548
K87f

70764

Fundamentals of
Inorganic Crystal Chemistry

Consulting Editor

P. Sykes, M.Sc., Ph.D.,

Fellow of Christ's College,
University of Cambridge

Other titles in the European Chemistry Series

BANWELL: Fundamentals of Molecular Spectroscopy
BARNARD: Theoretical Basis of Inorganic Chemistry
BARNARD & CHAYEN: Modern Methods of Chemical Analysis
BARNARD & MANSELL: Fundamentals of Physical Chemistry
BRENNAN & TIPPER: A Laboratory Manual of Experiments in
   Physical Chemistry
BU'LOCK: The Biosynthesis of Natural Products
HALLAS: Organic Stereochemistry
KEMP: Practical Organic Chemistry
WILLIAMS & FLEMING: Spectroscopic Methods in Organic Chemistry
WILLIAMS & FLEMING: Spectroscopic Problems in Organic Chemistry

Fundamentals of
Inorganic Crystal
Chemistry

H. Krebs

Professor of Inorganic Chemistry,
Technical University, Stuttgart

translated by

P. H. L. Walter

Assistant Professor of Chemistry,
Skidmore College, Saratoga Springs, New York

McGRAW-HILL · LONDON

New York · Toronto · Sydney · Mexico · Johannesburg · Panama

Published by

McGRAW-HILL PUBLISHING COMPANY LIMITED
MAIDENHEAD · BERKSHIRE · ENGLAND.

94066

Grundzüge der Anorganischen Kristallchemie first published by Ferdinand Enke Verlag, 1968.

PRINTED AND BOUND IN GREAT BRITAIN

Preface to the German Edition

Our knowledge of the structure of condensed materials is today so extensive and diverse that only the main points can be illustrated in a textbook. If one attempts to arrange all this material in an orderly fashion, and if one further hopes to understand the structures and properties of crystals, he must begin farther back with those theories of the chemical bond developed in the formalism of wave and quantum mechanics. The first part of this book seeks to introduce the reader to these theories without presupposing an extensive mathematical background. Only later when the theory of many-electron systems (chapter 8) is developed are those techniques of quantum mechanics employed which might cause difficulties for the mathematically inexperienced reader. Since the product functions which are developed in that chapter form the basis of crystal field theory, the author feels compelled to include this material. The book is written, however, so that it can be profitably read even if this chapter cannot be fully comprehended.

The structures of the elements and of the simple AB and AB_2 types of compounds are treated in some detail so that from these geometrically simple crystals those points of view which are important to the understanding of crystalline phases and their structures can be developed for the students. The book emphasizes how the structures and properties of crystals are determined to a great extent by the electronic structures of the atoms and by the form, extent, and electron occupation of the atomic orbitals. In listing representatives of a structure type the author has attempted to illustrate the diverse types of materials which can crystallize with that structure. No attempt was made to list all known examples of a given type. The structures discussed in this book were chosen so that general regularities and theoretical relationships would be made apparent by simple examples. Simultaneously, however, it was necessary to include as broad as possible a cross-section. The mode of interpretation and explanation of the structure types frequently go back to the author's own work. They may thus tend to give the book a personal touch. To simplify the readers' access to the literature, newer publications have been frequently cited in addition to the basic, older references. The many illustrations which are essential to a book on crystal chemistry were for the most part newly designed and drawn.

The author received many valuable suggestions in conversations with scientific co-workers and students. He would especially like to mention B. Reiser and H. Thurn, Stuttgart, who also helped with reading the proofs. Many improvements in the text can be attributed to P. H. L. Walter, Wilmington, Delaware, and R. W. Haisty, Dallas, Texas, who spent some time as guests in the author's laboratory. K. Krogmann, Stuttgart, and H. G. v. Schnering, Münster, assisted the author in writing chapter 27 on structures containing metal-metal bonds.

Heinz Krebs

Stuttgart
July, 1967.

Foreword to the English Edition

During the past decade the field of solid state science has taken immense steps forward. Despite both the technical importance of this field and the number of scientists involved in it, no book has been available which attempts as its primary goal to correlate the structures and bonding in condensed phases. Professor Krebs has applied modern theories of chemical bonding derived from quantum mechanics and the approach of solid state physics to form a basis by which the vast amount of experimental observation in crystal chemistry can be ordered and explained. The ionic model which is too often applied in crystal chemistry because of its simplicity is treated briefly but seldom used because it generally hinders the deeper understanding of the behaviour of condensed matter. This present volume, which explains in a unified fashion, the author's ideas on covalent bonding, opens up to scientist and student alike new paths to the understanding of solids and their properties. In addition, and perhaps more important, it is the first book on crystal chemistry to go beyond an essentially descriptive approach.

I want to thank the Central Research Department of E. I. Du Pont de Nemours and Co. which allowed me while in their employ to spend a very profitable year with the author in Stuttgart. In addition they provided secretarial help for much of the translation. Thanks must also be given to Dr R. W. Haisty who assisted in parts of the translation upon my return to America.

Paul H. L. Walter

Saratoga Springs, New York
February, 1968

Contents

1

The Atom and its Components

1.1 Evidence for the Existence of Atoms

In the year 1808, Dalton asserted, on the basis of the laws of multiple and constant proportions, that there existed a small indivisible particle of matter, the atom. In 1865, Loschmidt succeeded in calculating the number of atoms in a gram-atom at about 6×10^{23}. From the mass of the gram-atom and Loschmidt's Number, it was then possible to determine the mass of an individual atom, e.g., $m_H = 1 \cdot 008 \div (6 \cdot 02 \times 10^{23}) = 1 \cdot 673 \times 10^{-24}$ g. Although these assertions were derived indirectly and could consequently be put forward only as hypotheses, the existence of atoms has since often been proved experimentally.

1.2 Evidence for the Existence of Electrons

Faraday's electrolysis experiments showed that an electric charge can be separated from atoms. In 1833 Faraday found that for the electrolytic deposition of one gram-equivalent, 96,530 coulombs (C) of electricity is required. This experimental result can be most easily explained by assuming that each atom contains a definite amount of electricity and that there exists an indivisible particle of electricity, the *electron*. The charge on an electron can be calculated from Faraday's Constant and the Loschmidt Number: $96530 \div (6 \cdot 02 \times 10^{23}) = 1 \cdot 602 \times 10^{-19}$ C $= 1e$. The first direct experimental determination of this number was carried out in 1910 by Millikan in his famous oil-drop experiment, in which he observed the velocity of descent of a very small oil drop through an electric field. On the basis of Stoke's Law, the velocity of descent, v, of the drop is given by the equation:

$$Mg = 6\pi\eta av,$$

where M = mass, a = radius of the drop, η = viscosity of air, g = the acceleration due to gravity. If now the drop is partially ionized by X- or ultraviolet radiation and passes between the plates of a condenser, then

$$Mg + Ec = 6\pi\eta av$$

where E is the field strength in the condenser and c is the electrical charge on the drop. Then $c = ne$, where n is always an integer.

1.3 Mass of the Electron

Lenard determined the mass of an electron during his research on the deflection of cathode rays by magnetic or electric fields in an evacuated glass tube (Fig. 1.1). Electrons are produced at a hot-cathode, G, and

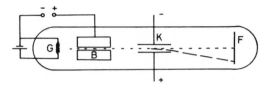

Fig. 1.1. Deviation of an electron beam in an electric field. G = glowing cathode, B = aperture, K = condenser, F = fluorescent screen.

are then accelerated by an electric field. The electron beam which passes through the slit, B, must then traverse the field of a condenser, K (or alternatively, the field of a magnet), before striking a fluorescent screen, F, or a photographic plate. From the degree of deflection of the cathode ray brought about by the electric field of the condenser K, the relationship between charge and mass of an electron can be determined as

$$e/m_e = 1.76 \times 10^8 \text{ C/g.}$$

On substituting the previously determined value of e in the above equation, one obtains for the mass of an electron:

$$m_e = \frac{1.602 \times 10^{-19}}{1.76 \times 10^8} = 9.109 \times 10^{-28} \text{ g.}$$

If the electron beam is replaced by an ion beam (e.g., H^+, He^+, He^{2+}), the mass of the corresponding ion can be determined in the same manner (e.g., the mass of H^+, $m_{H^+} = 1.672 \times 10^{-24}$ g). The mass of a hydrogen ion is much greater than that of an electron.

$$\frac{m_{H^+}}{m_e} = \frac{1.672 \times 10^{-24}}{9.109 \times 10^{-28}} = 1836.$$

The hydrogen atom, which is electrically neutral, must consist of a positively charged part in which the atomic mass is concentrated, and an electron. This positive part is called the nucleus. Correspondingly, helium has two electrons and its nucleus has twice the charge of the hydrogen nucleus. It is thus apparent that besides the negatively charged electron there is also a carrier of positive electricity, the proton. Proceeding further in the periodic system, the number of protons and electrons in an atom is always equal, and the number of each is given by the atomic number of the element.

1.4 Size of Atomic Nuclei and Atoms

The size of the atomic nucleus can be estimated from the deflection of α-particles (which consist of helium ions, He^{2+}), when they pass through a metal foil and thus pass by positively-charged atom nuclei. Radii of from 10^{-4} to 10^{-5} Å are found. However, the radius of an atom is of the order of 1 Å, so that the atom is 10^4 to 10^5 times larger than its nucleus.

1.5 Distribution of Electrons around Atomic Nuclei

The interference phenomena which are observed when X-rays pass through crystals result from the ability of electrons to influence the oscillations of the electric field of X-rays. From the intensity of the scattered rays, the distribution of electrons in a crystal can be inferred. Figure 1.2

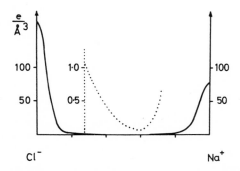

Fig. 1.2. Measured electron density[1.1] along the inter-atomic line between a Na and a Cl atom in a rock salt crystal.

shows the electron density (ordinate) as a function of distance along the line between a sodium and a chlorine atom in a sodium chloride crystal.[1.1] It is clear from this figure that the electrons remain primarily in the neighbourhood of the atomic nuclei, and that the probability of finding an electron at a given point decreases exponentially with increasing distance from the nucleus. However, thermal vibration of the atoms causes this simple curve to become so 'smeared-out' in practice that a detailed investigation of the electron distribution is made very difficult.

2

Filling of Electron Shells

2.1 Electron Energy Levels

In 1913, Franck and Hertz carried out experiments to determine bonding energies of an electron in an atom (Fig. 2.1a, b). A triode was filled

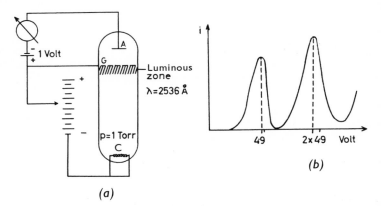

(a)

(b)

Fig. 2.1. (a) The Franck–Hertz arrangement for the determination of the excitation energy of atoms. C = glowing cathode, G = grid, A = anode. (b) Dependence of the anode current i on the grid potential at 1 Torr mercury pressure.

with mercury vapour at about 1 torr pressure. The anode current increased with increasing grid voltage, up to 4·9 V when the anode current dropped suddenly, apparently because the electrons had given up their kinetic energy of 4·9 eV shortly before reaching the grid. They thus could no longer overcome an anodic counterpotential of 1 V relative to the grid. Simultaneously, the mercury vapour in the vicinity of the grid began to glow. The emitted light was monochromatic with a wavelength of 2536 Å. By increasing the grid voltage the process could be repeated. Several luminous zones then formed in the tube. From these experiments one can conclude that an electron on an atom can accept only certain definite energies. When these energies are again given up, monochromatic light of a wavelength given by the Einstein equation, $E = hv$, is observed. Since $v = c/\lambda$, this can also be written in the form, $E = hc/\lambda$ (c is the velocity of light and v the frequency). The factor, h, is *Planck's constant* which is numerically equal to $6{\cdot}607 \times 10^{-27}$ erg. sec. in the c.g.s. system.

If the Franck–Hertz experiment is performed with still lower mercury pressure, the probability of an electron interacting with a mercury atom becomes small, and the mean free path of the electron is long enough to permit the electron to take on a higher energy. At a grid voltage of $10{\cdot}38$ V a sudden increase in the anode current is observed (Fig. 2.2). In this experiment the 'anode' has a negative potential relative to the cathode, so that only positive charged particles, here Hg^+-ions, can reach the anode.

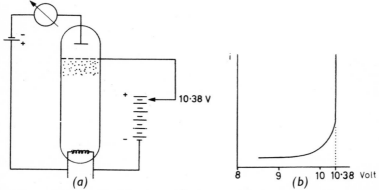

Fig. 2.2. (a) *Arrangement for measuring the ionization potential of the* Hg *atom.* (b) *Dependence of the anode current* i *on the grid potential.*

Thus, $10{\cdot}38$ V corresponds to the ionization energy of a mercury atom. The Einstein equation gives the corresponding light wavelength as 1203 Å.

The above experiments show that the electrons are bound in an atom with definite energy and that this energy can be radiated only in energy quanta, $E = hv$. From this principle, that light transports energy only in individual quanta, $E = hv$, one must conclude that a light beam as well as an electron beam consists of individual particles. These are called *photons*. On the other hand, the dispersion of light and interference phenomena are explained, as Huygens and Maxwell did, on the basis of electromagnetic waves. Light can thus be described by two pictures at the same time: the particle and the wave picture.

The particle character of light is also made apparent by the photo-emission effect. If one shines light on an alkali metal photocell (Fig. 2.3) a current begins to flow when the frequency (energy) of the light exceeds a certain minimum value called the work function. Each metal has its own characteristic work function. It is important to emphasize that if the frequency is not high enough a light beam of whatever intensity cannot remove an electron from the metal.

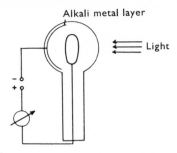

Fig. 2.3. Structure of an alkali photocell.

A further experiment on fluorescence (Fig. 2.4) also gives evidence for the acceptance of discrete amounts of energy by an electron. In a flask (K) is sodium vapour, which is irradiated (with the help of a lens) by the non-luminous flame of a Bunsen burner. If sodium is then added to the flame,

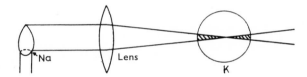

Fig. 2.4. Arrangement for the excitation of fluorescence in sodium vapour.

a yellow glow appears also in the flask. The energy of the photons of yellow light from the Bunsen flame can be accepted by the sodium atoms in the flask. The electrons in the flask are thereby raised to the same state as the thermally excited atoms of the sodium vapour in the Bunsen flame. When an electron returns to its ground state, it emits energy of the same wavelength which is then observed as a yellow fluorescence.

Extensive information on the binding energy of electrons in an atom can be obtained from the emission spectrum. Hydrogen, which contains only one electron, shows the simplest spectrum. The lines, which fall into individual series, become progressively more crowded together as they approach a so-called series limit (Fig. 2.5).

For the series of lines which lie principally in the visible range, Balmer

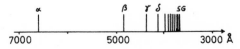

Fig. 2.5. Wavelengths of the lines in the Balmer series of hydrogen, SG-series limit.

developed a formula which describes the observed wavelengths. Further series in the infrared and ultraviolet were discovered by Lymann, Paschen, Brackett, and Pfund. The following relationship holds for these series:

$$\frac{1}{\lambda} = R_H Z^2 \left\{ \frac{1}{m^2} - \frac{1}{n^2} \right\}$$

In this equation, R_H is the *Rydberg Constant* for hydrogen. The corresponding constants for other elements differ only slightly (about 1 per cent) from R_H. m is an integer which is characteristic for a given series of lines: it equals 1, 2, 3, 4, and 5 for the Lymann, Balmer, Paschen, Brackett, and Pfund series, respectively. The quantity n is an integer, $m < n < \infty$, and Z is the atomic number of the element in question (for hydrogen $Z = 1$, for the corresponding series of He$^+$-ions, $Z = 2$, etc). Since, according to Einstein, $E = h\nu = hc/\lambda$, it is clear that the electrons in an

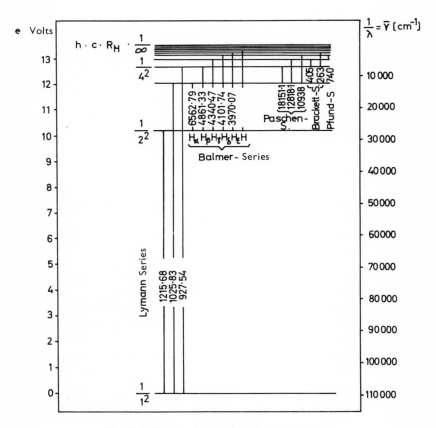

Fig. 2.6. Term scheme of the hydrogen atom.

atom can have only certain definite energy values (*terms*) (Fig. 2.6).

$$E = h\nu = \frac{hc}{\lambda} = hcR_{\mathrm{H}}Z^2\left\{\frac{1}{m^2} - \frac{1}{n^2}\right\}.$$

The transition of electrons from one term to another is thus connected with the absorption or emission of light of a definite wavelength. The series limit (SG), which can be determined through an experiment of the type of Franck and Hertz, corresponds to the ionization of the atom.

When an atom contains several electrons, the spectrum is in general complicated. Relatively simple patterns are, however, observed for the X-ray spectra. Figure 2.7 shows the lines obtained for tungsten. The lines

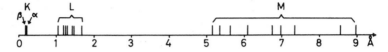

Fig. 2.7. Wavelengths of the lines in the K-, L-, and M-series of tungsten.

fall into series designated by the letters K, L, M, etc. Moseley showed in 1912 that in any series there is a relation between the value of the longest wavelength and the atomic number of the element.

$$\text{for the K-Series} \quad \frac{1}{\lambda} \simeq R(Z - 1)^2\left\{\frac{1}{1^2} - \frac{1}{2^2}\right\}$$

$$\text{for the L-Series} \quad \frac{1}{\lambda} \simeq R(Z - 7\cdot4)^2\left\{\frac{1}{2^2} - \frac{1}{3^2}\right\}.$$

For any given element the K-Series has the shortest wavelength, since it results from transitions of the electrons in the immediate neighbourhood of the atomic nucleus where the electrons' potential energy must be the greatest. What is surprising is that even in the formula for the K-series transitions, it is not the full nuclear charge which appears in the equation but a value which is nearly $Z - 1$. This leads to the postulate that the attractive force of the nucleus on the electron in question is partially shielded by another electron. In the L-series, there are yet more electrons which shield the electron under consideration from the nuclear charge. These phenomena clarify the arrangement of electrons in shells as Fig. 2.8 shows. The absorption of energy by the electron corresponds to the transition of the electron from an inner shell to one farther removed from the nucleus. The reverse transition is associated with the emission of X-rays.

In 1913, the Danish physicist, Bohr, developed the first atom model, but his description has largely been replaced by a wave-mechanical treatment. The Bohr model offers little explanation of the existence of chemical bonds. Only the basic outline of this model will be given here, since it is often used in chemical literature. Bohr postulated that an

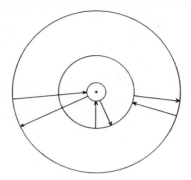

Fig. 2.8. Tentative representation of the electronic arrangement in shells about the atomic nucleus.

electron revolves around the nucleus in a circular or elliptical orbit, for which the following relationships hold:

(a) The centrifugal force is equal to the Coulombic attraction:

$$\frac{mv^2}{r} = \frac{e_1 e_2}{r^2}.$$

(b) The angular momentum of the electron is given by:

$$mvr = \frac{nh}{2\pi}.$$

m = electron mass
e_1, e_2 = charge of the electron and of the nucleus respectively
r = radius of the orbit
v = velocity of the electron
h = Planck's constant.

Bohr himself indicated that his model could not be correct since an electron moving in this way must radiate light, and must have associated with it a magnetic field. Bohr was forced to postulate that the radiation of light and the magnetic field are suppressed on those orbits determined by the simultaneous solution of the above two equations. No explanation of this 'suppression' could be given.

2.2 Wave Character of Electrons

The methods of classical physics did not provide a very good idea of the formation and structure of an atom, because the electron had been pictured as an electrically charged particle. While the wave character of light was accepted and the particle nature was much later developed, the situation with the electron was reversed. Its wave nature remained long hidden. When light is diffracted, interference patterns result. These can be described easily with the wave model by a summation of the amplitudes. The intensity of the light in the interference pattern is proportional to the square of the amplitude. In the particle model, the intensity is given as the number of photons which arrive at a given point in unit time, or as the probability that a photon will be found at a given point at a given time.

Interference phenomena can also be seen with electrons, as the following experiment demonstrates (Fig. 2.9). Electrons emitted from a hot cathode,

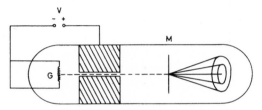

Fig. 2.9. Production of electron interference. G = glowing cathode, V = aperture voltage, M = metal foil.

(G), are accelerated by means of a positive voltage, (V), and collimated into a beam. On passing through a metal foil, they give a diffraction pattern. This is evidence that electrons have the properties of waves as well as particles. De Broglie had already postulated this in 1924 and the experiment described above was actually performed by Davison and Germer in 1926. Other elementary particles also have a wave character. Stern and Estermann have obtained corresponding interference patterns from proton beams. From the experimentally obtained interference patterns, the wavelength (λ) associated with the electron beam can be derived, using the *Einstein relationship*, $E = h\nu$ (E = total energy of the electron), and the *de Broglie equation* $p = h/\lambda$, where $p = mv$ = momentum.

$$\lambda = \frac{h}{p} = \frac{h}{\sqrt{2mE^*}} \left(\text{since } E^* = \frac{m}{2}v^2 \right)$$

In addition,

$$\lambda v = u = \frac{h}{\sqrt{2mE^*}} \cdot \frac{E}{h} = \frac{E}{\sqrt{2mE^*}} \quad \text{or} \quad \frac{1}{u^2} = \frac{2mE^*}{E^2}$$

E in this formula is the kinetic energy of the electron, which is here equal to the total energy, since an electron in field-free space has no potential energy, and u is the velocity of propagation of the wave. This is not identical to the velocity, v, of the electron. Both photons and electrons thus have a dual nature: wave and particle. It should therefore be possible to describe the behaviour of the electron by a wave equation.

2.3 Schrödinger Equation

For light, the amplitude, A, of the vibrations corresponds to the magnitude of the propagating electromagnetic field. For electrons, we know only that the oscillations can be described by an amplitude, Ψ. We do not, however, understand the physical significance of this 'amplitude'. This lack of a clear physical picture for one of the fundamental functions of wave mechanics creates great difficulty for the beginner.

Although Ψ itself is difficult to describe, the square of this factor can be understood. Employing the analogy to light, Ψ^2 may be visualized in three ways: (a) It is proportional to the intensity of the electron beam. (b) It corresponds to the number of electrons which arrive at a given point in unit time. (c) It is the probability that an electron will be found at a given point at any given time. Table 2.1 summarizes these ways of looking at light and electron beams:

Table 2.1. Analogues between light and electron beams

Photon	Electron
$I \sim A^2$	$I \sim \Psi^2$
(a) Intensity of the light beam	(a) Intensity of the electron beam
(b) The number of photons which arrive at a given point in unit time	(b) The number of electrons which arrive at a given point in unit time
(c) The probability of finding a photon at a given point in space at any given time	(c) The probability of finding an electron at a given point in space at any given time

It is thus possible to make a statement only about the physical significance of Ψ^2, but not about Ψ itself. Any calculations about the behaviour of electrons require an equation for the magnitude of Ψ, similar to that obtained from the interference phenomena for light. The equation which describes the behaviour of electrons in an electric force field is the *wave equation for electrons*. It reads:

$$\frac{\partial^2 \Psi(x, y, z, t)}{\partial x^2} + \frac{\partial^2 \Psi(x, y, z, t)}{\partial y^2} + \frac{\partial^2 \Psi(x, y, z, t)}{\partial z^2}$$

$$= \frac{2m(E - V)}{E^2} \cdot \frac{\partial^2 \Psi(x, y, z, t)}{\partial t^2}.$$

We thus have $\Psi = \Psi(x, y, z, t)$, a function of the three spatial co-ordinates and of time. This equation contains only the second derivative of Ψ with respect to the four co-ordinates. It can thus be handled mathematically as a so-called homogeneous differential equation of the second order, the solutions of which obey definite rules. The derivation of these solutions is beyond the scope of this book.

In this wave equation, E is the total energy of an electron; V is the potential energy. $E - V$ is thus the kinetic energy of the electron for which the equation $2m(E - V) = 2m[(m/2)v^2] = p^2$ holds. It therefore follows that for electrons which have both kinetic and potential energy $[2m(E - V)]/E^2 = 1/u^2$ should be substituted for $2mE^*/E^2 = 1/u^2$, which was derived (section 2.2) for electrons which have no potential energy. If this substitution is made, the equation becomes:

$$\frac{\partial^2 \Psi(x, y, z, t)}{\partial x^2} + \frac{\partial^2 \Psi(x, y, z, t)}{\partial y^2} + \frac{\partial^2 \Psi(x, y, z, t)}{\partial z^2} = \frac{1}{u^2} \cdot \frac{\partial^2 \Psi(x, y, z, t)}{\partial t^2} .$$

Now this equation, which is called the *general wave equation*, contains only the amplitude, $\Psi = \Psi(x, y, z, t)$, of a wave and the velocity of propagation, u. The nature of the wave no longer plays any part. The equation is equally valid for any kind of wave motion. It can serve for the propagation of light and for interference phenomena when Ψ is replaced by the electric vector ε, and u by the velocity of light c. It is just as valid for earthquake waves when $\Psi(x, y, z, t)$ describes the course of the pressure wave in the earth, and u is the velocity of the earthquake wave. The function $\Psi(x, y, z, t)$ assigns to each point of the earth, x, y, z, a definite pressure at a time, t, and is therefore a scalar and not a vector, as in the case of light. This equation also describes the propagation of sound waves and their interference phenomena. While interference is not easily heard with sound waves, it can be clearly observed at ultrasonic frequencies. If $\partial^2 \Psi/\partial z^2$ is set equal to zero, the equation describes the properties of plane waves, as for example water waves, if the z-axis is chosen so that it is perpendicular to the water surface. If $\partial^2 \Psi/\partial y^2$ is also set equal to zero, the equation is valid for a one-dimensional wave, having its propagation direction along the x-axis. Examples include the propagation of sound in a rail, or of a lateral displacement in an infinitely long cable.

Electrons in an electron beam have, as we have shown earlier, both particle and wave character. The physical significance of Ψ is unknown. We know only that a wave is associated with the motion of an electron, which is exactly described mathematically by the general wave equation.

Electrons in an atom are no longer free to move anywhere in space but are bound to the atom. The wave process associated with the electronic motion is then also confined to the space around the atom. In order to understand this, let us consider some examples from classical physics of wave propagation in a restricted space. In the case of a string fixed at both ends (e.g., on a violin), the waves reflected from the fixed ends reinforce the primary vibration to produce a standing wave, the vibrating string. Further examples are the vibrating circular membrane the edges of which are fixed (e.g., earphones, drum) or the standing waves of the air in a hollow sphere (Helmholz sphere).

The previous examples of standing waves can all be treated with the same wave equation, when the appropriate physical values are substituted for Ψ and u, and when the boundary conditions are properly taken into account. The mathematical solutions to the wave equation are generally not easily obtained. It is sufficient here to consider solutions for certain specific examples, in order to understand better the solution of the wave equation for an electron around an atomic nucleus.

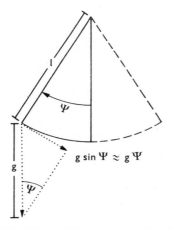

Fig. 2.10. Diagram for the derivation of the wave equation of a pendulum.
——————— *positive values of* Ψ (Ψ-*angle of deflection*)
- - - - - - - - - - - *negative values of* Ψ
. . . . *energy diagram*

Mathematically, the simplest case of a wave equation concerns the motion of a pendulum (Fig. 2.10). The amplitude of the pendulum swing is a function of time, $\Psi = \Psi(t)$. The acceleration of the mass point,

$$l\frac{d^2\Psi(t)}{dt^2}$$

is given by the component of g in the direction of motion, $g \sin \Psi(t)$. For small angles Ψ, $\sin \Psi \simeq \Psi$. Thus, for a small vibration, the equation becomes $d^2\Psi(t)/dt^2 = -(g/l) \cdot \Psi(t)$. The solution is then (as can be easily verified):

$$\Psi(t) = c \sin \sqrt{g/l}\, t = c \sin (2\pi/\tau)t, \quad \text{with the period:} \quad \tau = 2\pi\sqrt{l/g}.$$

For $t = (n + \frac{1}{4})\tau$ (n = an integer), there results the maximum amplitude, $\psi = c$. The solution of the wave equation is thus characterized by the product of a constant, $\psi = c$, which gives the maximum amplitude of the pendulum, with one and only one time function, $\sin (2\pi/\tau)t$. There are no other solutions for the wave equation.

For the vibrating string, there are a series of solutions to the wave equation. For the fundamental vibration the solution is:

$$\Psi_1(x, t) = c_1 \sin (\pi x/a) \sin (2\pi t/\tau_1).$$

The string (Fig. 2.11), which is fixed at points $x = 0$ and $x = a$, vibrates back and forth between the maximum positive amplitude ($t = (n + \frac{1}{4})\tau_1$,

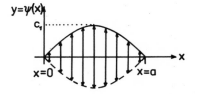

Fig. 2.11. Fundamental vibration of a string fastened at $x = 0$ and $x = a$.

———————————— Ψ_1 *(for $t = (n + \frac{1}{4})\tau_1$)* $= \psi_1$

— — — — — — — — Ψ_1 *(for $t = (n + \frac{3}{4})\tau_1$)* $= -\psi_1$

solid curve) and the maximum negative amplitude ($t = (n + \frac{3}{4})\tau_1$, dashed curve). Here, n is an integer and τ_1 is the period of the vibration. If the string is observed at a given time, $t = (n + \frac{1}{4})\tau_1$, the shape of the curve at maximum positive amplitude is seen. The shape of the string can then be given through a pure position function, $\psi = \psi(x)$. When c_1 is chosen positive, ψ has the form $\psi_1(x) = c_1 \sin (\pi x/a)$. The function $\psi_1(x)$ assigns to every point, $o \leqslant x \leqslant a$, a maximum displacement vector which is parallel to the y-axis and the magnitude of which is given by the function $\psi_1(x)$. The fundamental vibration can also be written in the form:

$$\Psi_1 = \psi_1 \sin (2\pi/\tau_1)t.$$

The string can also, however, have harmonic vibrations. The first harmonic (Fig. 2.12) is described by the equation:

$$\Psi_2 = c_2 \sin \frac{\pi}{a} 2x \sin \frac{2\pi t}{\tau_2}$$

where

$$\psi_2 = c_2 \sin \frac{\pi}{a} 2x.$$

The general equations for higher harmonics are:

$$\Psi_n = c_n \sin \frac{\pi}{a} nx \sin \frac{2\pi t}{\tau_n}$$

where

$$\psi_n = c_n \sin \frac{\pi}{a} nx.$$

The functions ψ_n have $n + 1$ zero positions, *nodes*, including the nodes at both ends of the string. At every node, the function $\psi(x, y, z)$ changes its sign.

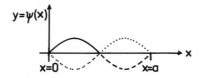

Fig. 2.12. *First harmonic vibration of a string fastened at* $x = 0$ *and* $x = a$.
——————— $\psi_2 > 0$ *and* – – – – – – $\psi_2 < 0$ $\left[\text{for } t = (n + \frac{1}{4})\tau_2\right]$
. . . . . .$-\psi_2 > 0$ *and* .. .. $-\psi_2 < 0$ $\left[\text{for } t = (n + \frac{3}{4})\tau_2\right]$

The differential equation for the vibrating string permits a number of solutions, which differ in the period of vibration and in the numbers of nodes. The functions can be distinguished by the running variable, $n = 1, 2, 3, \ldots$ and through the associated periods of vibration τ_n, which are called *eigenvalues* of the differential equation. The solution of the differential equation, $\psi_n(x)$, which corresponds to a given eigenvalue is called an *eigenfunction*.

One important property of homogeneous differential equations should be noted: the sum of any two solution functions $\Psi = \Psi_1 + \Psi_2$ is again a solution of the differential equation, as can readily be verified by substitution. Physically, this means that on a vibrating string, various vibrations can be superimposed.

In the two-dimensional case, as for example a vibrating circular membrane, the relationships and their analytical description are more complicated. The function again consists of the product of a position function, $\psi(x, y)$, which is now dependent on two co-ordinates, and a time-dependent sine function, $\sin (2\pi t)/\tau$. In this case $\psi(x, y)$ specifies the magnitude of the maximum displacement vector in the z-direction. Each vibration period (eigenvalue) and each eigenfunction is now, however, characterized by two running variables: n and l, where n is the number of all nodal lines and l gives the number of straight-line nodes. l must always be smaller than n. We can now draw up Table 2.2:

Table 2.2. Eigenvalues, eigenfunctions, and nodal lines of a vibrating circular membrane

Eigenvalue $\tau_{n,l}$ Vibration period	Eigenfunction $\psi_{n,l}(x, y)$	Nodes	Remarks
$\tau_{1,0}$	$\psi_{1,0}(x, y)$		1 circular node, the edge of the membrane remains at rest
$\tau_{2,0}$	$\psi_{2,0}(x, y)$		2 circular nodes—the edge and one inner ring remain at rest
$\tau_{3,0}$	$\psi_{3,0}(x, y)$		3 circular nodes—edge and two inner rings remain at rest
$\tau_{2,1}$	$\psi_{2,1}(x, y)$		In addition to the circular nodes there is also a linear node
$\tau_{3,1}$	$\psi_{3,1}(x, y)$		

Once again, at every node the spatial eigenfunction changes its sign. These changes are noted in the table by $+$ and $-$.

If we consider now a three-dimensional vibrating model such as a Helmholtz sphere (i.e., a hollow sphere in which the air vibrates), the motion of the air at any point (x, y, z) in the sphere can be described by a function $\vec{\Psi}(x, y, z, t)$ which is now a displacement vector dependent on x, y, z, and t. This function is now much more complex, since not only the magnitudes, but also the directions of the displacement vectors must be specified. The function can again be described as the product of a spatial function $\vec{\psi}(x, y, z)$, which gives the direction and maximum displacement of the air from the position of rest, and the sine function, $\sin (2\pi t)/\tau$. The eigenfunctions $\vec{\psi}(x, y, z)$ and the eigenvalues (period of vibration), τ are now characterized by a series of three integers: n, l, and λ, which specify the number and kind of nodal surfaces.

The vibration of the air in a Helmholtz sphere can also be described by specifying the density fluctuations as a function, $\Psi(x, y, z, t)$ of both the spatial and temporal co-ordinates. We then associate with each point within the sphere a scalar which varies with time. These Ψ-functions are therefore more simply constructed. They also can be written in the form of a product. One factor, $\psi(x, y, z)$ gives, for each point, the maximum variation in density; the other remains as before, $\sin(2\pi t)/\tau$. Again in this description of the vibrational process, the eigenfunction, $\psi(x, y, z)$ and the period of vibration τ are characterized by three running variables.

An atom forms a three-dimensional structure. Generally, the electrons are in stationary states. Any transition of the electrons among these stationary states is associated with the absorption or emission of electromagnetic radiation, such as light. However, so long as ionization does not occur, the atomic nucleus holds the electron fast. The Coulombic force therefore restricts the motion of the electron, just as the walls of the Helmholtz sphere restrict the motion of the enclosed air. Such motions of the electron can be described by the wave equation for electrons. Further, the frequency of the emitted light corresponds to the frequency of the wave which describes the electronic transition. At the end of the transition, the electron is in another stationary state. Since the electron as a particle cannot disappear, it must be possible to describe it by a stationary field distribution, $\psi(x, y, z)$, which is independent of time. These stationary states have no analogue in the Helmholtz sphere experiment, since a stationary state there is distinguished by the fact that the air is everywhere in equilibrium; no vibration or density variation is then possible, and $\psi(x, y, z)$ is everywhere zero.

Schrödinger[2.1] showed how the previously mentioned (p. 11), time-dependent wave equation, which describes the motion of electrons, can be transformed for stationary states into a differential equation which is time-independent. This reads:

$$\frac{\partial^2 \psi(x, y, z)}{\partial x^2} + \frac{\partial^2 \psi(x, y, z)}{\partial^2 y} + \frac{\partial^2 \psi(x, y, z)}{\partial^2 z}$$
$$+ \frac{8\pi^2 m}{h^2} (E - V)\psi(x, y, z) = 0.$$

This, too, is a homogeneous differential equation of the second order. It can be derived from the time-dependent equation for electrons by separating $\Psi(x, y, z, t)$ into two parts:

$$\Psi(x, y, z, t) = \psi(x, y, z) \cdot e^{-2\pi i E t/h}.$$

Differentiating Ψ twice with respect to time we obtain:

$$\frac{\partial \Psi}{\partial t} = -\psi \frac{2\pi i E t}{h} e^{-2\pi i E t/h} = -\frac{2\pi i E}{\lambda} \Psi$$

$$\frac{\partial^2 \Psi}{\partial t^2} = (-2\pi i E/h)^2 \Psi = -(4\pi^2 E^2/h^2)\Psi.$$

3

Substituting this back into the wave equation for electrons we have

$$e^{-(2\pi iEt/h)}\left\{\frac{\partial^2\psi}{\partial x^2} + \frac{\partial^2\psi}{\partial y^2} + \frac{\partial^2\psi}{\partial z^2}\right\} + \frac{2m(E - V)}{E^2}\cdot\frac{4\pi^2 E^2}{h^2}e^{-(2\pi iEt/h)}\psi = 0.$$

After cancelling out the common factor $e^{-2\pi iEt/h}$, we obtain the *time-independent Schrödinger equation* given above.†

In the case of the hydrogen atom, the potential is given by $V = e_1 e_2/r$, where e_1 and e_2 are the charges on the electron and on the nucleus respectively and r is the distance between them. The time-independent Schrödinger equation is soluble only for certain definite eigenvalues, in this case the energy, $E_{n,l,\lambda}$, which, just as with the Helmholtz sphere, depend on three running variables called *quantum numbers*. To each set of quantum numbers there corresponds one eigenfunction, $\psi_{n,l,\lambda}(x, y, z)$. The square of this function, $\psi^2_{n,l,\lambda}(x, y, z)$, gives the density-probability that an electron will be found at the point with the co-ordinates x, y, z. It gives a density-probability distribution in the atom. In order to make this concept more descriptive it is often said that an electron is more or less strongly present at a given point. The electron is frequently compared to a cloud, so that one can speak of an electron-density distribution, although only one electron is being considered.

The quantum numbers which we have introduced so far are:

$n = $ principal quantum number
$l = $ azimuthal or angular momentum quantum number
$\lambda = $ axial quantum number.

† In addition

$$\frac{2m(E - V)}{E^2}\cdot\frac{\partial^2\Psi}{t^2} = -\frac{2m(E - V)}{E^2}\cdot\frac{2\pi iE}{h}\cdot\frac{\partial\Psi}{\partial t}$$

$$= -\frac{4\pi im}{h}\cdot\frac{\partial\Psi}{\partial t} + \frac{4\pi im}{h}\cdot\frac{V}{E}\cdot(-1)\frac{2\pi iE}{h}\Psi$$

$$= -\frac{4\pi im}{h}\cdot\frac{\partial\Psi}{\partial t} + \frac{8\pi^2 m}{h}V\Psi.$$

From the wave equation for electrons it then follows that

$$\frac{\partial^2\Psi(x, y, z, t)}{\partial x^2} + \frac{\partial^2\Psi(x, y, z, t)}{\partial y^2} + \frac{\partial^2\Psi(x, y, z, t)}{\partial z^2}$$

$$+ \frac{4\pi im}{h}\cdot\frac{\partial\Psi(x, y, z, t)}{\partial t} - \frac{8\pi^2 m}{h^2}V\Psi(x, y, z, t) = 0.$$

This is the time-dependent Schrödinger equation, which is generally valid for the motion of electrons in an electrical force field. Since this equation will not be used in this book, we only mention this fundamental formula of wave mechanics here.

Just as in the case of the membrane, the various quantum numbers are interdependent: n can take any integral value from 1 to ∞, l can vary from 0 to $(n - 1)$ and λ runs from 0 to $+l$. For the various values of l and λ certain letters of the alphabet are often used:

Table 2.3. Symbols for the azimuthal and axial quantum numbers

Value of l and λ	0	1	2	3	4
Designation of l	s	p	d	f	g
Designation of λ	σ	π	δ	φ	γ

When $\lambda \neq 0$ there are two eigenfunctions for each λ, which differ only in their spatial orientation.

2.4 Solutions of the Schrödinger Equation for the Hydrogen Atom

The analytic representation of the eigenfunctions, $\psi(x, y, z)$ and the solutions of the time-independent Schrödinger equation will now be discussed. For the simple case of the hydrogen atom, when the electron is in the ground state, $n = 1$, and consequently $l = \lambda = 0$, the appropriate eigenfunction is:

$1s\sigma$: $$\psi_{1,0,0} = Ne^{-(Zr/1a_0)} = 2\left(\frac{Z}{1a_0}\right)^{3/2} \cdot e^{-(Zr/1a_0)} \cdot \frac{1}{2\sqrt{\pi}},$$

where Z = the nuclear charge, $a_0 = 0.5284$ Å, the *Bohr radius*, and r is the distance of the point (x, y, z) from the nucleus. So-called *atomic units* are used in calculation. Here the unit of electrical charge is the charge on one electron (or proton) and the unit of length is the Bohr radius, a_0. N is a *normalization factor* which is chosen so that the probability of finding an electron somewhere in space is numerically equal to 1.

$$\int \psi_{1,0,0}^2 d\tau = \int N^2 e^{-2Zr/a_0} d\tau = 1.$$

In this equation $d\tau$ is a volume element and the integration is carried out over the volume of the atom. The integral gives the probability of finding the electron in the atom. This probability is naturally 1. Integration gives the value of N as:

$$N = 2\left(\frac{Z}{1a_0}\right)^{3/2} \cdot \frac{1}{2\sqrt{\pi}}.$$

The function, $\psi_{1,0,0}$ depends only on r and is thus spherically symmetric.

As r increases, the value of Ψ decreases exponentially. Thus the probability of finding an electron in the neighbourhood of the atomic nucleus is high, but decreases sharply with increasing distance. Figure 2.13 reproduces the

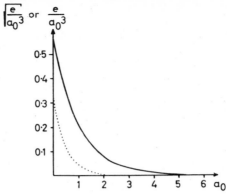

Fig. 2.13. —— *Value of the function* $\psi_{1,0,0}$ *(in units of* $\sqrt{e/a_0{}^3}$ *)*; ... *Value of the function* $\psi_{1,0,0}^2$ *(in units of* $e/a_0{}^3$ *), as a function of the distance from the atomic nucleus in the hydrogen atom.*

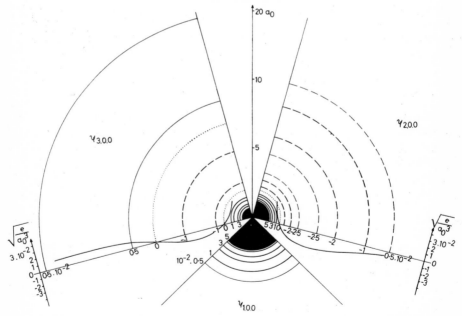

Fig. 2.14. *Values of the functions* $\psi_{1,0,0}$, $\psi_{2,0,0}$, *and* $\psi_{3,0,0}$, *represented by contour lines each on a sector of a central section through a hydrogen atom.*

—— $\psi > 0$ – – – – $\psi < 0$ ...... $\psi = 0$

$\psi_{2,0,0}$ *and* $\psi_{3,0,0}$ *are additionally plotted as functions of* r, *the distance from the atomic nucleus.*

shape of the functions $\psi_{1,0,0}(xyz)$ and $\psi^2_{1,0,0}(xyz)$ as a function of the distance from the nucleus to the point in question. In the lower segment of Fig. 2.14, the function $\psi_{1,0,0}(xyz)$ on a cross-section through the centre of the atom is shown by means of a contour line.

Figure 2.15 shows how the electron density is distributed over the individual spherical shells. When the spatial electron density, $\psi^2(r)$, is multiplied by the surface area of a sphere $(4\pi r^2)$ at the radius, r, from the nucleus, the distribution curve shown in the upper section of Fig. 2.15 is obtained. The maximum of this curve is seen to be at $r = a_0 = 0.5284$ Å.

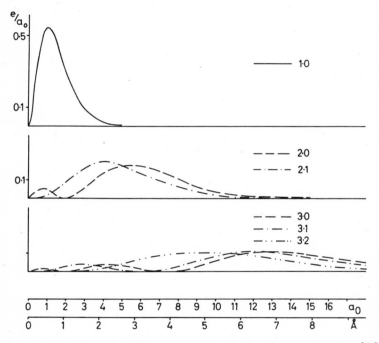

Fig. 2.15. *Distribution of the electron density over the spherical shells* $(4\pi r^2\psi^2)$ *in the hydrogen atom for various n and l.*

In the case of $n = 2$, $l = \lambda = 0$, the wave function is an exponential function multiplied by a polynomial:

$2s\sigma$: $\psi_{2,0,0} = N.e^{-(Zr/2a_0)}.\left[1 - \dfrac{Zr}{2a_0}\right]$

$$= 2\left(\frac{Z}{2a_0}\right)^{3/2}.e^{-(Zr/2a_0)}.\left[1 - \frac{Zr}{2a_0}\right].\frac{1}{2\sqrt{\pi}}.$$

The polynomial in this equation, $\left[1 - Zr/2a_0\right]$, is zero when $r = 2a_0/Z$ and therefore negative for $r > 2a_0/Z$. However, because of the exponential function, $\psi_{2,0,0}$ goes to zero for large values of r. Figures 2.16 and 2.14 show also the dependence of $\psi_{2,0,0}$ on r, and across a central cut through the atom respectively. A spherical nodal surface exists where both ψ and ψ^2 are zero. Within this sphere the function ψ may be chosen as positive; outside it will then be negative. When ψ^2 is integrated over both regions, the electron is 5·4 per cent within the nodal sphere and 94·6 per cent outside. This can be seen easily in Fig. 2.15. The area between the curve, $4\pi r^2 \psi_{2,0,0}^2(r)$ and the abscissa is equated to 1 (certainty of finding the electron). The portion of the area between 0 and $2a_0$ is then 0·054, while that outside of $2a_0$ is 0·946.

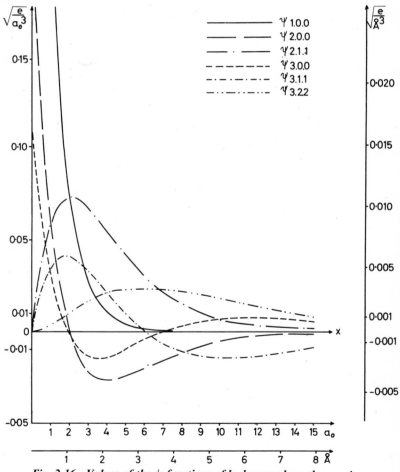

Fig. 2.16. Values of the ψ-functions of hydrogen along the x-axis.

For $n = 3, l = \lambda = 0$, Schrödinger's equation reads:

$$3s\sigma: \quad \psi_{3,0,0} = 2\left(\frac{Z}{3a_0}\right)^{3/2} \cdot e^{-(Zr/3a_0)} \cdot \left[1 - 2\left(\frac{Zr}{3a_0}\right) + \frac{2}{3}\left(\frac{Zr}{3a_0}\right)^2\right] \cdot \frac{1}{2\sqrt{\pi}}.$$

Here too, the entire function vanishes when the polynomial is equal to zero. Since the polynomial is quadratic in r, there are two solutions, which in the special case of the hydrogen atom are: $r_1 = 1.90a_0 = 1.004$ Å, $r_2 = 7.10a_0 = 3.652$ Å (see Figs. 2.14, 2.15, 2.16). Here two nodal surfaces are obtained. The probability of finding the electron is 1.5 per cent within the first nodal surface, 9.5 per cent between the surfaces, and 89 per cent outside the second nodal surface.

In the three cases considered above, with $l = 0$, the number of spherical nodal surfaces was $n - 1$. We shall now consider cases where $l > 0$, e.g., $n = 2, l = 1, \lambda = 0$.

$$2p\sigma: \quad \psi_{2,1,0} = \underbrace{\frac{2}{\sqrt{3}} \cdot \left(\frac{Z}{2a_0}\right)^{3/2} \cdot e^{-(Zr/2a_0)} \cdot \left(\frac{Zr}{2a_0}\right)}_{\chi_{2,1}(r)} \cdot \underbrace{\frac{1}{2}\sqrt{3/\pi} \cdot \frac{z}{r}}_{Y_1{}^0}, \quad \text{or } z$$

The $\psi_{2,1,0}$-function (as also its square) has rotational symmetry about an axis (which is chosen by convention as the z-axis of a Cartesian system) Fig. 2.17. When $z = 0$, the entire function becomes zero. The xy-plane,

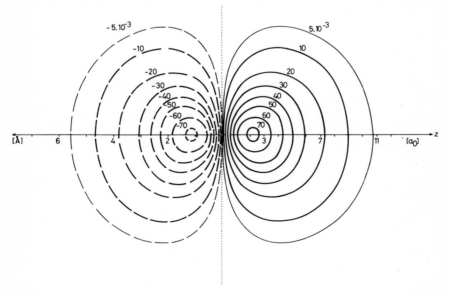

Fig. 2.17. Values of $\psi_{2,1,0}$ (p_z-electron) of hydrogen along a central section which contains the z-axis.

therefore, forms a nodal-surface. For positive values of z, the function may also be chosen as positive, in this case it changes to negative on passing through the nodal surface (i.e., for negative values of z).

In order to shorten and simplify the equations, the factor, (z/r), will be replaced by z. This 'z' is then the z-co-ordinate of the intersection of a unit sphere ($r = 1a_0$) around the nucleus and the radius vector to the point (x, y, z). In Fig. 2.18, when this z-value is plotted onto the proper radius vector, the angular dependence of the eigenfunction is obtained by a kind

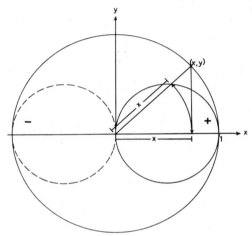

Fig. 2.18. Construction of a polar diagram for the spherical harmonic of a p_x-electron.

of polar diagram. By this process, two spheres are obtained which appear as circles in cross section.

For every $\lambda \neq 0$, there are two ψ-functions which can be transformed into each other by rotation about the z-axis. The two functions are differentiated by the symbols: λ and $\bar{\lambda}$.

$$\psi_{2,1,1} = \frac{2}{\sqrt{3}} \cdot \left(\frac{Z}{2a_0}\right)^{3/2} \cdot e^{-(Zr/2a_0)} \cdot \left(\frac{Zr}{2a_0}\right) \cdot \frac{1}{2}\sqrt{3/\pi} \cdot (y/r), \quad \text{or } y$$

$2p\pi$:

$$\psi_{2,1,1} = \underbrace{\frac{2}{\sqrt{3}} \cdot \left(\frac{Z}{2a_0}\right)^{3/2} \cdot e^{-(Zr/2a_0)} \cdot \left(\frac{Zr}{2a_0}\right)}_{\chi_{2,1}(r)} \cdot \underbrace{\frac{1}{2}\sqrt{3/\pi} \cdot (x/r)}_{Y_1^1}, \quad \text{or } x.$$

All three functions: $\psi_{2,1,0}$, $\psi_{2,1,1}$, and $\psi_{2,1,\bar{1}}$ can be transformed into each other by exchange of the axes. The first two factors in all three functions are alike, depending only on r, and can be represented as a single function, $\chi(r)$, the so-called *radial factor*. The second factor, Y_l^λ depends only on the direction of the radius vector from the atomic nucleus to the point (x, y, z). A given number is associated with the point at which the radius vector to the point (x, y, z) intersects the surface of the unit sphere. In the case of the three p-functions, these numbers are the values of the x, y, or z-co-ordinate of this point of intersection, multiplied by a numerical factor, $\frac{1}{2}\sqrt{3/\pi}$. This function is called a *spherical harmonic* and is analogous to the circular functions (sine, cosine, etc.), which associate a definite number—the x or the y co-ordinate—with every point on the periphery of a circle.

The lower index of Y_l^λ gives the azimuthal (angular momentum) quantum number, or the *order of the spherical harmonic*, while the upper index is the axial quantum number.

A point (x, y, z) within an atom can also be described by spherical co-ordinates (r, ϑ, φ) Fig. 2.19. The angular co-ordinate, ϑ of a point is

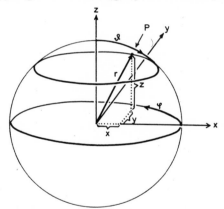

Fig. 2.19. *Cartesian co-ordinates* (x, y, z) *and polar co-ordinates* (r, ϑ, φ) *of a point P on a unit sphere.*

measured not as on earth from the 'equator', but from the 'pole', that is from the z-axis. φ corresponds to longitude on earth. The following transformations allow one to convert from Cartesian to spherical polar co-ordinates:

$$z = r \cos \vartheta$$

$$y = r \sin \vartheta \, . \, \sin \varphi$$

$$x = r \sin \vartheta \, . \, \cos \varphi.$$

If we consider a unit sphere, for which $r = 1$, the character of the spherical harmonics as pure angle functions becomes clear.

Table 2.4. The real normalized orthogonal eigenfunctions of the hydrogen atom $(Z = 1)$: $\psi_{n,l,\lambda} = \chi(r)_{n,l} \times Y_l^\lambda(x, y, z)$ *or* $Y_l^\lambda(\vartheta, \varphi)$

Electron Symbol	n l $\frac{\bar{\lambda}}{\lambda}$	$\chi_{n,l}(r)$	$\times$ $Y_l^\lambda(x, y, z)$	$Y_l^\lambda(\vartheta, \varphi)$
$1s\sigma$	1 0 0	$2 \cdot \left(\dfrac{Z}{1a_0}\right)^{3/2} \cdot e^{-Zr/1a_0}$	$\times \dfrac{1}{2\sqrt{\pi}}$	$\dfrac{1}{2\sqrt{\pi}}$
$2s\sigma$	2 0 0	$2 \cdot \left(\dfrac{Z}{2a_0}\right)^{3/2} \cdot e^{-Zr/2a_0} \cdot \left[1 - \dfrac{Zr}{2a_0}\right]$	$\times \dfrac{1}{2\sqrt{\pi}}$	$\dfrac{1}{2\sqrt{\pi}}$
$2p\sigma$	2 1 0	$\dfrac{2}{\sqrt{3}} \cdot \left(\dfrac{Z}{2a_0}\right)^{3/2} \cdot e^{-Zr/2a_0} \cdot \left[\dfrac{Zr}{2a_0}\right]$	$\times \dfrac{\sqrt{3}}{2\sqrt{\pi}} \cdot z$	$\dfrac{\sqrt{3}}{2\sqrt{\pi}} \cdot \cos\vartheta$
$2p\pi$	2 1 1	$\dfrac{2}{\sqrt{3}} \cdot \left(\dfrac{Z}{2a_0}\right)^{3/2} \cdot e^{-Zr/2a_0} \cdot \left[\dfrac{Zr}{2a_0}\right]$	$\times \dfrac{\sqrt{3}}{2\sqrt{\pi}} \cdot \begin{cases} y \\ x \end{cases}$	$\dfrac{\sqrt{3}}{2\sqrt{3}} \cdot \sin\vartheta \begin{cases} \sin\varphi \\ \cos\varphi \end{cases}$
$3s\sigma$	3 0 0	$2 \cdot \left(\dfrac{Z}{3a_0}\right)^{3/2} \cdot e^{-Zr/3a_0} \cdot \left[1 - 2\dfrac{Zr}{3a_0} + \dfrac{2}{3}\left(\dfrac{Zr}{3a_0}\right)^2\right]$	$\times \dfrac{1}{2\sqrt{\pi}}$	$\dfrac{1}{2\sqrt{\pi}}$
$3p\sigma$	3 1 0	$\dfrac{2}{3}\sqrt{2} \cdot \left(\dfrac{Z}{3a_0}\right)^{3/2} \cdot e^{-Zr/3a_0} \cdot \left[\dfrac{Zr}{3a_0}\left(2 - \dfrac{Zr}{3a_0}\right)\right]$	$\times \dfrac{\sqrt{3}}{2\sqrt{\pi}} \cdot z$	$\dfrac{\sqrt{3}}{2\sqrt{\pi}} \cdot \cos\vartheta$
$3p\pi$	3 1 1	$\dfrac{2}{3}\sqrt{2} \cdot \left(\dfrac{Z}{3a_0}\right)^{3/2} \cdot e^{-Zr/3a_0} \cdot \left[\dfrac{Zr}{3a_0}\left(2 - \dfrac{Zr}{3a_0}\right)\right]$	$\times \dfrac{\sqrt{3}}{2\sqrt{\pi}} \cdot \begin{cases} y \\ x \end{cases}$	$\dfrac{\sqrt{3}}{2\sqrt{\pi}} \cdot \sin\vartheta \begin{cases} \sin\varphi \\ \cos\varphi \end{cases}$
$3d\sigma$	3 2 0	$\dfrac{4}{3\sqrt{10}} \cdot \left(\dfrac{Z}{3a_0}\right)^{3/2} \cdot e^{-Zr/3a_0} \cdot \left[\left(\dfrac{Zr}{3a_0}\right)^2\right]$	$\times \dfrac{\sqrt{5}}{2\sqrt{\pi}}\dfrac{1}{2}(3z^2 - 1)$	$\dfrac{\sqrt{5}}{2\sqrt{\pi}}\dfrac{1}{2}(3\cos^2\vartheta - 1)$
$3d\pi$	3 2 1	$\dfrac{4}{3\sqrt{10}} \cdot \left(\dfrac{Z}{3a_0}\right)^{3/2} \cdot e^{-Zr/3a_0} \cdot \left[\left(\dfrac{Zr}{3a_0}\right)^2\right]$	$\times \dfrac{\sqrt{5}}{2\sqrt{\pi}} \cdot \sqrt{3} \begin{cases} yz \\ zx \end{cases}$	$\dfrac{\sqrt{5}}{2\sqrt{\pi}} \cdot \sqrt{3}\cos\vartheta\sin\vartheta \begin{cases} \sin\varphi \\ \cos\varphi \end{cases}$

Symbol	n l m	Radial function	× Cartesian angular	Spherical angular
$3d\delta$	3 2 2	$\dfrac{4}{3\sqrt{10}}\left(\dfrac{Z}{3a_0}\right)^{3/2}\cdot e^{-Zr/3a_0}\cdot\left[\left(\dfrac{Zr}{3a_0}\right)^2\right]$	$\times\dfrac{\sqrt5}{2\sqrt\pi}\cdot\sqrt3\begin{cases}xy\\\frac12(x^2-y^2)\end{cases}$	$\dfrac{\sqrt5}{2\sqrt\pi}\dfrac12\sqrt3\sin^2\vartheta\begin{cases}\sin2\varphi\\\cos2\varphi\end{cases}$
$4s\sigma$	4 0 0	$2\cdot\left(\dfrac{Z}{4a_0}\right)^{3/2}\cdot e^{-Zr/4a_0}\cdot\left[1-3\dfrac{Zr}{4a_0}+2\left(\dfrac{Zr}{4a_0}\right)^2-\dfrac13\left(\dfrac{Zr}{4a_0}\right)^3\right]$	$\times\dfrac{1}{2\sqrt\pi}$	$\dfrac{1}{2\sqrt\pi}$
$4p\sigma$	4 1 0	$2\sqrt{\dfrac53}\left(\dfrac{Z}{4a_0}\right)^{3/2}\cdot e^{-Zr/4a_0}\cdot\left[\dfrac{Zr}{4a_0}\left(1-\dfrac{Zr}{4a_0}+\dfrac15\left(\dfrac{Zr}{4a_0}\right)^2\right)\right]$	$\times\dfrac{\sqrt3}{2\sqrt\pi}\cdot z$	$\dfrac{\sqrt3}{2\sqrt\pi}\cdot\cos\vartheta$
$4p\pi$	4 1 1	$2\sqrt{\dfrac53}\left(\dfrac{Z}{4a_0}\right)^{3/2}\cdot e^{-Zr/4a_0}\cdot\left[\dfrac{Zr}{4a_0}\left(1-\dfrac{Zr}{4a_0}+\dfrac15\left(\dfrac{Zr}{4a_0}\right)^2\right)\right]$	$\times\dfrac{\sqrt3}{2\sqrt\pi}\begin{cases}y\\x\end{cases}$	$\dfrac{\sqrt3}{2\sqrt\pi}\cdot\sin\vartheta\begin{cases}\sin\varphi\\\cos\varphi\end{cases}$
$4d\sigma$	4 2 0	$\dfrac{2}{\sqrt5}\left(\dfrac{Z}{4a_0}\right)^{3/2}\cdot e^{-Zr/4a_0}\cdot\left[\left(\dfrac{Zr}{4a_0}\right)^2\left(1-\dfrac13\dfrac{Zr}{4a_0}\right)\right]$	$\times\dfrac{\sqrt5}{2\sqrt\pi}\dfrac12(3z^2-1)$	$\dfrac{\sqrt5}{2\sqrt\pi}\dfrac12(3\cos^2\vartheta-1)$
$4d\pi$	4 2 1	$\dfrac{2}{\sqrt5}\left(\dfrac{Z}{4a_0}\right)^{3/2}\cdot e^{-Zr/4a_0}\cdot\left[\left(\dfrac{Zr}{4a_0}\right)^2\left(1-\dfrac13\dfrac{Zr}{4a_0}\right)\right]$	$\times\dfrac{\sqrt5}{2\sqrt\pi}\cdot\sqrt3\begin{cases}yz\\zx\end{cases}$	$\dfrac{\sqrt5}{2\sqrt\pi}\cdot\sqrt3\cos\vartheta\sin\vartheta\begin{cases}\sin\varphi\\\cos\varphi\end{cases}$
$4d\delta$	4 2 2	$\dfrac{2}{\sqrt5}\left(\dfrac{Z}{4a_0}\right)^{3/2}\cdot e^{-Zr/4a_0}\cdot\left[\left(\dfrac{Zr}{4a_0}\right)^2\left(1-\dfrac13\dfrac{Zr}{4a_0}\right)\right]$	$\times\dfrac{\sqrt5}{2\sqrt\pi}\cdot\sqrt3\begin{cases}xy\\\frac12(x^2-y^2)\end{cases}$	$\dfrac{5}{2\sqrt\pi}\dfrac12\sqrt3\sin^2\vartheta\begin{cases}\sin2\varphi\\\cos2\varphi\end{cases}$
$4f\sigma$	4 3 0	$\dfrac{2}{3\sqrt{35}}\left(\dfrac{Z}{4a_0}\right)^{3/2}\cdot e^{-Zr/4a_0}\cdot\left[\left(\dfrac{Zr}{4a_0}\right)^3\right]$	$\times\dfrac{\sqrt7}{2\sqrt\pi}\dfrac12(5z^3-3z)$	$\dfrac{\sqrt7}{2\sqrt\pi}\dfrac12(5\cos^3\vartheta-3\cos\vartheta)$
$4f\pi$	4 3 1	$\dfrac{2}{3\sqrt{35}}\left(\dfrac{Z}{4a_0}\right)^{3/2}\cdot e^{-Zr/4a_0}\cdot\left[\left(\dfrac{Zr}{4a_0}\right)^3\right]$	$\times\dfrac{\sqrt7}{2\sqrt\pi}\sqrt{\dfrac38}(5z^2-1)\begin{cases}y\\x\end{cases}$	$\dfrac{\sqrt7}{2\sqrt\pi}\sqrt{\dfrac38}(5\cos^2\vartheta-1)\sin\vartheta\begin{cases}\sin\varphi\\\cos\varphi\end{cases}$
$4f\delta$	4 3 2	$\dfrac{2}{3\sqrt{35}}\left(\dfrac{Z}{4a_0}\right)^{3/2}\cdot e^{-Zr/4a_0}\cdot\left[\left(\dfrac{Zr}{4a_0}\right)^3\right]$	$\times\dfrac{\sqrt7}{2\sqrt\pi}\sqrt{\dfrac{15}{4}}\begin{cases}2xyz\\(x^2-y^2)z\end{cases}$	$\dfrac{\sqrt7}{2\sqrt\pi}\sqrt{\dfrac{15}{4}}\cos\vartheta\sin^2\vartheta\begin{cases}\sin2\varphi\\\cos2\varphi\end{cases}$
$4f\varphi$	4 3 3	$\dfrac{2}{3\sqrt{35}}\left(\dfrac{Z}{4a_0}\right)^{3/2}\cdot e^{-Zr/4a_0}\cdot\left[\left(\dfrac{Zr}{4a_0}\right)^3\right]$	$\times\dfrac{\sqrt7}{2\sqrt\pi}\sqrt{\dfrac58}\begin{cases}(3x^2-y^2)y\\(3y^2-x^2)x\end{cases}$	$\dfrac{\sqrt7}{2\sqrt\pi}\sqrt{\dfrac58}\sin^3\vartheta\begin{cases}\sin3\varphi\\\cos3\varphi\end{cases}$

In Table 2.4 are displayed the eigenfunctions of the hydrogen atom as the product of a radial function and a spherical harmonic. The spherical harmonics are given both in Cartesian and in spherical polar co-ordinates. The eigenfunctions have been normalized by the condition $\int \psi^2 d\tau = 1$, which in spherical polar co-ordinates reads:

$$\int_{r=0}^{\infty} \int_{\vartheta=0}^{\pi} \int_{\varphi=0}^{2\pi} \psi^2(r, \vartheta, \varphi) dr \cdot r d\vartheta \cdot r \sin \vartheta d\varphi =$$

$$\int_{r=0}^{\infty} \chi^2(r) r^2 dr \cdot \int_{\vartheta=0}^{\pi} \int_{\varphi=0}^{2\pi} Y^2(\vartheta, \varphi) \sin \vartheta d\vartheta d\varphi = 1.$$

The normalization is carried out so that *both* $\int_{r=0}^{\infty} \chi^2(r) r^2 dr = 1$ and $\int_{\vartheta=0}^{\pi} \int_{\varphi=0}^{2\pi} Y^2(\vartheta, \varphi) \sin \vartheta d\vartheta d\varphi = 1$. It can also be shown that the *orthogonality condition* is preserved:

$$\int_{\vartheta=0}^{\pi} \int_{\varphi=0}^{2\pi} YY' \sin \vartheta d\vartheta d\varphi = 0, \quad \text{when } Y \neq Y'.$$

That is, the surface integral over the entire sphere of the product of two different spherical harmonics (Y and Y') is equal to zero.

Electrons having an azimuthal quantum number $l = 1$, are called *p*-electrons or individually: p_x, p_y, p_z electrons. If the axial quantum number $\lambda = 0$, there is always rotational symmetry about the unique *z*-axis. An electron having such symmetry is designated by the letter σ. When $\lambda = 1$ the unique axis (z) lies in a nodal plane and one speaks of π-electrons. When $\lambda \geqslant 2$, there are λ nodal planes which meet in a straight line coincident with the *z*-axis.

The next group of electrons, the *d*-electrons, have an angular momentum quantum number, $l = 2$, and are first observed when $n = 3$. The function $\psi_{3,2,0}$ ($3d\sigma$-electron) is:

$$3d\sigma: \quad \psi_{3,2,0} = \underbrace{\frac{4}{3\sqrt{10}} \cdot \left(\frac{Z}{3a_0}\right)^{3/2} \cdot e^{-(Zr/3a_0)} \cdot \left(\frac{Zr}{3a_0}\right)^2}_{\chi_{3,2}(r)} \cdot \underbrace{\frac{1}{2}\sqrt{5/\pi} \cdot \frac{1}{2}(3z^2 - 1)}_{Y_3^0}.$$

The first factors depend only on r, and can, as in the equation above, be combined into the single function $\chi(r)$. The exponential function remains the same as for $3s$- and $3p$-electrons.

The special geometric shape and the location of the nodal surfaces is determined by the spherical harmonic, Y_3^0, and especially by the factor $(3z^2 - 1)$, which (because $x^2 + y^2 + z^2 = 1$), is frequently written as $\{2z^2 - (x^2 + y^2)\}$. Rotational symmetry about the *z*-axis results from this factor (Fig. 2.20a). The two conical nodal surfaces which come together at a point are determined by the condition that at their intersection with the unit sphere, $3z^2 = 1$. This corresponds to $\cos \vartheta = \sqrt{\frac{1}{3}}$ or $\vartheta \simeq 55°$.

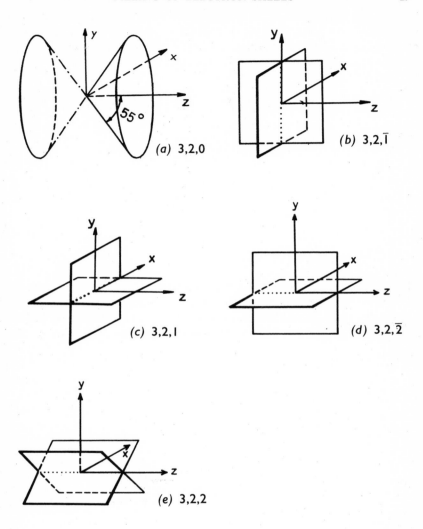

Fig. 2.20. The nodal surfaces of d-eigenfunctions ($l = 2$).

The electron is most likely to be found within the cone and in the neighbourhood of the z-axis within a certain distance from the nucleus. In the space between the two cones there is also a finite electron density in a torus perpendicular to and concentric with the z-axis (Fig. 2.21).

When the quantum number λ is varied, the following functions are

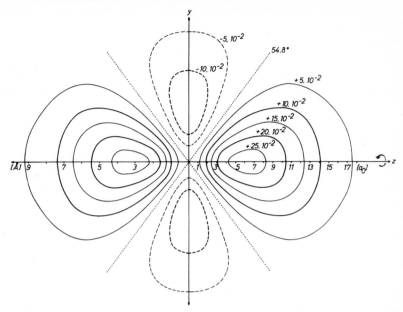

Fig. 2.21. *Representation of the function* $\psi_{3,2,0}(d_{3z^2-1})$ *of the H-atom on a central section which includes the z-axis.*

obtained in which the $\chi(r)$ factor is the same as that for the $3d\sigma$ electrons:

$3d\pi$:

$$\psi_{3,2,\bar{1}} = \frac{4}{3\sqrt{10}} \cdot \left(\frac{Z}{3a_0}\right)^{3/2} \cdot e^{-(Zr/3a_0)} \cdot \left(\frac{Zr}{3a_0}\right)^2 \cdot \frac{1}{2}\sqrt{5/\pi} \cdot \sqrt{3}\, yz$$

$$\psi_{3,2,1} = \frac{4}{3\sqrt{10}} \cdot \left(\frac{Z}{3a_0}\right)^{3/2} \cdot e^{-(Zr/3a_0)} \cdot \left(\frac{Zr}{3a_0}\right)^2 \cdot \frac{1}{2}\sqrt{5/\pi} \cdot \sqrt{3}\, zx$$

. . . .

$3d\delta$:

$$\psi_{3,2,\bar{2}} = \frac{4}{3\sqrt{10}} \cdot \left(\frac{Z}{3a_0}\right)^{3/2} \cdot e^{-(Zr/3a_0)} \cdot \left(\frac{Zr}{3a_0}\right)^2 \cdot \frac{1}{2}\sqrt{5/\pi} \cdot \sqrt{3}\, xy$$

$$\psi_{3,2,2} = \underbrace{\frac{4}{3\sqrt{10}} \cdot \left(\frac{Z}{3a_0}\right)^{3/2} \cdot e^{-(Zr/3a_0)} \cdot \left(\frac{Zr}{3a_0}\right)^2 \cdot \frac{1}{2}\sqrt{5/\pi}}_{\chi_{3,2}(r)} \quad \underbrace{\sqrt{3}\frac{1}{2}(x^2 - y^2).}_{Y_2^\lambda}$$

As can easily be derived for $\lambda = 1$ or 2, the nodal surfaces are planar. These can also be regarded as degenerate cones with a cone angle of 180° (Fig. 2.20). The planes are perpendicular to each other. For $\lambda = 1$, their intersection coincides with the y- or x-axis respectively. The two functions for $\lambda = 1$ can be transformed into each other by rotation about the z-axis. In the case of $\lambda = 2$, the line of intersection of the two nodal planes must be coincident with the z-axis. In this case the two functions can be superposed by a rotation of $45°$ about the z-axis. Figure 2.22 shows the eigenfunctions $\psi_{3,2,2}$ through a central section of the atom perpendicular to the z-axis.

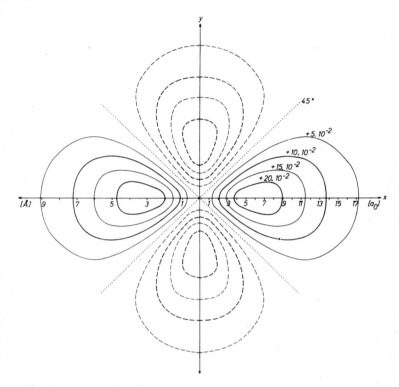

Fig. 2.22. *Representation of the function $\psi_{3,2,2}(d_{x^2-y^2})$ of the H-atom on a central section which contains both the x- and the y-axis.*

When $l = 3$, f-electrons occur. These functions will be only briefly given and represented by their nodal surfaces.

$$4f\sigma: \quad \psi_{4,3,0} = \frac{2}{3\sqrt{35}} \cdot \left(\frac{Z}{4a_0}\right)^{3/2} \cdot e^{-(Zr/4a_0)} \cdot \left(\frac{Zr}{4a_0}\right)^3 \cdot \frac{1}{2}\sqrt{7/\pi} \cdot$$
$$\frac{1}{2}(5z^3 - 3z).$$

This eigenfunction is rotationally symmetric about the z-axis and has three conical nodes, one of which has a cone angle of $180°$ (Fig. 2.23a). In the neighbourhood of the z-axis, this function looks similar to a p_z-eigenfunction. In both cases the eigenfunctions have a maximum near the z-axis and change sign on going from positive to negative z.

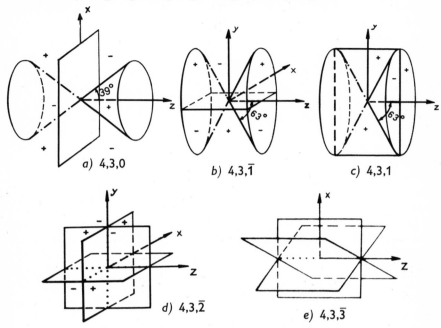

Fig. 2.23. *The nodal surfaces of f-eigenfunctions.*

The functions:

$4f\pi:$ $\psi_{4,3,\overline{1}} = \dfrac{2}{3\sqrt{35}} \cdot \left(\dfrac{Z}{4a_0}\right)^{3/2} \cdot e^{-(Zr/4a_0)} \cdot \left(\dfrac{Zr}{4a_0}\right)^3 \cdot \dfrac{1}{2} \sqrt{7/\pi}\,.$

or 4, 3, 1

$$\sqrt{\tfrac{3}{8}}\,(5z^2 - 1) \begin{cases} y, \text{ or} \\ x \end{cases}$$

have one nodal plane which contains the z-axis and two conical nodal surfaces (Fig. 2.23b, c).

$4f\delta:$ $\psi_{4,3,\overline{2}} = \dfrac{2}{3\sqrt{35}} \cdot \left(\dfrac{Z}{4a_0}\right)^{3/2} \cdot e^{-(Zr/4a_0)} \cdot \left(\dfrac{Zr}{4a_0}\right)^3 \cdot \dfrac{1}{2} \sqrt{7/\pi}\,.$

or 4, 3, 2

$$\sqrt{\tfrac{15}{4}} \begin{cases} (2xyz) \text{ or} \\ (x^2 - y^2)z \end{cases}$$

have three mutually perpendicular nodal planes. Rotation by $45°$ about the z-axis transforms $\Psi_{4,3,\overline{2}}$ into $\Psi_{4,3,2}$ (Fig. 2.23d).

The two functions $\Psi_{4,3,3}$ and $\Psi_{4,3,\bar{3}}$,

$4f\varphi:$ $\psi_{4,3,\bar{3}} = \dfrac{2}{3\sqrt{35}} \cdot \left(\dfrac{Z}{4a_0}\right)^{3/2} \cdot e^{-(Zr/4a_0)} \cdot \left(\dfrac{Zr}{4a_0}\right)^3 \cdot \dfrac{1}{2}\sqrt{7/\pi} \cdot$
or $4,3,3$
$\qquad\qquad\qquad\qquad\qquad\qquad\qquad\qquad\qquad \sqrt{\tfrac{5}{8}}\begin{cases}(3x^2 - y^2)y \text{ or} \\ (3y^2 - x^2)x\end{cases}$

have three planar nodal surfaces which cut each other at angles of $120°$. The line of intersection is the z-axis. The functions are transformed into each other by a rotation of $90°$ about the z-axis (Fig. 2.23e).

p-, d-, and f-electrons always have non-spherical nodal surfaces. When, however, the principal quantum number, n, is greater than in the cases considered above, additional spherical nodal surfaces are obtained, the number of which is given by $n - l - 1$. The following general rules can be given for the nodes:

(a) The total number of nodal surfaces is $n - 1$.

(b) The number of non-spherical nodes is given by l.

(c) The number of nodal planes which contain the z-axis is given by λ.

Figures 2.15 and 2.16 (pages 21 and 22) show the influence of the two quantum numbers, n and l, on the shape of the eigenfunction and the probability density for the electron being considered. Figure 2.16 shows the values of several eigenfunctions as a function of distance from the nucleus along the positive x-direction. In Fig. 2.15 $4\pi r^2\psi^2$, the probability distribution over spherical surfaces drawn about the nucleus, is plotted for several lower states of the hydrogen atom. Both figures show clearly that with increasing principal as well as azimuthal quantum number the electrons are forced farther and farther from the nucleus. The influence of the principal quantum number can be seen by comparing the curves for $\psi_{1,0,0}$, $\psi_{2,0,0}$, and $\psi_{3,0,0}$; or $\psi_{2,1,0}$ and $\psi_{3,1,0}$, that of the azimuthal number by comparison of $\psi_{3,0,0}$. $\psi_{3,1,0}$, and $\psi_{3,2,0}$. It is important to note that in the neighbourhood of the nucleus the value of the ψ-function becomes smaller as the azimuthal quantum number becomes larger. Only at 1.5 Å is the magnitude of the $3d$ eigenfunction (Fig. 2.15) great enough for the curve to leave the abscissa in the scale used. At greater distances, the electron density probability over spherical surfaces is not strongly dependent on the angular momentum quantum number. (Compare the curves for quantum numbers 2,0 with 2,1 or 3,0 with 3,1 and 3,2.)

For chemical bonding, it is very important to remember that because of the increasing number of nodal surfaces as l increases, an electron with high l is strongly directional. This directionality is shown in Figs. 2.24a–e, where the spherical harmonics $Y_0{}^0$, $Y_1{}^0$, $Y_2{}^0$, $Y_3{}^0$, and $Y_2{}^1$ are plotted on polar diagrams. Because of their shape on a polar diagram p- and d-electrons are frequently represented by the symbols ⬿⬾ and ✻ respectively.

4

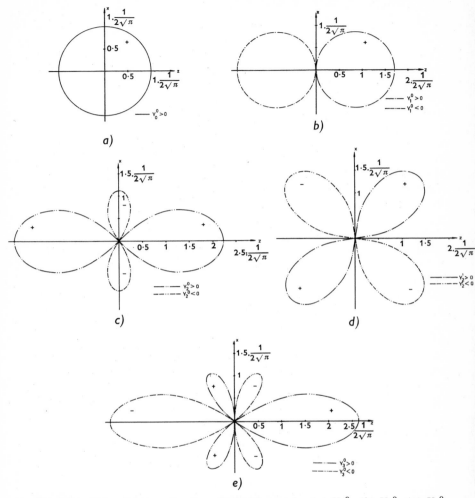

Fig. 2.24. Polar diagrams for the spherical harmonics (a) $Y_0{}^0$, (b) $Y_1{}^0$, (c) $Y_2{}^0$, (d) $Y_2{}^1$, and (e) $Y_3{}^0$, i.e., for (a) s-, (b) p_z-, (c) d_{3z^2-1}-, (d) d_{zx}-, and (e) f_{5z^3-3z}-electrons.

One apparent peculiarity of the eigenfunctions should be noted. This is their behaviour when reflected at the origin of the co-ordinate system, which is called *inversion*. For s- and d-electrons, the two eigenfunctions, $\psi(x, y, z)$, and $\psi(-x, -y, -z)$, are identical. With p- and f-electrons, however, $\psi(x, y, z) = -\psi(-x, -y, -z)$. The former functions (i.e., those which are unchanged on inversion) are called *gerade* functions. The others, which change sign on inversion are called *ungerade* functions.

Eigenfunctions which differ only in their orientation in space, as for example, the p-eigenfunctions p_x, p_y, p_z or the three d-eigenfunctions d_{xy}. d_{yz}, d_{xz} have naturally the same energy eigenvalues. In the free atom, these eigenfunctions are indistinguishable and are referred to as *degenerate* eigenfunctions. Only when the atom is, for example, placed in a magnetic field or forms a chemical bond, is it possible to differentiate these orbitals. The eigenvalues then differ; the associated electronic terms are *split*, and the degeneracy is either partially or completely removed.

As seen from the spectra of atoms or ions, all eigenfunctions (of a given atom or ion) having the same n and l are degenerate. When the spin (see later) is excepted the terms of the alkali-metal spectra are characterized by the principal and azimuthal quantum numbers. The axial quantum number is not spectroscopically observable, and both d_{xy} and $d_{x^2-y^2}$ have the same energy. They are thus mutually degenerate. In the special case of the hydrogen atom and those ions which are isoelectronic with it (e.g., He$^+$), all eigenfunctions with the same n are degenerate. Thus in Balmer's formula only the principal quantum number is involved.

The interaction of an electron with a magnetic field will be briefly discussed. A p_z-eigenfunction is rotationally symmetric about the z-axis. The square of this function, which represents the probable electron-density, has the same rotational symmetry. Rotation about the z-axis does not change the orientation of the electron, and hence no circular current flows. If, however, a p_x- or a p_y-electron is rotated about the z-axis, a circular current results which has associated with it a magnetic moment. This so-called *orbital moment* can be oriented either parallel or antiparallel to an external field in the z-direction depending on the direction in which the electron moves. By means of quantum mechanical calculations, supported by experiment, this moment, parallel to the z-axis, can be shown to be

$$\pm (eh/4\pi mc)$$

where e and m are respectively the charge and mass of an electron, h is Planck's constant, and c is the velocity of light. The quantity $eh/4\pi mc$, is called the *Bohr magneton* and is often denoted by μ_B.

If the factor $3/4\pi$ is neglected one p_x and one p_y electron together give the electron density

$$\chi^2(r) \cdot x^2 + \chi^2(r) \cdot y^2 = \chi^2(r) \cdot (x^2 + y^2).$$

The state of this system is thus also circularly symmetrical about the z-axis and no magnetic moment is possible.

In general, the orbital magnetic moment of an electron in a magnetic field is $\pm \lambda$ Bohr magneton. With several d- or f-electrons, more complicated relations hold, which will be developed later.

3

The Basis of the Periodic System
of the Elements

3.1 Electron Spin and the Pauli Principle

Dirac deduced from the theory of relativity that every electron has a magnetic moment. This moment is called a *spin moment* in the earlier quantum theory, where the spin was supposed to be a result of the rotation of an electron about its axis. Associated with this moment is a quantum number, which can be either $+\frac{1}{2}$ (α-electron) or $-\frac{1}{2}$ (β-electron). The sign is determined by whether the spin moment is aligned parallel or antiparallel to an external magnetic field.

The spin moment of an electron can be experimentally determined by the 'Stern–Gerlach experiment'. A beam of atoms having an odd number of s-electrons (H, Na, Ag) is made to pass through an inhomogeneous magnetic field, M (Fig. 3.1). In this way the atoms will be differently

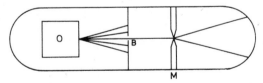

Fig. 3.1. *Splitting of an atomic beam in a magnetic field according to Stern–Gerlach. O-oven with an aperture to produce the atomic ray, B-aperture, M-pole face of the magnet.*

displaced depending on the orientation of the electron spin moment relative to the magnetic field (parallel or antiparallel). The magnitude of the spin moment determined by this experiment agrees with that predicted by the theory, i.e., $\sqrt{s(s+1)} = \sqrt{3}/2$ Bohr magneton.

For a complete description of the state of an electron in an atom, four quantum numbers: n, l, λ, s, are thus required. In 1925, Pauli[3.1] stated, for the first time, an important principle which applies to all electrons bound in an atom: 'no two electrons in an atom can have all four quantum numbers the same'. Naturally, λ and $\bar{\lambda}$ must be distinguished.

The following combinations of quantum numbers are then possible for the various principal quantum numbers:

Table 3.1. Possible combinations for the quantum numbers n, l, λ, and s

Shell	n	l	λ	s	Sum of all possibilities
K	1	0		$\pm\frac{1}{2}$	2
L	2	0	0	$\pm\frac{1}{2}$	8
		1	1, $\bar{1}$, 0	,,	
M	3	0	0	$\pm\frac{1}{2}$	18
		1	1, $\bar{1}$, 0	,,	
		2	2, $\bar{2}$,..0	,,	
N	4	0	as M	$\pm\frac{1}{2}$	32
		1	,,	,,	
		2	,,	,,	
		3	3, $\bar{3}$,..0		
O	5	0	as N	$\pm\frac{1}{2}$	50
		1	,,	,,	
		2	,,	,,	
		3	,,	,,	
		4	4, $\bar{4}$,..0	,,	

This summary brings out the parallel between the maximum number of electrons for a given principal quantum number and the length of a given period on the periodic table.

3.2 Discussion of the Periodic System

Applying the above results to a step-by-step build-up of the periodic system, we obtain the following:

Table 3.2. The periodic system and electron arrangement

	K	L	M	N	O	P	Q	Eff. Nuclear charge Z^*
n	1	2	3	4	5	6	7	
l	s	s p	s p d	s p d f	s p d f	s p d	s	
H	1							1·00
He	2							1·35

Table 3.2. The periodic system and electron arrangement —*cont.*

	K	L		M			N				O				P			Q	Eff. Nuclear charge Z*
n	1	2		3			4				5				6			7	
l	s	s	p	s	p	d	s	p	d	f	s	p	d	f	s	p	d	s	
Li	2	1																	1·26
Be	2	2																	1·65
B	2	2	1																1·56
C	2	2	2																1·82
N	2	2	3																2·07
O	2	2	4																2·00
F	2	2	5																2·26
Ne	2	2	6																2·52
Na	2	2	6	1															1·85
Mg				2															2·25
Al				2	1														1·98
Si				2	2														2·32
P				2	3														2·72
S				2	4														2·62
Cl				2	5														2·95
Ar				2	6														3·24
K	2	2	6	2	6		1												2·25
Ca							2												2·68
Sc						1	2												2·78
Ti						2	2												2·82
V						3	2												2·82
Cr						5	1												2·80
Mn						5	2												2·94
Fe						6	2												3·04
Co						7	2												3·03
Ni						8	2												3·00
Cu						10	1												3·00
Zn						10	2												3·32
Ga						10	2	1											2·64
Ge						10	2	2											3·04
As						10	2	3											3·42
Se						10	2	4											3·38
Br						10	2	5											3·72
Kr						10	2	6											4·06
Rb	2	2	6	2	6	10	2	6			1								2·77
Sr											2								3·24

	K	L		M			N				O				P			Q	Eff. Nuclear charge Z^*
n	1	2		3			4				5				6			7	
l	s	s	p	s	p	d	s	p	d	f	s	p	d	f	s	p	d	s	
Y									1		2								3·47
Zr									2		2								3·58
Nb									4		1								—
Mo									5		1								3·69
Tc									6		1								—
Ru									7		1								3·77
Rh									8		1								3·77
Pd									10		0								—
Ag									10		1								3·73
Cd									10		2								4·07
In									10		2	1							3·26
Sn									10		2	2							3·67
Sb									10		2	3							3·96
Te									10		2	4							4·07
I									10		2	5							4·43
Xe									10		2	6							4·73
Cs	2	2	6	2	6	10	2	6	10		2	6			1				3·21
Ba															2				3·72
La													1		2				3·86
Ce										2					2				4·17
Pr										3					2				3·93
Nd										4					2				4·10
Pm										5					2				—
Sm										6					2				4·19
Eu										7					2				3·88
Gd										7			1		2				4·23
Tb										9					2				—
Dy										10					2				—
Ho										11					2				—
Er										12					2				—
Tm										13					2				—
Yb										14					2				4·35
Lu										14			1		2				—
Hf										14			2		2				—
Ta										14			3		2				—
W										14			4		2				4·62
Re										14			5		2				—
Os										14			6		2				—
Ir										14			7		2				—
Pt										14			9		1				4·87

Table 3.2. The periodic system and electron arrangement —cont.

	K	L	M	N	O	P	Q	Eff. Nuclear charge Z^*
n	1	2	3	4	5	6	7	
l	s	s p	s p d	s p d f	s p d f	s p d	s	
Au				14	10	1		4·96
Hg				14	10	2		5·27
Tl				14	10	2 1		4·02
Pb				14	10	2 2		4·44
Bi				14	10	2 3		4·62
Po				14	10	2 4		—
At				14	10	2 5		—
Rn				14	10	2 6		5·34
Fr	2	2 6	2 6 10	2 6 10 14	2 6 10	2 6	1	—
Ra							2	4·37
Ac						1	2	—
Th						2	2	—
Pa					2	1	2	—
U					3	1	2	—
Np					4	1	2	—
Pu					5	1	2	—
Am					7		2	—
Cm					7	1	2	—
Bk					8	1	2	—
Cf					10		2	—
Es					11		2	—
Fm					12		2	—
Md					13		2	—
102 (No)					14		2	—
Lw					14·	1	2	—
Kt					14	2	2	—

Observations on the First Period

If the energy for the electron in the He^+-ion is calculated from the equation previously given for the spectral lines of hydrogen, the following is obtained:

$$E = h\nu = hcR_{He}2^2\left(\frac{1}{1^2} - \frac{1}{n^2}\right) \text{ with } n = \infty.$$

It is immediately apparent that this electron is four times as strongly bound as is the electron of a hydrogen atom, since the nuclear charge ($Z = 2$)

appears as the square. If a second electron is now added, it will occupy the same quantum state as the first electron, except that the spins will be opposed. In this way, the second electron comes as closely as possible to the nucleus and gives up the greatest amount of energy. If electron 1 is in a $1s$-state, its electron terms are given by:

$$E = h\nu = hcR_{He}Z^2_{n, l, \text{eff}} \frac{1}{n^2}.$$

$Z_{n, l, \text{eff}}$ is the *effective nuclear charge* which operates on the second electron (quantum numbers n, l). This is smaller than 2, since a part of the nuclear charge is shielded by the first electron.

In a helium atom, both electrons are described by the same spatial function, $\psi_{1, 0, 0}(x, y, z)$. They are differentiated only by their spins. The shielding of the nuclear charge acting on one electron by the second electron is minimal in the immediate neighbourhood of the atomic nucleus, where Z_{eff} is only slightly less than two. In the outermost regions of the atom, the mutual shielding is greatest and Z_{eff} tends toward a value of 1. Z_{eff} is therefore a function of r, the distance from the atomic nucleus. The energy of the two electrons, their term level, is given by an average effective nuclear charge, $\bar{Z}_{\text{eff}}$. This can be easily calculated, in the special case of the ground state of helium, from the ionization energy He $\rightarrow$ He^{2+} + 2e^- + 1818 kcal/mol. When one compares this value with the ionization energy of the hydrogen atom, H $\rightarrow$ H$^+$ + e^- + 313 kcal/mol, then

$$\frac{\text{Ionization energy He} \rightarrow \text{He}^{2+}}{\text{Ionization energy H} \rightarrow \text{H}^+} = \frac{1818}{313} = 2\bar{Z}^2_{1, 0, \text{eff}} = 2(1 \cdot 7)^2.$$

In other cases, the determination of $\bar{Z}_{\text{eff}}$ and especially Z_{eff} as a function of r is very complicated and is possible only through approximation methods. Therefore another effective nuclear charge, which we shall designate as Z^*_{eff}, is frequently used. This is given by the ratio of the ionization energy, e.g., He $\rightarrow$ He$^+$ + e^-, to that of hydrogen in the comparable electronic state. For example, for the $1s$-electrons on the two atoms:

$$\frac{\text{Ionization energy He} \rightarrow \text{He}^+}{\text{Ionization energy H} \rightarrow \text{H}^+} = \frac{566 \text{ kcal/mol}}{313 \text{ kcal/mol}} = Z^{*2}_{\text{eff}} = 1 \cdot 35^2.$$

In this way the increase in nuclear bonding by one electron, when the other is removed, is ignored.

If now the effective nuclear charge in the excited state of the helium atom, $1s^1 2s^1$ (one electron in the $1s$ state and one in the $2s$ state), is considered, a value for

$$Z^*_{2, 0, \text{eff}} = 1 \cdot 08$$

can be calculated from the spectrum. This calculation is made by comparing the ionization energy of a 2s-electron of an excited helium atom to that for a 2s electron of hydrogen. This latter value can be calculated by substituting higher values of n in the equation for the terms of hydrogen. In our case, $n = 2$ and the excitation energy,

$$E_1 - E_2 = hv = hcR_H(1/n^2 - 1/m^2).$$

For the ionization energy, $E = hcR_H(1/n^2)$, since $m = \infty$. The ionization energy of hydrogen, which from the ground state ($n = 1$) is 313 kcal is 78·2 kcal from the first excited state ($n = 2$) and 34·8 kcal from the next higher excited state ($n = 3$).

Since the 2s-electron in an excited helium atom is farther removed from the nucleus than a 1s-electron, the first electron is better able to shield it from the nucleus, as is also shown by the lower effective nuclear charge. On the same basis, the shielding is still better for a 2p-electron ($1s^1 2p^1$). Here, the effective nuclear charge is only slightly greater than one, namely 1·03.

The two K-shell electrons in the ground state of helium are in the immediate neighbourhood of the nucleus, and can shield the nuclear charge very effectively from the region of space farther removed from the nucleus. There is, therefore, no appreciable force tending to attract electrons from neighbouring atoms to produce an He^--ion. Also the ionization energy is so high that no He^+-ion can be formed by chemical processes. Helium is therefore a 'noble' gas, i.e., it is chemically inert.

The effective nuclear charge on helium is greater than unity; therefore, the diameter of the helium atom must be smaller than that of the hydrogen atom. This is so because here the exponential factor $e^{-(Z_{eff} \cdot r/n \cdot a)}$ in the radial part, $\chi(r)$, of the eigenfunction, $\psi_{1,0,0}$, is determinative. As Table 3.2 shows, the noble gases are always distinguished by a high effective nuclear charge. In any given period of the Periodic Table, the noble gas atom has the smallest diameter, while the alkali metal has the largest.

All atoms and ions such as H and He^+ which have unpaired electrons, are paramagnetic, while atoms and ions with only paired electrons are diamagnetic, since here the spin moments are all compensated.

The Schrödinger equation for a system of two electrons around one nucleus (Fig. 3.2) is:

$$\frac{\partial^2 \psi(x_1 y_1 z_1 x_2 y_2 z_2)}{\partial x_1{}^2} + \frac{\partial^2 \psi(x_1 y_1 z_1 x_2 y_2 z_2)}{\partial y_1{}^2} + \frac{\partial^2 \psi(x_1 y_1 z_1 x_2 y_2 z_2)}{\partial z_1{}^2}$$

$$+ \frac{\partial^2 \psi(x_1 y_1 z_1 x_2 y_2 z_2)}{\partial x_2{}^2} + \frac{\partial^2 \psi(x_1 y_1 z_1 x_2 y_2 z_2)}{\partial y_2{}^2} + \frac{\partial^2 \psi(x_1 y_1 z_1 x_2 y_2 z_2)}{\partial z_2{}^2}$$

$$+ \frac{8\pi^2 m}{h^2}\left(E + \frac{e_1 Ze}{r_1} + \frac{e_2 Ze}{r_2} - \frac{e_1 e_2}{r_{12}} \right)\psi(x_1 y_1 z_1 x_2 y_2 z_2) = 0.$$

In this equation, ψ is a function of the co-ordinates of both electrons 1 and 2, r_1 and r_2 are the distances of the respective electrons from the nucleus with charge Ze, and r_{12} is the relative distance between the two electrons. E is the eigenvalue of this Schrödinger equation and represents the sum of the binding energies of the two electrons, $E = E_1 + E_2$. An equation such as this is no longer analytically soluble. Instead, complicated approximation methods must be used in order to approach closer and closer to the solution of the equation. In the case of the lithium atom, the equation is dependent on the co-ordinates of three electrons, a total of nine co-ordinates, and the equation is still more intractable. Further

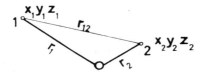

Fig. 3.2. Co-ordinates of the two electrons (1 and 2) in a He-*atom.*

considerations on the build up of the periodic system can therefore be only qualitative. These more complex cases are approximately described by so-called one-electron functions, or *orbitals*, in which co-ordinates of one electron only are considered. The fact that the properties of electrons in a many-electron system are interdependent is ignored in this approximation.

Comments on the Second Period

The filling of the L-shell begins with lithium, where the first 2s-electron appears. Here the effective nuclear charge is found to be $Z_{eff} = 1.26$.

When yet another electron is added (beryllium) it too goes into the s-shell, because s-orbitals have greater values in the neighbourhood of the nucleus than do p-orbitals. The shielding is thus poorer for s-electrons. The first p-electron is added at boron. The additional electrons in carbon and nitrogen occupy states in which they experience a minimum of shielding from the electrons already present. Since shielding is better for electrons in the same p-state, this means that the second and third p-electrons enter the unoccupied p-states. In fact, all states in a free atom having the same azimuthal quantum number (some heavy transition elements excepted) are first singly occupied, and the spin moments are parallel. This is *Hund's*[3.2] *Rule*, which will be treated in more detail later. (See chapter 8, section 4.3.)

When a third p-electron is added, the nuclear charge is again optimally shielded. Therefore, Z_{eff}^* becomes smaller for the addition of a fourth electron. This is easier to understand if one considers the electron density distribution on an atom with half and completely occupied subshells. For the p-subshell this can be described by the following equation:

$$\psi_{p_x}^2 + \psi_{p_y}^2 + \psi_{p_z}^2 = N^2\chi^2(r)(x^2 + y^2 + z^2).$$

The electron density is thus spherically symmetric, which explains the unexpected properties and increased stability of all elements and ions with either half or completely filled subshells. An electron which either half or completely fills a subshell is always especially firmly bound. The ionization energy and Z_{eff}^* are large since the electron is built into a hole (further reasons will be given later, chapter 8.4.3).

While the sum of the ψ^2-functions is spherically symmetric, the sum of the ψ-functions,

$$\psi_{p_x} + \psi_{p_y} + \psi_{p_z} = N\chi(r)(x + y + z),$$

is not. Further, the Cartesian axes remain characterized by large values of the ψ-functions. This fact is very important for chemical bonding.

The later elements of the second period (oxygen, fluorine, neon) show a decrease in paramagnetic susceptibility with increasing electron pairing.

Comments on the Third Period

In the third period, the filling of the M-shell begins. This shell, however, is completed in this period only up to the $3p$-levels. Argon is a noble gas, even though there is an empty $3d$-subshell available.

Remarks on the Fourth Period

The fourth period is the first of the so-called long periods. Potassium and calcium add $4s$-electrons as would be expected. With scandium, however, the next electron goes not into a $4p$-shell, but rather into the still empty $3d$-shell. Scandium and those elements following it which add electrons in the $3d$-shell are called *transition elements*. This seeming anomaly is due to the fact that the probability density of the $4s$-electrons in the neighbourhood of the nucleus is greater than in the case of the $3d$-electrons. This is not too surprising since a d-electron has two, non-spherical, nodal surfaces which go through the nucleus, making the magnitude of the ψ-function around the nucleus quite small.

The previously-mentioned enhanced stability of half-filled sub-shells is clearly shown by the electronic configuration of chromium. While one might expect this to be $1s^2 2s^2 2p^6 3s^2 3p^6 3d^4 4s^2$, the tendency to form a half-filled shell is so great that one of the $4s$-electrons is 'demoted' to the $3d$-level, giving a configuration, $\ldots 3d^5 4s^1$. A similar deviation from the expected order of sub-shell filling occurs with copper. The easy formation of Fe^{3+} is understandable from the build-up of the electron shells, since here, as in the case of Mn^{2+}, a half-filled d-shell and, therefore, spherical symmetry occurs. Compound formation is dependent on still other factors, since both iron and manganese have different valence states.

While both zinc and calcium have the same electronic configuration ($4s^2$) in the outermost shell, the elements differ greatly in their effective nuclear charge. Because of the two nodal surfaces, the $3d$-electrons of zinc are pressed outwards to the periphery of the atom. Since the nuclear charge is poorly shielded, the two $4s$-electrons are relatively strongly bound (high ionization energy) and are drawn closer to the nucleus. The zinc atom, despite its larger number of electrons, is thus smaller than the calcium atom. Since $4s$-electrons on calcium can be easily removed, calcium tends to form salt-like compounds, while the electrons on zinc are strongly bound and it tends to form complexes.

Remarks on the Fifth Period

This series is similar to the fourth period. First the $5s$- and $4d$-shells are filled, and then the $5p$. In the fifth period, however, there is a much stronger competition between the $5s$- and $4d$-levels, than between the corresponding levels of the fourth period. This competition shows itself in the greater number of cases where the s-electron is pulled into the d-shell, and in the easier valence changes among these elements.

Remarks on the Sixth Period

After the $6s$-level is filled at caesium and barium, one would expect filling of the $5d$-levels to begin. However, there are still vacant $4f$-orbitals, and following lanthanum, which has one $5d$-electron, it is the $4f$-shell which is filled (cerium, praseodymium, ... lutetium). Indeed, the $4f$-shell becomes energetically so favourable that the electron which is in the $5d$-shell in lanthanum falls into the $4f$-level in cerium. No $5d$-electron reappears until gadolinium, where a half-filled $4f$-shell can be retained. The late filling of the $4f$-level is due to the number of non-spherical nodal surfaces (three), which push the f-electrons away from the nucleus. The valence of these fourteen *rare earth elements* is generally three. However, where it is possible to form or retain a half- or completely-filled shell bivalence and tetravalence is observed (e.g., Eu^{2+} and Tb^{4+}).

Remarks on the Seventh Period

The building up of the periodic system now continues regularly until the *actinide elements* are reached. Here again an f-level is being filled and there is strong competition for electrons between the $5f$- and $6d$-levels. This results in many oxidation states for these elements, and also leads to difficulty in determining the position of these elements in the periodic table. The electron configurations given in Table 3.2 have not been experimentally confirmed from berkelium onwards.

Remarks on Groups IA, IIA, IB, and IIB

With the addition of an electron to start a new s-level in the alkali metals, there is a large increase in size of the atom. This occurs because in the expression $e^{-(Z_{eff}r/na)}$, the principal quantum number, n, increases by 1 while Z_{eff} is relatively small. In any given period of the periodic table, the electrons in the outermost shells become more and more strongly held as the nuclear charge increases, so that the diameters of the atoms decrease, although not always regularly, until the next inert gas is reached.

If one considers the alkali and alkaline earth groups, the ionization energy is seen to decrease monotonically with increasing atomic weight (Tables 3.2, 3.3). If in contrast, one looks at the subgroup elements (copper, silver, gold; zinc, cadmium, mercury), the effective nuclear charges and ionization energies are generally higher and they both increase with increasing atomic weight. It should be especially noted that the elements gold and mercury in the third long period have extremely high effective nuclear charges and correspondingly high ionization energies. The subgroup elements with completed d-shells are therefore distinguished by tightly bound valence electrons, and they tend to form typical co-ordination compounds.

Table 3.3. Ionization energies in kilocalories/mole

			$Me \rightarrow Me^+ + e^-$			
Me	E_{ion}	$Z^*_{eff.}$	Me	E_{ion}	$Z^*_{eff.}$	E_{ion} calculated for H with $n = 1-7$
H	313	1				313
Li	123·5	1·26				78·2
Na	117·7	1·85				34·8
K	99·5	2·25	Cu	177	3·00	19·6
Rb	95·8	2·8	Ag	174	3·73	12·5
Cs	89·2	3·2	Au	212	4·94	8·7
Fr						6·4
Be	213·8	1·65				
Mg	175·3	2·25				
Ca	140·3	2·68	Zn	216	3·33	
Sr	130·6	3·62	Cd	207	4·07	
Ba	119·6	3·70	Hg	242	5·28	
			$Me \rightarrow Me^{2+} + 2e^-$			
Ca	414		Zn	629		
Sr	384		Cd	595		
Ba	350		Hg	674		

4

Single Bond Systems

4.1 Bonding in the Hydrogen Molecule

The following forces are involved in the formation of the hydrogen molecule (Fig. 4.1):

(a) Mutual repulsion of the nuclei, A and B
(b) Mutual repulsion of the electrons, 1 and 2
(c) Attractions between nuclei and electrons: A,1; A,2; B,1; B,2.

If we consider both nuclei to be fixed in space, the Schrödinger equation for the 'simple' case of a hydrogen molecule reads:

$$\frac{\partial^2 \psi(x_1 y_1 z_1 x_2 y_2 z_2)}{\partial x_1^2} + \frac{\partial^2 \psi(x_1 y_1 z_1 x_2 y_2 z_2)}{\partial y_1^2} + \frac{\partial^2 \psi(x_1 y_1 z_1 x_2 y_2 z_2)}{\partial z_1^2}$$

$$+ \frac{\partial^2 \psi(x_1 y_1 z_1 x_2 y_2 z_2)}{\partial x_2^2} + \frac{\partial^2 \psi(x_1 y_1 z_1 x_2 y_2 z_2)}{\partial y_2^2} + \frac{\partial^2 \psi(x_1 y_1 z_1 x_2 y_2 z_2)}{\partial z_2^2}$$

$$+ \frac{8\pi^2 m}{h^2} \left(E + \frac{e_1 e}{r_{1A}} + \frac{e_1 e}{r_{1B}} + \frac{e_2 e}{r_{2A}} + \frac{e_2 e}{r_{2B}} - \frac{e_1 e_2}{r_{12}} - \frac{ee}{r_{AB}} \right)$$

$$\times \psi(x_1 y_1 z_1 x_2 y_2 z_2) = 0$$

where r_{1A} represents the distance of electron 1 from nucleus A (etc.); r_{12} is the distance between the two electrons; r_{AB} is the distance between the two nuclei, and e is the charge on a hydrogen nucleus. The eigenfunctions depend on the six spatial co-ordinates $(x_1 y_1 z_1 x_2 y_2 z_2)$ of the two electrons. The eigenvalue of the two electrons, $E = E_1 + E_2$, is specified by four quantum numbers. To each eigenvalue, there belong one or more eigenfunctions, $\psi(x_1 y_1 z_1 x_2 y_2 z_2)$. Just as we found previously for helium, the equation is not analytically soluble. There are essentially two approximate methods which allow us to come close to the correct solution. These are the *valence bond theory* of Heitler, London,[4.1] Pauling,[4.2] and Slater,[4.3] and the *molecular orbital theory* of Hund[4.4] and Mulliken.[4.5] Since the valence bond theory is more familiar to chemists, this will be discussed primarily.

If two hydrogen atoms are brought close enough to form a hydrogen molecule, and the attractive force is calculated for the case where each electron remains localized about its original nucleus, a bond energy of only 5 kcal/mol is obtained. Experimentally, however, the bond energy is found to be 103 kcal/mol. The greater part of the bonding energy must be based on a special effect. This effect is that in the bonding state, the electrons are not required to remain on a particular nucleus. In the above

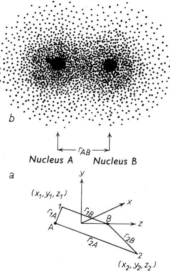

Fig. 4.1. (a) Co-ordinates for the two electrons, 1 and 2, for setting up the Schrödinger equation of the H_2-molecule. (b) Approximate electron density distribution in a H_2-molecule along a section which contains both atom nuclei.

Schrödinger equation for the hydrogen molecule there is also no assignment of an electron to a certain nucleus. Each electron experiences equal attractive forces from both nuclei. The Schrödinger equation contains the expressions $(e_1 e)/r_{1B}$, $(e_1 e)/r_{1A}$, etc. in equal weights. If one postulates that the two electrons have opposed spins, there is no reason why electron 2 for example, say a β-electron, cannot wander over to nucleus A, since there is still a free $1s\beta$-orbital there. Correspondingly, there is a vacant $1s\alpha$-quantum state on nucleus B available for electron 1. Thus both electrons can, and in fact do, belong to both nuclei. The assignment of the electrons to both nuclei can be approximately visualized by imagining that the two electrons exchange their positions. The energy gain resulting from such a process is called the *exchange energy*. Naturally, because of Coulombic repulsion, if electron 1 is on atom A, there is a high probability of finding electron 2 on atom B.

The exchange energy and correspondingly, the bonding energy in general increase as: (a) the nucleus bonds the valence electrons more strongly, and (b) the two atomic orbitals more deeply interpenetrate. This latter process is referred to as *overlapping* of the atomic eigenfunctions or orbitals, respectively. The bonding would be strongest if both eigenfunctions could be made to coincide. This is, of course, prevented by the Coulombic repulsion of the nuclei. The bonding function for each electron is, to a first approximation, the appropriately normalized sum of the eigenfunctions of the separated atoms. A definite increase in electron density in the neighbourhood of the middle of the bonding line between the two nuclei can occur only when both eigenfunctions have the same sign. Then the bonding function $(1/\sqrt{2})(\psi_A + \psi_B)$ is formed and $\frac{1}{2}(\psi_A + \psi_B)^2$ becomes especially large midway between the two nuclei, due to the $2\psi_A\psi_B$ term.

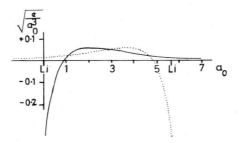

Fig. 4.2. *Values of the 2s-orbitals of two* Li-*atoms along the bonding line between the nuclei in the* Li_2-*molecule.*

———— *2s-orbital of the left* Li-*atom*

.... *2s-orbital of the right* Li-*atom.*

The alkali-metal atoms can also form diatomic molecules. Figure 4.2 shows the electron density distribution for the ψ_{2s}-orbitals along the principal axis of an Li_2-molecule. Only those parts of the orbitals which are between the two nodal surfaces ($r = 0.83a_0 = 0.44$ Å) can overlap, giving a gain in bonding energy. On crossing the nodal surface, $(1/\sqrt{2})(\psi_A + \psi_B)$ becomes small because of the change in sign. This, like the 'antibonding function' (see page 78) is unfavourable for the bonding energy. A limit is thus set to the interpenetration of the orbitals, resulting in the extremely diminished bond energies of alkali metal molecules, relative to those of hydrogen (Table 4.1).

Further, the two positively charged atomic cores with noble gas configuration repel each other, since the two valence electrons no longer shield the charge on the core sufficiently. The bonding energy is strongly reduced by this effect, also.

Table 4.1. Bonding energies and interatomic distances in diatomic alkali metal molecules

Molecule	Bonding energy	Internuclear distance
H_2	103 kcal/mol	0·74 Å
Li_2	26	2·67
Na_2	17	3·08
K_2	12	3·92
Rb_2	11	
Cs_2	10	

4.2 Hybrid Functions from *s*- and *p*-States

Some simple molecules, such as H_2O, NH_3, and CH_4, are found to be angular. How can these valence angles be explained?

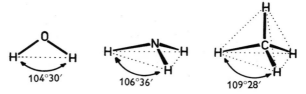

To answer this, let us first refer back to the Schrödinger equation for one electron:

$$\frac{\partial^2 \psi}{\partial x^2} + \frac{\partial^2 \psi}{\partial y^2} + \frac{\partial^2 \psi}{\partial z^2} + \frac{8\pi^2 m}{h^2} (E - V) = 0.$$

For the principal quantum number, $n = 2$, there are several solutions with $l = 0$ and $l = 1$. If these belong to the same eigenvalue of energy, E, then they cannot be distinguished from one another in the free atom; the solutions are degenerate. For degenerate eigenfunctions it is always true that any linear combination of these is also a solution to the Schrödinger equation. Thus, a valid solution would be:

$$\frac{\partial^2 (\gamma\psi_s + \delta\psi_p)}{\partial x^2} + \frac{\partial^2 (\gamma\psi_s + \delta\psi_p)}{\partial y^2} + \frac{\partial^2 (\gamma\psi_s + \delta\psi_p)}{\partial z^2}$$

$$+ \frac{8\pi^2 m}{h^2} (E - V)(\gamma\psi_s + \delta\psi_p) = 0.$$

This can be separated into

$$\frac{\partial^2 \gamma\psi_s}{\partial x^2} + \frac{\partial^2 \gamma\psi_s}{\partial y^2} + \frac{\partial^2 \gamma\psi_s}{\partial z^2} + \frac{8\pi^2 m}{h^2} (E - V)\gamma\psi_s = 0; \quad \text{and}$$

$$\frac{\partial^2 \delta\psi_p}{\partial x^2} + \frac{\partial^2 \delta\psi_p}{\partial y^2} + \frac{\partial^2 \delta\psi_p}{\partial z^2} + \frac{8\pi^2 m}{h^2} (E - V)\delta\psi_p = 0.$$

The normalization condition for the numbers γ and δ is $\gamma^2 + \delta^2 = 1$. Only in hydrogen are s- and p-electrons with the same principal quantum number degenerate. For all other atoms, there are somewhat different eigenvalues for s- and p-states, since Z_{eff} is then different for these two states. Nevertheless the energy difference is small in comparison to the energy of a chemical bond, and as Pauling[4.6] has shown, it is possible even here to treat the valence electron states as if they were degenerate. Our task is now to seek out those linear combinations, *hybrid functions*, which have large values on that side of the atom pointing toward a bonding partner. In this way, the overlap will be as great as possible, and a high bond energy will result.

4.2.1 *The (sp)-Hybrid*

The simplest case of a linear combination between an s- and p-function will be considered, first with the coefficients $\gamma = \delta = 1/\sqrt{2}$, and later $\gamma = 1/\sqrt{2}$, $\delta = -1/\sqrt{2}$ being chosen. The hybrid function in the initial case is then:

$$\varphi_+ = \frac{1}{\sqrt{2}} (\psi_s + \psi_p).$$

It can be easily shown that this hybrid function is normalized since:

$$\int \varphi_+^2 d\tau = \int \tfrac{1}{2}(\psi_s + \psi_p)^2 d\tau = \tfrac{1}{2}\left(\int \psi_s^2 d\tau + \int \psi_p^2 d\tau + \int \psi_s \psi_p d\tau \right) = 1.$$

The first two integrals within the brackets equal 1, since both these functions are normalized. The third function contains the product of a gerade (ψ_s) with an ungerade (ψ_p) function and results therefore, in equal positive and negative values. The integral is then equal to zero.

When we choose the second combination of coefficients:

$$\gamma = +\frac{1}{\sqrt{2}}, \qquad \delta = -\frac{1}{\sqrt{2}},$$

the eigenfunction reads:

$$\varphi_- = \frac{1}{\sqrt{2}} (\psi_s - \psi_p).$$

Conversely, by addition or subtraction of the φ_+ and φ_- functions, ψ_s or ψ_p are again obtained.

The radial distributions of s- and p-electrons are generally different. In the outer regions of an atom, however, these differences are not too great, so that to a first approximation they can be ignored. Then, one can associate with every point on a spherical surface a product, the first factor of which is given by the fixed value of the radial factor while the second factor is a purely angular function. The latter can again be reproduced on a polar diagram. Figure 4.3 shows to this approximation how the (sp)- and (sp^3) hybrid functions are directed to one side of an atom.

The hybrid functions φ_+ and φ_- are orthogonal to each other. They have the same shape but extend to opposite sides of an atom, so that two

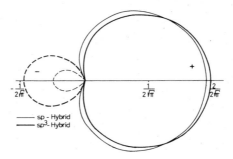

Fig. 4.3. Polar diagram of an (sp)- and an (sp^3)-hybrid. Negative values of the hybrid are designated by broken lines.

partners in these directions can be very firmly bound. One example of this arrangement is the single-bond framework of acetylene. In order to form an (sp)-hybrid, the carbon atom, which in the ground state has the outer electron configuration $2s^2 2p^2$, must be raised in energy to an excited state, in which one s-electron is promoted to the vacant p-state. This gives carbon a configuration $2s^1 2p_x^{\,1} 2p_y^{\,1} 2p_z^{\,1}$, having only unpaired electrons. Contrary to a real excited state, the spin moments of the valence electrons are now made independent of each other so that they can suitably take part in pairing. This electronic configuration is called the *valence state*. In carbon it is energetically *ca.* 90 kcal/mol. above the $2s^2 2p^2$ ground state. If

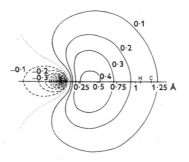

Fig. 4.4. Values of a (sp)-hybrid function of carbon, calculated[4.7] using the values of the $2s$- and $2p$-orbitals of carbon in the ground state. The position of the C and H atoms in acetylides is also given.

the z-axis is chosen as the molecular axis, then the hybrid functions (Fig. 4.4) on each atom are:

$$\varphi_+ = \frac{1}{\sqrt{2}}(\psi_s + \psi_{p_z}), \quad \text{and}$$

$$\varphi_- = \frac{1}{\sqrt{2}}(\psi_s - \psi_{p_z}).$$

The ψ_{p_y} and ψ_{p_x} orbitals as will be shown later, are involved in the formation of two additional bonds which are, however, of a different type. The (sp)-hybrids of carbon and the $1s$-eigenfunctions of hydrogen are represented in Fig. 4.5 by contour lines.

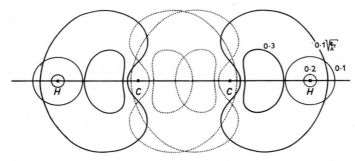

Fig. 4.5. *Overlap of the $1s$-orbital of hydrogen and the (sp)-hybrid function of carbon in the acetylene molecule.*

4.2.2 *The (sp^2)-Hybrid*

In the ethylene molecule

the carbon atoms have (sp^2)-hybrid orbitals. These are formed from the $2s$-, $2p_z$-, and $2p_y$-orbitals, while the $2p_x$-orbitals do not take part in the hybridization and are still available to form a double bond. The observed bond angle of $120°$ is obtained from the linear combinations:

$$\varphi_1 = \frac{1}{\sqrt{3}}\left(\psi_s + \sqrt{2}\,\psi_{p_z}\right)$$

$$\varphi_2 = \frac{1}{\sqrt{3}}\left(\psi_s - \frac{1}{\sqrt{2}}\psi_{p_z} + \sqrt{\frac{3}{2}}\,\psi_{p_y}\right)$$

$$\varphi_3 = \frac{1}{\sqrt{3}}\left(\psi_s - \frac{1}{\sqrt{2}}\psi_{p_z} - \sqrt{\frac{3}{2}}\,\psi_{p_y}\right).$$

The normalization factor $1/\sqrt{3}$ results from the normalization condition,

$$\int \varphi_n^2 d\tau = 1, \quad (n = 1, 2, \text{ or } 3).$$

It is immediately apparent that the φ_1-function, just as the φ_+-function is principally directed toward the positive side of the z-axis. φ_2 and φ_3 are equivalent to φ_1 except that they are rotated by $120°$ about the x-axis. This is not too difficult to see, since the $\psi_s + \sqrt{3/2}\,\psi_{p_y}$ factor gives a hybrid function which is directed toward the positive side of the y-axis. If now $-(1/\sqrt{2})\psi_{p_z}$ is added to this, the electron density is increased in the direction of the $(-z)$-axis, moving the centre of gravity of the φ_2-function in this direction.

4.2.3 The (sp^3)-Hybrid

In the tetrahedral bonds characteristic of aliphatic carbon atoms, the p_x-electron is also involved in hybridization, forming the four tetrahedrally-directed (sp^3)-hybrids.

$$\varphi_1 = \frac{1}{\sqrt{4}}(\psi_s + \psi_{p_x} + \psi_{p_y} + \psi_{p_z})$$

$$\varphi_2 = \frac{1}{\sqrt{4}}(\psi_s + \psi_{p_x} - \psi_{p_y} - \psi_{p_z})$$

$$\varphi_3 = \frac{1}{\sqrt{4}}(\psi_s - \psi_{p_x} - \psi_{p_y} + \psi_{p_z})$$

$$\varphi_4 = \frac{1}{\sqrt{4}}(\psi_s - \psi_{p_x} + \psi_{p_y} - \psi_{p_z})$$

The contribution from the s-function drops to $1/\sqrt{4} = \frac{1}{2}$. This results in an increase in the electron density in the concave side of the nodal surface, relative to that for the (sp)- or (sp^2)-hybrid (Figs. 4.3, 4.6). Figure 4.7 illustrates the spatial orientation of all four hybrids. From this diagram one can see that in the upper, right, rear octant (1), all four functions contribute positive values to φ_1. In the opposite direction, the contribution of the three p-functions is negative while that of the s-function remains positive. In the left, upper, forward octant all contributions of the four functions are positive for φ_4. Corresponding positive contributions hold for the octants designated 2 and 3, which correspond to φ_2 and φ_3 respectively. The body diagonals of these cubic octants are separated from each other by the tetrahedral angle, $109°\ 28'$.

If the substitution on the four carbon atoms is not identical, the coefficients in the linear combinations can be somewhat altered. In this way, one φ-function will have a larger s-contribution, while another will have a correspondingly greater *p*-contribution. The bonds are then not identical, and the angles between the bonds are changed more or less from those of a tetrahedron. Such deviations are possible since the coefficients in the linear combinations are continuously variable and do not have to be integers like the quantum numbers.

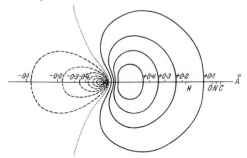

Fig. 4.6. Values of the (sp^3)-hybrid function of carbon[4.7], calculated using the values for the 2s- and 2p-orbitals of carbon in the ground state.[4.8] Added are the positions of singly bonded C, N, O, and H atoms.

In addition to CH_4, tetrahedral structures are also found for such compounds as: CCl_4, SiH_4, $SiCl_4$, and NH_4^+. When NH_3 and BF_3 combine, both the nitrogen and boron atom have slightly distorted tetrahedral configurations.

The bond angles in ammonia (106° 36') and in water (104° 30') correspond neither to the hybrid functions previously considered, nor to pure *p*-functions. From the bond angles in ammonia, one can conclude that the

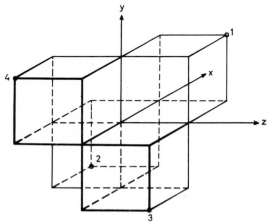

Fig. 4.7. Orientation of the axes of (sp^3)-hybrid functions from the centre of a Cartesian co-ordinate system to the points 1, 2, 3, and 4.

three N–H bonds have a somewhat higher p-character, and the free electron pair a somewhat higher s-character than that which would be expected for a completely symmetrical (sp^3)-hybrid. This can be easily seen in Fig. 4.8. On the left side of this diagram, the positive branches of the p-functions are represented by solid arrows, the negative branches in the backward direction by arrows with broken lines. The lengths of the arrows serve as a measure of the magnitudes of the functions in the two directions. The three p-functions are thus represented by double-headed arrows which extend equally in both directions and are directed along the axes of a Cartesian co-ordinate system.

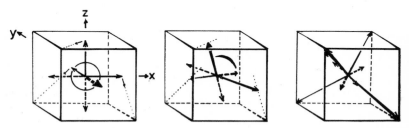

Fig. 4.8. Schematic representation of the transition from one s- and three p-orbitals (left) into four (sp^3)-hybrid functions, (right). The axes of the functions (bond directions) are represented by arrows (see text).

In an (sp^3)-hybrid (right part of the figure) the four positive, long branches (large values of the hybrid functions) point toward the corners of a tetrahedron. In the reverse, negative direction, the magnitudes of the hybrid functions are small, and the arrows are correspondingly short.

When only a small s-component is added to the three p-functions, these are augmented on one side (longer arrows), and attenuated on the other side (shorter arrows). In addition, the angles between the positive parts of the axes of the functions are widened if, simultaneously, the p-functions are slightly mixed. On the other hand, small portions of the three p-functions are then admixed with the s-functions. It can be mathematically shown that with this admixture the spherically symmetrical s-function becomes distorted, so that it appears more like a crescent.

The extent of mixing of the functions determines the angles between the axes and the preference for one bonding direction over the other. When the s-function and the three p-functions are completely mixed, one obtains finally the tetrahedral picture (left). The crescent-shaped function is then transformed into the fourth tetrahedral function.

Water has a planar molecular structure. The p-orbital which has its axis perpendicular to the molecular plane cannot take part in the bonding because of its symmetry. It therefore remains unchanged, and describes one of the two free electron pairs. Starting with an (sp^2)-hybrid, we associate with the bonds to hydrogen a higher p-content, and with the second free electron pair a somewhat higher s-content. In this way, the reduction in the bond angle from $120°$ to $105°$ can be easily explained.

The broadening of the bond angle from $90°$ (pure p-bonding) to $105°$ or $106° 36'$ is caused first by the fact that the hydrogen nuclei in water and ammonia are rather close to each other, and therefore mutually repel one another. The valence electrons on oxygen and nitrogen yield to these forces by hybridization. The second cause for hybridization is that the hybrid orbitals overlap with the $1s$-function on hydrogen better than do pure p-orbitals.

In order to explain the bonding in HCl, we first examine the electronic configuration of chlorine, $3s^2p_x^2p_y^2p_z^1$. While the possibility exists for bond formation by the overlap of the p_z-function on chlorine with the s-eigenfunction on hydrogen, this overlap is poorer than with an (sp)-hybrid. From the configuration s^2p_z, two (sp_z)-hybrids can be formed. One of these is occupied by one electron and forms the bond with hydrogen, while the other contains a free electron pair. The electronic configuration on the chlorine atom in the valence state can then be written: $(sp_z)^3p_x^2p_y^2$, where the parentheses indicate hybrid formation. The large dipole moment of HCl arises from the accumulation of negative charge in the doubly occupied (sp)-hybrid.

5

Multiple Bond Systems

5.1 Double Bonds

As seen above, (sp^2)-hybrids on carbon form the single bond framework of the ethylene molecule. In this frame, every bonding function is symmetrical about the corresponding bonding line. Because of this rotational symmetry, this is designated a *σ-bond*. Since each carbon atom has four electrons available for bond formation, and only three are used in forming the hybrid bonds, there remains one electron free on each carbon atom. In the case of ethylene, this electron occupies the *p*-orbital whose axis is perpendicular to the molecular plane and is not included in the (sp^2)-hybrid formation. According to Hückel,[5.1] lateral overlap can now take

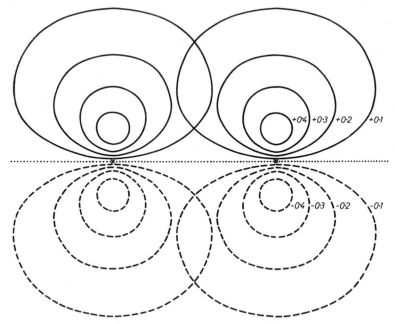

Fig. 5.1. Overlap of the pπ-orbitals of two C atoms[4.7, 4.8] of the ethylene molecule.

place (Fig. 5.1). This overlap is, however, not as good as with a σ-bond, and the bond energy is therefore less. Chemically, this decrease in bond energy results in increased chemical reactivity. Since the molecular plane is at the same time the nodal plane for the two p-functions, here is a case where a nodal plane passes through a unique axis, the molecular axis. In this case, the bond is referred to as a π-*bond*, and the electrons involved in the bond as π-*electrons*. In the rather rare case where the molecular axis contains two nodal planes of a bonding electron pair, δ-bonding occurs.

5.2 Triple Bonds

When carbon forms (sp)-hybrid functions as in acetylene (Figs. 4.3, 4.5), two p-functions on each carbon atom remain free to form π-bonds, just as they do in ethylene (Fig. 5.2). In acetylene, however, the two p-functions

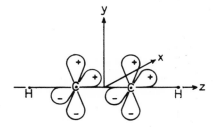

Fig. 5.2. Scheme of π-bonding in acetylene.

are perpendicular to each other and each pair has a nodal plane through the molecular axis, leading to double π-bonding. The strong coupling between carbon atoms which exists with double and triple bonds is reflected in shortened C—C bond distances (Table 5.1). As the table shows, N—N distances are also shortened by multiple bonding. In N_2 a triple bond is found and two (sp)-hybrids are occupied by free electron pairs.

Table 5.1. Interatomic distances for multiple bonding

C—C	1·54 Å	N—N	1·40 Å
C=C	1·32	N=N	1·20
C≡C	1·20	N≡N	1·09

5.3 Adjacent Multiple Bonds

The simplest case of directly adjacent double bonds is found in allene. The basic framework of this molecule is formed from (sp^2)-hybrids on the two outer carbon atoms and from (sp)-hybrids on the middle carbon atom.

Thus there are still available on the middle carbon atom the p_y- and p_x-electrons. If these are to form double bonds to each side of the middle atom, one of the outer carbon atoms must have a singly-occupied p_y, and the other a singly-occupied p_x-state available for double bonding. Since the two functions p_x and p_y are perpendicular to each other, the planes of the two outer CH_2-groups must also be mutually perpendicular (Fig. 5.3). This structure can be considered as a tetragonally distorted tetrahedron, which must be optically active. This activity has been experimentally observed.

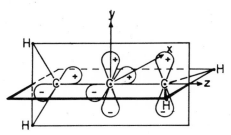

Fig. 5.3. Scheme of π-bonding in allene.

The bonding in allene does not form an isolated case but is found also in other structures such as carbon dioxide. As Fig. 5.4 shows, of the sixteen valence electrons in CO_2, eight fit into (*sp*)-hybrid states on the individual atoms. Six *p*-orbitals remain for the eight electrons left over. This gives two π-bonds and two lone *p*-electron pairs. These latter are designated in Fig. 5.4 by shading the electron symbols. There are two equivalent ways to form allenic bonds. Both belong to the same eigenvalue of energy. Consequently, any linear combination of the two solutions is also a solution of the Schrödinger equation. As shown by calculation, a linear combination of approximate solutions results in a gain in energy and a consequent strengthening of the bond which is shown by the shorter interatomic distance (Table 5.2). This energy gain is greatest when the linear combination contains equal proportions of the independent solutions (that is, equal coefficients on the components). These are not,

Table 5.2. Distances between C and O atoms

$\diagdown$ $-C-O-$ $\diagup$	1·43 Å (C—O distance in ethers)
$\diagdown$ $C=O$ $\diagup$	1·22 Å (C—O distance in ketones)
$O=C=O$	1·15 Å (C—O distance in CO_2)

however, all the possibilities, since it is possible for both doubly-occupied states to be on one oxygen atom, as the lower part of Fig. 5.4 shows. This corresponds to an ionic structure with one single and one triple bond. Since, however, all atoms have a tendency to be electrically neutral (Pauling[5.2, 5.3] electrical neutrality principle), mesomeric structures with

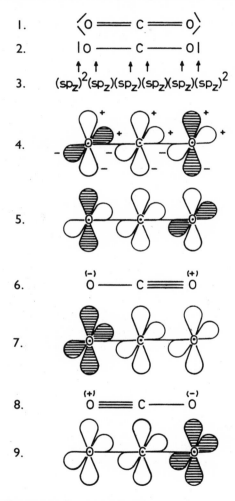

Fig. 5.4. *The bonding system in carbon dioxide:*
1st line: Formulation of the bonding using valence lines.
2nd and 3rd lines: σ-bonding system, diagram of the (sp_z)-hybrid electrons.
4th and 5th lines: The two mesomeric possibilities for allenic bonding systems.
6–9th lines: Mesomeric triple bonding. Double occupation of an orbital is represented here and in the following figures by hatched lines.

ionic components are not favoured. They nevertheless do enter into the total bonding function, but their influence is relatively small.

The carbon dioxide molecule thus forms an intermediate state which can be looked upon as a linear combination of four unique structures. In cases like this, one speaks of *mesomerism*, or using Pauling's[5.3, 5.4] terminology, of *resonance*. The theory of mesomerism had already been developed before quantum mechanics, principally by Thiele,[5.5] Ingold,[5.6] Arndt,[5.7] and Eistert,[5.8, 5.9] in order to explain the properties of conjugated organic systems. In conventional chemical notation the mesomerism in a CO_2 molecule is described:

$$O=C=O \quad \longleftrightarrow \quad |\overset{-}{\underline{O}}-C\equiv\overset{+}{O}| \quad \longleftrightarrow \quad |\overset{+}{O}\equiv C-\overset{-}{\underline{O}}|$$

The two other mesomeric forms of Fig. 5.4 cannot be given by a chemical formula, since they result from a rotation of 90° around the molecular axis.

The azide ion, N_3^- and the nitryl ion, NO_2^+, are isoelectronic with CO_2. Consequently the same mesomeric bonding systems also apply to them.

5.4 Conjugated Multiple Bonds

The C—C—C bond angle on both internal carbon atoms of butadiene is 124°. This is nearly the same as for an (sp^2)-hybrid as already seen with ethylene (Fig. 5.5). With a double bond, an interatomic distance of 1·32 Å would be expected and with a single bond, 1·54 Å. Instead, one finds a single bond distance of 1·46 Å, and a double bond distance of 1·35 Å. This phenomenon can be explained if it is realized that the spin moments of

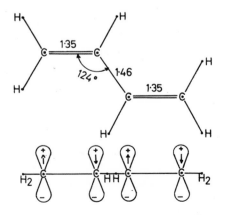

Fig. 5.5. Scheme of π-bonding in butadiene.

the *p*-electrons can be antiparallel, not only within the double bond, but also between carbon atoms 2 and 3. In this way, overlap and bonding are also possible between atoms 2 and 3, when the bonds between atoms 1 and 2, or 3 and 4 are broken. The two electrons on carbon atoms 1 and 4 appear radical-like in the limiting formula. As a result of the antiparallel

H   H

(1) (2) (3) (4)

C—C=C—C

H   H

alignment of the two electrons in the first formula (Fig. 5.5), a formal bonding can be represented between them. This formal bond, however, results in no gain in energy, since there is no overlap between the two orbitals. The second formula, with the double bond in the middle, is therefore at a disadvantage relative to the first, and does not make a substantial contribution to the mesomerism. Nevertheless, the middle bond gains a weak double-bond character and the two other double bonds are correspondingly weakened. The theory of partial valences developed by Thiele can thus be explained in quantum mechanical terms.

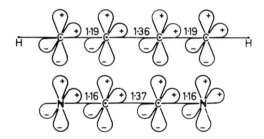

Fig. 5.6. Scheme of π-bonding in diacetylene and in dicyanogen.

This same phenomenon is also found in conjugated triple-bonded systems, such as diacetylene and dicyanogen (Fig. 5.6). Two systems analogous to butadiene can be represented, one of which lies in the plane of the paper and the other perpendicular to it. In both molecules, the central C—C single bond distance is shortened (1·36 Å and 1·37 Å respectively).

Mesomerism stabilizes a molecule. This does not, however, necessarily mean a reduction in reactivity. A mesomeric bonding system can very easily adapt itself to the molecular distortions brought about by thermal shocks and vibrations, since electrons are much more mobile than the relatively heavy atomic nuclei. Further, the coefficients of the various factors in the linear combination are variable. If, for example, carbon atoms 2 and 3 in a butadiene molecule are brought closer together and the distance between the other carbon atoms is increased, then that resonance form is preferred which gives greater weight to a double bond between carbon atoms 2 and 3, and single bonds between 1 and 2, and 3 and 4. Mesomerism makes such an electron displacement easier, and the molecule is described as 'polarizable'. A definite degree of distortion and its corresponding linear combination can be an advantage in facilitating a given chemical reaction. This is what an organic chemist means when he says that a molecule with a mesomeric bonding system reacts from a given limiting structure.

5.5 Aromatic Systems

Kekulé and Dewar concerned themselves with the formal representation of the mesomeric possibilities in benzene. Quantum mechanically, the true state is represented as a stationary ψ-function, which results from the superposition of the five possible double-bonded structures (Fig. 5.7). The plane of the ring represents the nodal plane for all six π-electrons.

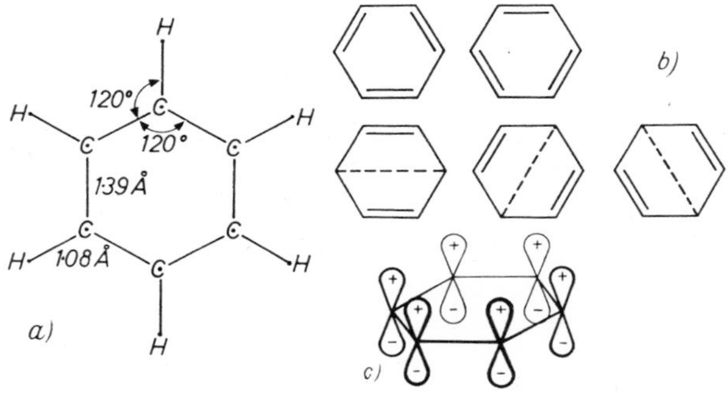

Fig. 5.7. The benzene molecule: (a) Geometry of the molecule. (b) Structural formulae according to Kekulé and Dewar. (c) Representation of the $p\pi$-electrons of benzene.

The three Dewar resonance structures are not as favourable as the Kekulé forms, since some bonds in the former, such as the 1,4-bond in butadiene, are only formal. The large number of mesomeric possibilities and the high symmetry of the molecule bring about a stabilization. As a result of this, the C—C bond distance, 1·39 Å, is shorter than the average (1·43 Å) of single and double bond distances.

Let us now consider several aromatic molecules with substituents on the ring, such as aniline (Fig. 5.8). The configuration on nitrogen, which has a free electron pair, is somewhere between $(sp^2)^3p^2$ and $(sp^3)^5$. Proceeding from the former structure, five mesomeric forms result, some benzene type and others quinoid type. The superposition of these forms explains the properties of aniline. In formulae III–V, the nitrogen gives up an electron to the benzene ring, and a double bond is formed between nitrogen and the neighbouring carbon atom. Nitrogen then becomes positively charged, and its basicity is diminished. Furthermore, the positions *ortho* and *para* to nitrogen become negative. This favours the addition of cationic substituents in these positions and thereby explains the directive influence of the amino group.

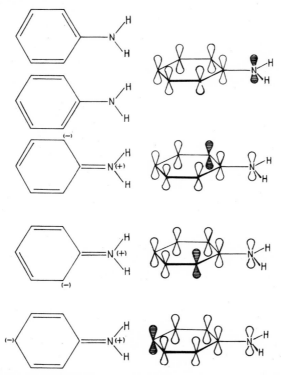

Fig. 5.8. The five mesomeric formulae of aniline and the associated occupation of pπ-orbitals.

If the amino group in aniline is now replaced by a chlorine atom, two (*sp*)-hybrid functions in the direction of the σ-bond are formed; one is occupied by a single electron, and the other by a free electron pair (Fig. 5.9). In addition, there are two doubly-occupied *p*-states. That *p*-electron pair, whose probability density is greatest on the ring plane, cannot for symmetry reasons interact with the π-electrons of the ring. Only that *p*-electron pair, whose charge distribution in the ring plane is zero,

6

remains available for interaction. With it, the same mesomerism possibilities exist as with aniline.

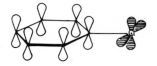

Fig. 5.9. Occupation of p-orbitals in chlorobenzene.

When a nitro group is present as a substituent, it gives rise to other mesomeric structures (Fig. 5.10). Of the five electrons on nitrogen, three go into (sp^2)-hybrid states and form the framework of single bonds between nitrogen, oxygen, and the ring. One electron of nitrogen now wanders to one of the oxygen atoms, giving oxygen a negative charge. The other p-electron still remaining on nitrogen then takes part in π-bonding with the lone p-electron on the other oxygen atom. Two mesomeric forms result, since the roles of the two oxygen atoms can be interchanged. In addition to these, one must consider the two Kekulé structures of the ring, giving a total of four possible resonance forms. The lone p-electron of

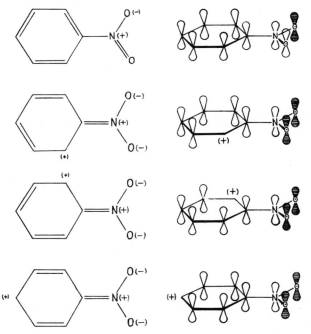

Fig. 5.10. The mesomeric formulae of nitrobenzene and the corresponding occupation of pπ-orbitals.

nitrogen can also, however, take part in bonding with the neighbouring carbon atom. In order, then, to retain a doubly-bonded system in the benzene ring, it is necessary for a π-electron in either the *ortho-* or *para-*position to migrate to the previously doubly-bonded oxygen atom. A superposition of all these structures results in a *meta*-position which is negative relative to its surroundings. Therefore, a substituent which would normally add in the *ortho-* or *para*-position in aniline is attracted instead to the *meta*-position in nitrobenzene.

In heterocyclic structures too, similar mesomeric phenomena occur. In the case of pyrrole, nitrogen is built into the ring resulting in an even stronger participation by the electron pair of nitrogen in the resonance.

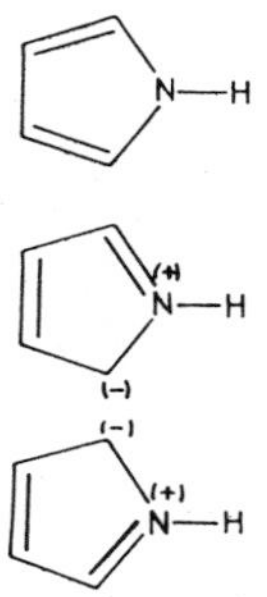

Fig. 5.11. The mesomeric formulae of pyrrole.

Thus, structures II and III of Fig. 5.11 have more weight, and the basicity of the nitrogen in pyrrole is considerably weaker than in aniline. Indeed, it is so weak that the hydrogen bound to nitrogen can be replaced by potassium.

5.6 Mesomeric Double-Bonded Systems in Simple Inorganic Compounds

The complex ions BO_3^{3-}, CO_3^{2-}, and NO_3^- are isoelectronic with BF_3. Similar mesomeric relationships are therefore to be found for this entire series. How these pertain to the carbonate ion is shown in Fig. 5.12.

On each oxygen, there are two (sp)-hybrid functions. One takes part in σ-bonding with a carbon atom which has an (sp^2)-hybrid configuration in the molecular plane. The other (sp)-hybrid function is occupied by a free electron pair of oxygen. Those p-orbitals on oxygen, the axes of which lie in the molecular plane, are filled by electron pairs. On two oxygen atoms the p-orbitals, the axes of which are perpendicular to the molecular plane, are doubly-occupied, and on the third oxygen atom, only singly-occupied. This lone electron can, with the fourth valence electron of carbon, a *p*-electron, enter into π-bonding. Since the roles of the three oxygen atoms can be interchanged, three mesomeric forms are possible. In the mean, a $1\frac{1}{3}$ bond results, so that the distance C—O is

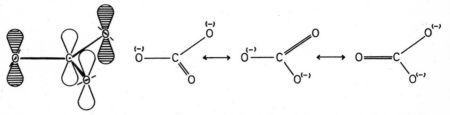

Fig. 5.12. *The three mesomeric structural formulae of the carbonate ion and the occupation of pπ-orbitals in one mesomeric form.*

between that for a single and a double bond (see Table 5.3). On acidification this mesomerism is destroyed since the added H^+-ions must be bound to two definite oxygen atoms. The elimination of mesomeric stabilization is demonstrated by the instability of free carbonic acid.

Table 5.3. *Bond lengths in $1\frac{1}{3}$, single, and double bonds*

Bond length	C—O	N—O
In anion XO_3	1·29 Å	1·22 Å
Single Bond	1·43 Å	1·46 Å (NH_2OH)
Double Bond	1·22 Å	1·15 Å (NOCl)

Double-bonded compounds containing heavy atoms have a tendency to polymerize, forming single bonds in the process since the π-electrons

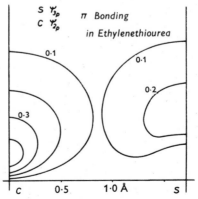

Fig. 5.13. *Overlap of the pπ-electrons of a C═S-double bond in a thiourea derivative.*[4.7] *Values calculated according to Watson and Freeman.*[5.10]

involved overlap insufficiently. Figure 5.13 shows the contours of the p-π-orbitals in a C$=$S double bond in a thiourea derivative. Carbon disulphide, an endothermic compound, can be obtained and kept in monomeric form, but CSe_2 and CTe_2 polymerize very readily. Similarly, SO_2 is gaseous and monomeric, while both SeO_2 and TeO_2 are solid and polymeric at room temperature.

6

Hybrid Functions in Low Spin Complexes

6.1 Hybrid Functions from *s*- and *p*-States

A tetrahedral atomic arrangement is found in complex ions such as $[ClO_4]^-$, $[SO_4]^{2-}$, $[PO_4]^{3-}$, or $[Zn(CN)_4]^{2-}$ and $[Cu(CN)_4]^{3-}$. The electronic arrangement around the central atom is that of an (sp^3)-hybrid. In this way, the central atom achieves the electronic configuration of the next noble gas; all occupied electronic shells are completely filled.

(sp^2)-Hybrids on a central heavy metal atom are rare. $K[Cu(CN)_2]$ is, as has recently been shown,[6.1] highly polymeric and the arrangement of the ligands about the copper atom is a distorted version of that observed in the carbonate ion (Fig. 6.1).

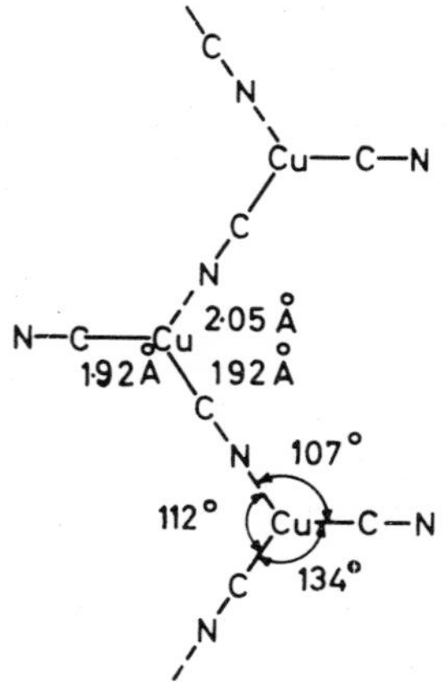

Fig. 6.1. *Geometry of a* $[Cu(CN)_2]_n^{n-}$-*chain in* $K[Cu(CN)_2]$.

(sp)-Hybrids are found principally in compounds of heavy metals of the first and second subgroups, such as H_3C—Zn—CH_3 and the corresponding compounds of cadmium and mercury. This structure is also found in compounds such as $ZnCl_2$ (vapour phase), $HgCl_2$, $[CuCl_2]^-$, and $[Ag(NH_3)_2]^+$. Mercury(II) chloride is found in molecular form, even in solution. A thallium compound, $[H_3C—Tl—CH_3]^+Cl^-$, is also known to belong to this series.

The difference between the elements of the zinc and alkaline earth groups, the chlorides of which are salt-like, is conditioned by the effective nuclear charge. For zinc, the excitation energy $Zn(4s^2 \rightarrow 4sp)$ is 95 kcal. This is small, relative to the 629 kcal. required for the transition $Zn \rightarrow Zn^{2+}$. A similar energy difference is observed with mercury: $Hg(6s^2 \rightarrow 6sp)$ 115 kcal., $Hg \rightarrow Hg^{2+}$, 674 kcal. The high energy required for ionization hinders the formation of ionic bonds; rather, the electrons remain essentially on the metal atom so that both atoms share in the possession of the electron pair. In order to form an electron pair bond, the metal atom requires only the relatively small (sp)-hybridization energy. While it is true that the hybridization energies of calcium and barium (44 and 37 kcal/mole) are also minimal, the ionization energies are low too: $Ca \rightarrow Ca^{2+}$ 444 kcal/mole, $Ba \rightarrow Ba^{2+}$ 350 kcal/mole.

The relatively low ionization energies result from the small effective nuclear charge, as we have already noted. This small charge permits the valence electron cloud to spread out from the nucleus. These electrons then find themselves essentially under the influence of the halogen atom. Consequently, the bonding can better be described by the ionic model. The influence of the (sp)-hybrid function on the calcium and barium atoms is too small to make mutual bonding of the atoms in a crystal lattice noticeable. Only in the vapour state do we find linear molecules such as $CaCl_2$ and $BaCl_2$ with (sp)-hybrids on the central atom.

If the ligand possesses free electron pairs, as chlorine does, then the electron pairs of the ligand can form semipolar π-bonds with the still unoccupied, free p- and d-quantum states on the metal atoms (e.g., in $HgCl_2$). Thus, these molecules are stabilized by weak double bonding.

6.2 Hybrid Functions from d-, s-, and p-States

To make clear the reason for the formation of low spin complexes it is expedient to begin with the electron configuration of the ionized central atom. In explaining the formation of the hexaminocobaltate(III) complex ion, the Co^{3+}-ion is first examined. The cobalt atom has the electronic configuration $3d^7 4s^2$:

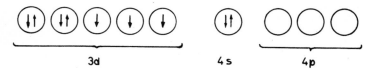

$$\underbrace{\qquad\qquad\qquad}_{3d} \qquad \underbrace{\quad}_{4s} \qquad \underbrace{\qquad\qquad}_{4p}$$

while Co^{3+}, in accordance with Hund's Rule, has $3d^6$:

The formation of the hexamine complex begins with a rearrangement of the electrons in such a way that doubly-occupied as well as unoccupied cells are available:

$$d_{xy} \quad d_{yz} \quad d_{zx} \quad d_{3z^2-1} \quad d_{x^2-y^2} \qquad s \qquad p_x \quad p_y \quad p_z$$

This rearrangement corresponds to the formation of the valence state of carbon; it has, however, the reverse direction. From the six free orbitals six (d^2sp^3)-hybrid functions are formed, which are occupied by the free electron pairs of ammonia, giving cobalt the electronic configuration of krypton.

Since these complexes exhibit an octahedral structure, the hybrid functions must be directed to the six directions of a Cartesian co-ordinate system. Of the individual functions involved, p-functions have this spatial arrangement to begin with, the s-function is spherical and thus contributes equally in all directions. Of the d-functions, d_{3z^2-1} and $d_{x^2-y^2}$ have the proper symmetry. The remaining three d-states, which are already doubly-occupied, have their nodal planes exactly in the axis directions so that the free electron pairs are between the ligands. From the above-named six functions, the following hybrids can be constructed:

$$\varphi_1 = \frac{1}{\sqrt{6}}\left(\psi_s + \sqrt{3}\,\psi_{p_z} + \sqrt{2}\,\psi_{d_{3z^2-1}}\right)$$

$$\varphi_2 = \frac{1}{\sqrt{6}}\left(\psi_s - \sqrt{3}\,\psi_{p_z} + \sqrt{2}\,\psi_{d_{3z^2-1}}\right)$$

Hybrids in z-direction

$$\varphi_3 = \frac{1}{\sqrt{6}}\left(\psi_s + \sqrt{3}\,\psi_{p_x} - \frac{1}{\sqrt{2}}\psi_{d_{3z^2-1}} + \sqrt{\frac{3}{2}}\,\psi_{d_{x^2-y^2}}\right)$$

$$\varphi_4 = \frac{1}{\sqrt{6}}\left(\psi_s - \sqrt{3}\,\psi_{p_x} - \frac{1}{\sqrt{2}}\psi_{d_{3z^2-1}} + \sqrt{\frac{3}{2}}\,\psi_{d_{x^2-y^2}}\right)$$

Hybrids in x-direction

$$\varphi_5 = \frac{1}{\sqrt{6}}\left(\psi_s + \sqrt{3}\,\psi_{p_y} - \frac{1}{\sqrt{2}}\psi_{d_{3z^2-1}} - \sqrt{\frac{3}{2}}\,\psi_{d_{x^2-y^2}}\right)$$

$$\varphi_6 = \frac{1}{\sqrt{6}}\left(\psi_s - \sqrt{3}\,\psi_{p_y} - \frac{1}{\sqrt{2}}\psi_{d_{3z^2-1}} - \sqrt{\frac{3}{2}}\,\psi_{d_{x^2-y^2}}\right)$$

Hybrids in y-direction

For each of the six φ-functions, the values of all the component orbitals add in the chosen direction and subtract in the opposite direction. Ignoring the differences in the radial component of s-, p-, and d-functions, a polar diagram for the (d^2sp^3)-hybrid function can be constructed. As Fig. 6.2 shows, the six hybrid functions are strongly directed to one side.

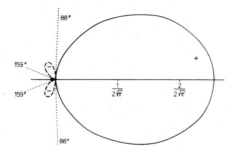

Fig. 6.2. Polar diagram of a (d^2sp^3)-hybrid.

In the complex ion $[Co(NH_3)_6]^{3+}$, the free electron pairs on ammonia occupy the above mentioned (d^2sp^3)-hybrids. If the binding electron pairs are counted and considered as belonging half to nitrogen and half to cobalt, the three positive charges are then distributed among the six nitrogen atoms, and the cobalt atom has a triply negative charge. This contradicts the tendency of atoms to remain, where possible, electrically neutral. Therefore, the electron pairs cannot be divided in this way. Rather, the relatively high effective nuclear charge on nitrogen causes the electron pairs to associate more closely with it. How extensively the electrons are associated with nitrogen cannot at present be calculated. However, the electrical charge on cobalt can be assumed to be small. Then the nitrogen atoms must accept the positive charge on the ion. The nitrogen atoms can also conduct the charges further, repelling the positively charged hydrogen nuclei and giving rise to strengthened hydrogen bridge bonds to the water surrounding the complex. The positive charge on the ion is, as Pauling[5.3] has shown, spread over all the atoms in the complex ion, including the solvent sheath. The strong tendency to hydrogen bonding is made apparent by the pronounced tendency to form acid salts such as $[Co(NH_3)_6]^{3+}SO_4^{2-} \cdot HSO_4^-$. The ions Fe^{2+}, Ni^{4+}, and Pt^{4+} are isoelectronic in their valence shells with Co^{3+} and are also distinguished by their tendency to form complexes with (d^2sp^3)-hybrids.

Cyanide complexes are especially stable. Even the free acids, $H_4[Fe(CN)_6]$, $H_3[Co(CN)_6]$, and $H_2[Pt(CN)_6]$ exist. Double bonding is primarily responsible for this enhanced stability Figure 6.3a shows a d_{xy}-electron pair on cobalt and the two p_x-electrons of a cyanide double bond. If now one of the *d*-electrons of cobalt migrates to nitrogen, a π-bond can result between carbon and cobalt (Fig. 6.3b). For the formation of such double bonds, exactly those *d*-states which do not take part in the (d^2sp^3)-hybrid are used. Since there are two singly occupied *p*-states on carbon, such mesomerism is possible in two ways: once in the plane of the diagram and once perpendicular to it. A large number of double bonded structures results.

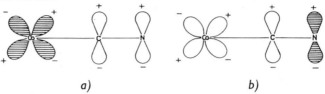

a)   b)

Fig. 6.3. Schematic representation of a mesomeric π-bonding system in the $[Co(CN)_6]^{3-}$-ion.

On cyanide ions, because of both the negative charge and the low nuclear charge on carbon, the free electron pairs on carbon are not too strongly bound. By comparison with $[Co(NH_3)_6]^{3+}$ then, these electron pairs can be brought much closer to the cobalt atom. The central atom would get a negative charge, were it not for the π-bonding system which permits the electrons to migrate through to the nitrogen atom and thereby to the periphery of the complex.

It is this stability of the cyanide complex which allows $[Fe(CN)_6]^{4+}$ to be oxidized to $[Fe(CN)_6]^{3+}$ without essential alteration of the electronic configuration. The missing electron leaves one unpaired electron making the ion paramagnetic. Experimentally, a paramagnetic susceptibility equivalent to $1.33\mu_B$ is found, while $1.29\mu_B$ would be expected for a single electron.

It is not necessary in all cases that the noble gas configuration be arrived at by the single bond system. The tetracyanonickelate(II) ion, for example, lacks two electrons from the krypton configuration. Proceeding from the excited Ni^{2+}-state with eight 3*d*-electrons:

a specific hybrid having the square planar structure observed in the complex is sought. The (dsp^2)-hybrid has the required form. If the molecule lies in the *xy*-plane, the p_z- and d_{3z^2-1}-states can be ignored and the s, p_x, p_y, and $d_{x^2-y^2}$ used to form four hybrid functions:

$$\varphi_1 = \frac{1}{\sqrt{4}} \left(\psi_s + \sqrt{2}\, \psi_{p_x} + \psi_{d_{x^2-y^2}} \right)$$

$$\varphi_2 = \frac{1}{\sqrt{4}} \left(\psi_s - \sqrt{2}\, \psi_{p_x} + \psi_{d_{x^2-y^2}} \right)$$

Hybrids in direction of x-axis

$$\varphi_3 = \frac{1}{\sqrt{4}} \left(\psi_s + \sqrt{2}\, \psi_{p_y} - \psi_{d_{x^2-y^2}} \right)$$

$$\varphi_4 = \frac{1}{\sqrt{4}} \left(\psi_s - \sqrt{2}\, \psi_{p_y} - \psi_{d_{x^2-y^2}} \right)$$

Hybrids in direction of y-axis

These form the single-bond framework. In addition a double-bond system of the following type occurs. The d_{xy}-function, which lies in the molecular plane, is occupied by an electron pair. Double bonds, such as we discussed in the case of $[Co(CN)_6]^{3-}$ (Fig. 6.4), can be formed with the

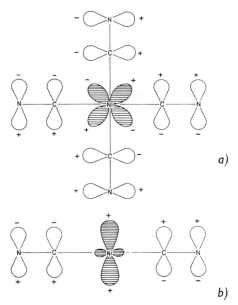

Fig. 6.4. (a) Schematic representation of the π-bonding system in the $[Ni(CN)_4]^{2-}$-*ion. (b) Destruction of π-symmetry by a* d_{3z^2-1}-*orbital.*

four cyanide groups in the xy-plane. Also, the d_{yz}- and d_{xz}-electron pairs can form double bonds with pairs of cyanide groups lying opposite using the p_z-electrons of the latter. The d_{3z^2-1}-electron pair, however, cannot form π-bonds here, since it is a gerade function, while p_z is ungerade.

  Characteristic for the above low spin complexes is the occupation by electron pairs of hybrid functions, which are directed to one side and mutually overlap. Other π-bonding systems have also been discussed. The bonding scheme is closely related to that in organic compounds, and could thus be developed rather early by Pauling. Bonding in the 'ionic complexes' was not explained until 1950, by Hartmann and Ilse.[6.2] To understand the bonding in these latter complexes requires some knowledge of electron relationships in partially-filled shells. Such systems will be discussed more fully later.

7

Molecular Orbital Theory

7.1 The Hydrogen Molecule

The Heitler–London method of calculating chemical bonding which we have been discussing up to now considers the behaviour of two valence electrons as two bonding partners approach each other. Proceeding from the separated orbitals of the individual atoms, the exchange interaction which results from the approximation is introduced into the calculation. Each bond (each solid line in a formula) corresponds to one electron pair. Because it considers the bonding between two atoms, this is called the '*valence bond theory*' (VB).

As Hund[4.4] and Mulliken[4.5] have shown, there is another approximate method, the so-called '*molecular orbital theory*' (MO). This latter model does not correspond very closely to the conceptions common to chemists, since the bond line in this theory frequently loses its significance. In addition, the molecular orbital theory is considerably more difficult, because the molecule is considered as a whole. In the case of diatomic molecules, however, it is possible to develop the essence of molecular orbital theory relatively easily.

If we consider two atoms A and B with valence electrons 1 and 2, orbitals can be assigned to the complete molecule just as we have done for individual atoms. If electron 1, for example, is in the vicinity of nucleus A, its condition can be described by an atomic orbital, ψ_{A1}. If, however, it is close to nucleus B, the proper atomic orbital is ψ_{B1} (Fig. 4.1). The behaviour of an electron in a molecule can then be approximated by a molecular orbital, which is given by the sum,

$$\Psi_+ = N_+ \frac{1}{\sqrt{2}} (\psi_{A1} + \psi_{B1}).$$

The capital Ψ here designates a molecular function which is only dependent on the spatial coordinates. This molecular orbital can still accept a second electron provided its spin moment is antiparallel to that of the first electron.

ψ_{A1} and ψ_{B1} in the hydrogen molecule are the $1s$ orbitals of the two hydrogen atoms A and B. Figure 7.1 shows the magnitude of these functions along the molecular axis, as well as the magnitude of the summed function, Ψ_+. The electron density is:

$$\Psi_+^2 = N_+^2 \frac{1}{2} (\psi_{A1}^2 + \psi_{B1}^2 + 2\psi_{A1}\psi_{B1}).$$

The last term in this equation, $\psi_{A1}\psi_{B1}$, increases the electron density in the middle of the line connecting the two nuclei. The normalization factor

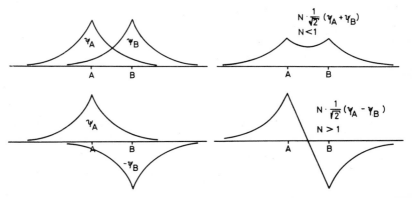

Fig. 7.1. *The development of bonding (above) and antibonding (below) molecular functions of the H_2-molecule from the $1s$-atomic eigenfunctions.*

is therefore <1. A state such as this represents an attraction between the atoms, a chemical bond. It is therefore called a '*bonding state*'. It is also possible to combine the atomic orbitals in such a way as to produce the molecular orbital,

$$\Psi_- = N_- \frac{1}{\sqrt{2}} (\psi_{A1} - \psi_{B1}).$$

This function is illustrated in the lower half of Fig. 7.1; it leads to a diminution in electron density in the space between the nuclei. The normalization factor, N_-, is slightly greater than one. The mutual repulsion of the nuclei here dominates and a so-called '*anti-bonding*' state results. In the case of H_2, this state is not occupied, because both available valence electrons can be accommodated in the bonding state. In the He_2^+-ion, which is found in gas discharges, the third electron must go into an anti-bonding state. This diminishes the bond strength in this ion relative to that in H_2.

Two helium atoms cannot come together to form He_2, since two valence electrons in bonding states and two in anti-bonding states cancel each other out. This same cancellation would occur in any diatomic noble gas. Neon will be further discussed later.

7.2 Diatomic Molecules from Light Atoms

The properties of molecular orbitals may be seen by examining the series: N_2^+, N_2, O_2^+, O_2, O_2^-, F_2, and Ne_2 (Fig. 7.2). The $2s$- and $2p$-orbitals on the individual atoms are available to form molecular orbitals.

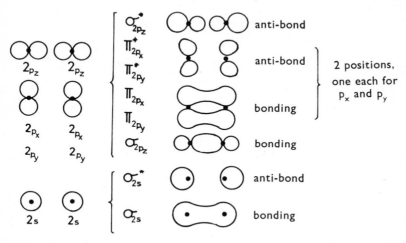

Fig. 7.2. *Bonding and anti-bonding molecular functions from two atoms with s- and p-valence electrons.*

Just as in the case of hydrogen, one bonding and one anti-bonding state can be formed from $2s$-orbitals. Both $2s$-molecular orbitals lie energetically deeper than those functions formed from $2p$-electrons, since the $2s$-electrons are more tightly bound in the isolated atom than are the $2p$-electrons.

Molecular orbitals are labelled according to their rotational symmetry about a unique axis (σ, π, δ, etc.) and according to the atomic orbitals involved in their formation (e.g., $2s$, $2p_x$, $2p_y$, etc.). Anti-bonding states are marked with an asterisk, e.g., σ^*2s. In Fig. 7.2, the molecular orbitals are represented by symbols which are related to their polar diagrams. The order of increasing energy can be different especially for the σ_{2p_z} and π_{2p} functions. Both p_z-orbitals give a low-lying bonding state with rotational symmetry (σ-state), and a high-energy, anti-bonding state having the same symmetry. Both p_x- and p_y-orbitals give bonding and anti-bonding states which have a nodal plane along the interatomic axis.

The eight states are now filled with electrons according to the Pauli principle starting with the lowest energy state and proceeding upwards in order (Table 7.1). Half the difference between the number of electrons in bonding states and the number in anti-bonding states is called the *bond order*, and corresponds to what the chemist customarily calls single, double, or triple bonding. In the last column, the dissociation energy of the molecule is given in electron-volts. This is seen to parallel closely the changes in bond order. The table shows further that O_2 must be paramagnetic since the two molecular orbitals $\pi*2p_x$ and $\pi*2p_y$ are each occupied by only one electron and in accordance with Hund's rule, the spins are parallel. The Heitler–London theory could not so unequivocally explain the paramagnetism of O_2.

Table 7.1. Molecular orbitals and their occupation by electrons in diatomic molecules

	$\sigma2s$	$\sigma*2s$	$\sigma2p_z$	$\pi2p_y$ $\pi2p_x$	$\pi*2p_y$ $\pi*2p_x$	$\sigma*2p_z$	No. of electrons Bond.	No. of electrons Anti.	B.O.	E_{diss} eV
N_2^+	2	2	1	2 + 2	—	—	7	2	2·5	6·4
N_2	2	2	2	2 + 2	—	—	8	2	3	7·4
O_2^+	2	2	2	2 + 2	1	—	8	3	2·5	6·5
O_2	2	2	2	2 + 2	1 + 1	—	8	4	2	5·1
O_2^-	2	2	2	2 + 2	2 + 1	—	8	5	1·5	
F_2	2	2	2	2 + 2	2 + 2	—	8	6	1	1·6
Ne_2	2	2	2	2 + 2	2 + 2	2	8	8	0	0

B.O. = bond order, ref. 6.3.

7.3 The Methane Molecule

Two further examples can now be given to help clarify the molecular orbital theory: methane and benzene. The 1*s*-eigenfunctions on the four

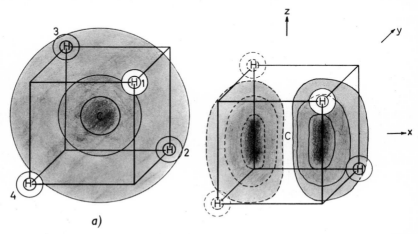

a)

Fig. 7.3. Representation of the molecular functions of methane with (a) 2s-orbitals, (b) one 2p-orbital of carbon.

hydrogen atoms: H_1, H_2, H_3, and H_4, are labelled: ψ_1, ψ_2, ψ_3, and ψ_4; the orbitals on carbon: s, p_x, p_y, and p_z. These atomic orbitals can be combined to form four molecular orbitals, $\Psi_1 \ldots \Psi_4$ (Fig. 7.3).

Symmetry designations for molecular orbital

$$\Psi_1 = \frac{1}{\sqrt{2}} \left\{ N_C\, s + N_H \frac{1}{\sqrt{4}} (+\psi_1 + \psi_2 + \psi_3 + \psi_4) \right\} \qquad \Sigma$$

$$\Psi_2 = \frac{1}{\sqrt{2}} \left\{ N_C'\, p_x + N_H' \frac{1}{\sqrt{4}} (+\psi_1 + \psi_2 - \psi_3 - \psi_4) \right\} \qquad \Pi_x$$

$$\Psi_3 = \frac{1}{\sqrt{2}} \left\{ N_C'\, p_y + N_H' \frac{1}{\sqrt{4}} (-\psi_1 + \psi_2 + \psi_3 - \psi_4) \right\} \qquad \Pi_y$$

$$\Psi_4 = \frac{1}{\sqrt{2}} \left\{ N_C'\, p_z + N_H' \frac{1}{\sqrt{4}} (+\psi_1 - \psi_2 + \psi_3 - \psi_4) \right\} \qquad \Pi_z$$

N_C, N_C', N_H, and N_H' are normalization factors.

7.4 The π-System of Benzene

Only the π-bonding system of benzene will be discussed. There are six possibilities for the formation of molecular orbitals, Ψ_1 to Ψ_6 from the $2p_z$ atomic functions of the six carbon atoms ψ_1, to ψ_6 (Fig. 7.4).

$\lambda = 0$

$$\Psi_1 = N_1 \frac{1}{\sqrt{6}} 1 \left(1\psi_1 + 1\psi_2 + 1\psi_3 + 1\psi_4 + 1\psi_5 + 1\psi_6 \right)$$

$\lambda = 1$

$$\Psi_2 = N_2 \frac{1}{\sqrt{6}} \sqrt{2} \left(1\psi_1 + \frac{1}{2}\psi_2 - \frac{1}{2}\psi_3 - 1\psi_4 - \frac{1}{2}\psi_5 + \frac{1}{2}\psi_6 \right)$$

$\bar{\lambda} = 1$

$$\Psi_3 = N_3 \frac{1}{\sqrt{6}} \sqrt{2} \left(0\psi_1 + \frac{\sqrt{3}}{2}\psi_2 + \frac{\sqrt{3}}{2}\psi_3 + 0\psi_4 - \frac{\sqrt{3}}{2}\psi_5 - \frac{\sqrt{3}}{2}\psi_6 \right)$$

$\lambda = 2$

$$\Psi_4 = N_4 \frac{1}{\sqrt{6}} \sqrt{2} \left(1\psi_1 - \frac{1}{2}\psi_2 - \frac{1}{2}\psi_3 + 1\psi_4 - \frac{1}{2}\psi_5 - \frac{1}{2}\psi_6 \right)$$

7

$\bar{\lambda} = 2$

$$\Psi_5 = N_5 \frac{1}{\sqrt{6}} \sqrt{2} \left(0\psi_1 + \frac{\sqrt{3}}{2}\psi_2 - \frac{\sqrt{3}}{2}\psi_3 + 0\psi_4 + \frac{\sqrt{3}}{2}\psi_5 - \frac{\sqrt{3}}{2}\psi_6 \right)$$

$\lambda = 3$

$$\Psi_6 = N_6 \frac{1}{\sqrt{6}} 1 \left(1\psi_1 - 1\psi_2 + 1\psi_3 - 1\psi_4 + 1\psi_5 - 1\psi_6 \right)$$

The above molecular functions can be calculated from the formula:

$$\Psi_j = N_j \frac{1}{\sqrt{6}} a_j \sum_{k=1}^{6} \left. \begin{matrix} \cos \\ \sin \end{matrix} \right\} (\lambda\varphi_k) \cdot \psi_k$$

where the rotation angle φ_k is defined in Fig. 7.4. The factors a_j are given from the normalization conditions for the individual atomic orbitals,

$$\frac{1}{6} \sum_{k=1}^{6} \left[a_j \cdot \left. \begin{matrix} \cos \\ \sin \end{matrix} \right\} (\lambda\varphi_k) \right]^2 = 1$$

while the normalization factors, N_j, take into account the contributions of the mixed members (e.g., $a_j^2 \int \cos \lambda\varphi_k \cos \lambda\varphi_l \cdot d\tau$). The positions of the nodal surfaces and the corresponding symmetry symbols are given in Fig. 7.4. In the ground state, only the Σ- and the two Π-states are occupied by electrons, while the Δ- and Φ-functions contain electrons only when benzene is raised to an excited state.

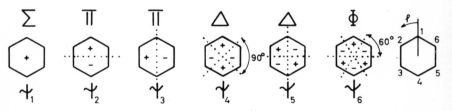

Fig. 7.4. The nodal surfaces of the molecular functions of the $p\pi$-electron system of benzene. Right: The angular co-ordinate φ, and numbering of the atoms.

The two Π-states, as well as the two Δ-states are degenerate, since they have the same energy. This becomes clearer when one looks at the complex orbitals, in which a_m always has the same value, $a_m = \sqrt{2}$:

$$\Psi_m = \frac{1}{\sqrt{2}} N_m \frac{1}{\sqrt{6}} a_m \sum_{k=1}^{6} (\cos \lambda\varphi_k \pm i \sin \lambda\varphi_k)\psi_k$$

$$= \frac{1}{\sqrt{2}} N_m \frac{1}{\sqrt{6}} a_m \sum_{k=1}^{6} e^{im\varphi_k}\psi_k \qquad -3 \leqslant m \leqslant +3.$$

For the case $m = +1$, the molecular function then reads:

$$\Psi_{+1} = \frac{1}{\sqrt{2}} N_{+1} \frac{1}{\sqrt{6}} \cdot \sqrt{2} (\underbrace{e^{2\pi i(0/6)}}_{= 1}\psi_1 + e^{2\pi i(1/6)}\psi_2 + e^{2\pi i(2/6)}\psi_3$$
$$+ \underbrace{e^{2\pi i(3/6)}}_{= -1}\psi_4 + e^{2\pi i(4/6)}\psi_5 + e^{2\pi i(5/6)}\psi_6)$$

When moving from one atom to the next, the phase factor in the molecular function changes by $e^{2\pi i m/6}$. For $m \neq 0$, these functions have a direction of rotation. Since those states with $m = \pm 1$ belong to the ground state of the molecule, benzene is strongly diamagnetic.

8

Many-Electron Systems

8.1 The Helium Atom

8.1.1 *Symmetrical and Antisymmetrical Product Functions Neglecting the Spin Component*

In order to describe ionic complexes, some knowledge of the behaviour of many-electron systems and their mathematical description is required. We have actually already encountered a many-electron system in the H_2-molecule. The Schrödinger equation for He is similar (compare Fig. 3.2):

$$\frac{\partial^2 \psi(x_1 y_1 z_1 x_2 y_2 z_2)}{\partial x_1^2} + \frac{\partial^2 \psi(x_1 y_1 z_1 x_2 y_2 z_2)}{\partial y_1^2} + \frac{\partial^2 \psi(x_1 y_1 z_1 x_2 y_2 z_2)}{\partial z_1^2}$$

$$+ \frac{\partial^2 \psi(x_1 y_1 z_1 x_2 y_2 z_2)}{\partial x_2^2} + \frac{\partial^2 \psi(x_1 y_1 z_1 x_2 y_2 z_2)}{\partial y_2^2} + \frac{\partial^2 \psi(x_1 y_1 z_1 x_2 y_2 z_2)}{\partial z_2^2}$$

$$+ \frac{8\pi^2 m}{h^2} \left(E + \frac{e_1 Ze}{r_1} + \frac{e_2 Ze}{r_2} - \lambda \frac{e_1 e_2}{r_{12}} \right) \cdot \psi(x_1 y_1 z_1 x_2 y_2 z_2) = 0$$

$$\text{with } Z = 2$$

The indices 1 and 2 refer to electrons 1 and 2, respectively, while r_{12} is their mutual separation. The term $-e_1 e_2 / r_{12}$ ($\lambda = 1$) takes account of the mutual repulsion of the electrons. As in the case of the H_2-molecule, this equation is not analytically soluble. If the interaction between the two electrons is diminished ($\lambda \to 0$) (the so-called *electron interaction-free field*), then the solution to the equation must approach the solution of the Schrödinger equation without interelectron interaction. This equation can be analytically solved by making the substitution:

$$\psi(x_1 y_1 z_1 x_2 y_2 z_2) = \psi_1(x_1 y_1 z_1) \cdot \psi_2(x_2 y_2 z_2)$$

Then

$$\psi_2(x_2y_2z_2)\left\{\frac{\partial^2\psi_1(x_1y_1z_1)}{\partial x_1^2} + \frac{\partial^2\psi_1(x_1y_1z_1)}{\partial y_1^2} + \frac{\partial^2\psi_1(x_1y_1z_1)}{\partial z_1^2}\right\}$$

$$+ \psi_1(x_1y_1z_1)\left\{\frac{\partial^2\psi_2(x_2y_2z_2)}{\partial x_2^2} + \frac{\partial^2\psi_2(x_2y_2z_2)}{\partial y_2^2} + \frac{\partial^2\psi_2(x_2y_2z_2)}{\partial z_2^2}\right\}$$

$$+ \frac{8\pi^2m}{h^2}\left\{E + \frac{e_1Ze}{r_1} + \frac{e_2Ze}{r_2}\right\}\psi_1(x_1y_1z_1) \cdot \psi_2(x_2y_2z_2) = 0$$

Division by $\psi_1(x_1y_1z_1) \cdot \psi_2(x_2y_2z_2)$ gives:

$$\frac{1}{\psi_1(x_1y_1z_1)}\left(\frac{\partial^2\psi_1(x_1y_1z_1)}{\partial x_1^2} + \frac{\partial^2\psi_1(x_1y_1z_1)}{\partial y_1^2} + \frac{\partial^2\psi_1(x_1y_1z_1)}{\partial z_1^2}\right)$$

$$+ \frac{8\pi^2m}{h^2}\left(E_1 + \frac{e_1Ze}{r_1}\right)$$

$$+ \frac{1}{\psi_2(x_2y_2z_2)}\left(\frac{\partial^2\psi_2(x_2y_2z_2)}{\partial x_2^2} + \frac{\partial^2\psi_2(x_2y_2z_2)}{\partial y_2^2} + \frac{\partial^2\psi_2(x_2y_2z_2)}{\partial z_2^2}\right)$$

$$+ \frac{8\pi^2m}{h^2}\left(E_2 + \frac{e_2Ze}{r_2}\right) = 0$$

with $E_1 + E_2 = E$.

Since this equation is valid for all values of electron co-ordinates, it can be separated into two independent equations:

$$\frac{\partial^2\psi_1(x_1y_1z_1)}{\partial x_1^2} + \frac{\partial^2\psi_1(x_1y_1z_1)}{\partial y_1^2} + \frac{\partial^2\psi_1(x_1y_1z_1)}{\partial z_1^2}$$

$$+ \frac{8\pi^2m}{h^2}\left(E_1 + \frac{e_1Ze}{r_1}\right)\psi_1(x_1y_1z_1) = 0$$

and

$$\frac{\partial^2\psi_2(x_2y_2z_2)}{\partial x_2^2} + \frac{\partial^2\psi_2(x_2y_2z_2)}{\partial y_2^2} + \frac{\partial^2\psi_2(x_2y_2z_2)}{\partial z_2^2}$$

$$+ \frac{8\pi^2m}{h^2}\left(E_2 + \frac{e_2Ze}{r_2}\right)\psi_2(x_2y_2z_2) = 0.$$

In a field free of electron–electron interaction the solutions of the Schrödinger equation are therefore given by the products of the eigenfunctions for the individual electrons (*product functions*).

The Schrödinger equation for n non-interacting electrons,

$$\sum_{i=1}^{n} \left\{ \frac{\partial^2 \psi(x_1 y_1 z_1 \ldots x_n y_n z_n)}{\partial x_i^2} + \frac{\partial^2 \psi(x_1 y_1 z_1 \ldots x_n y_n z_n)}{\partial y_i^2} \right.$$

$$\left. + \frac{\partial^2 \psi(x_1 y_1 z_1 \ldots x_n y_n z_n)}{\partial z_i^2} \right\} + \frac{8\pi^2 m}{h^2} \left(E + \sum_{i=1}^{n} \frac{e_i Z e}{r_i} \right) \psi(x_1 y_1 z_1 \ldots x_n y_n z_n)$$

$$= 0$$

shows that the solution to this equation consists of the products of n single-electron functions:

$$\psi(x_1 y_1 z_1 \ldots x_n y_n z_n) = \psi_1(x_1 y_1 z_1) \cdot \psi_2(x_2 y_2 z_2) \ldots \psi_n(x_n y_n z_n)$$

$$= \prod_{i=1}^{n} \psi_i(x_i y_i z_i)$$

For the ground state of helium, the product function then reads:

$$\psi(x_1 y_1 z_1 x_2 y_2 z_2) = N^I e^{-Zr_1/1a_0} \cdot N^{II} e^{-Zr_2/1a_0}$$

Here the nuclear charge is $Z = 2$ and not the effective nuclear charge Z_{eff}, since the screening of the nuclear charge has been eliminated by striking out the interaction potential, $(e_1 e_2/r_{12})$. For each electron the ψ-function is spherically symmetric, independent of the position of the other electron. The product function is also spherically symmetric. If the electron–electron interaction is now reintroduced, the two electrons within the atom will evade one another as much as possible, since they mutually repel. It can be shown mathematically that the spherical symmetry is maintained, but the dependence of the product function on the co-ordinates of the two electrons is altered.

If a helium atom in the excited state $1s^1 2s^1$ is now considered, the product function reads:

$$\psi(x_1 y_1 z_1 x_2 y_2 z_2) = \psi^I(x_1 y_1 z_1) \cdot \psi^{II}(x_2 y_2 z_2)$$

$$= N^I e^{-Zr_1/1a_0} \cdot N^{II} e^{-Zr_2/2a_0} \left(1 - \frac{Zr_2}{2a_0} \right)$$

The two electrons 1 and 2 can, however, be interchanged, giving a second solution to Schrödinger's equation:

$$\psi(x_1 y_1 z_1 x_2 y_2 z_2) = \psi^I(x_2 y_2 z_2) \cdot \psi^{II}(x_1 y_1 z_1)$$

$$= N^I e^{-Zr_2/1a_0} \cdot N^{II} e^{-Zr_1/2a_0} \left(1 - \frac{Zr_1}{2a_0} \right)$$

Since both solutions belong to the same eigenvalue of energy, E, they are mutually degenerate, as is any linear combination of solutions to the equation.

The Schrödinger equation for helium, including electron–electron interaction ($\lambda = 1$) has the property that exchanging both electrons leaves the system unaltered. Since real, normalized eigenfunctions remain real, normalized solutions of the Schrödinger equation only when left alone or multiplied by -1, the eigenfunctions of helium ($\lambda = 1$), must, by interchange of electrons, either remain unchanged or go into themselves with, however, a factor of -1. In the first case, one speaks of a *symmetrical function* relative to interchange of electrons while in the second case, one speaks of an *anti-symmetric function*.

If $\lambda \to 0$, the solutions go into the linear combinations of the electron-interaction free system. These are called the *adapted* eigenfunctions to the perturbation (electron interaction).

$$\psi_{sym}(x_1 y_1 z_1 x_2 y_2 z_2) = \frac{1}{\sqrt{2}} \{\psi^I(x_1 y_1 z_1)\psi^{II}(x_2 y_2 z_2) + \psi^I(x_2 y_2 z_2)\psi^{II}(x_1 y_1 z_1)\}$$

$$= \frac{1}{\sqrt{2}} \left\{ N^I e^{-Zr_1/1a_0} \cdot N^{II} e^{-Zr_2/2a_0}\left(1 - \frac{Zr_2}{2a_0}\right) \right.$$

$$\left. + N^I e^{-Zr_2/1a_0} \cdot N^{II} e^{-Zr_1/2a_0}\left(1 - \frac{Zr_1}{2a_0}\right) \right\}$$

$$\psi_{antis}(x_1 y_1 z_1 x_2 y_2 z_2) = \frac{1}{\sqrt{2}} \{\psi^I(x_1 y_1 z_1)\psi^{II}(x_2 y_2 z_2) - \psi^I(x_2 y_2 z_2)\psi^{II}(x_1 y_1 z_1)\}$$

$$= \frac{1}{\sqrt{2}} \left\{ N^I e^{-Zr_1/1a_0} \cdot N^{II} e^{-Zr_2/2a_0}\left(1 - \frac{Zr_2}{2a_0}\right) \right.$$

$$\left. - N^I e^{-Zr_2/1a_0} \cdot N^{II} e^{-Zr_1/2a_0}\left(1 - \frac{Zr_1}{2a_0}\right) \right\}.$$

8.1.2 *Product Functions Including Spin—The Pauli Principle*

The Pauli Principle was previously defined: 'No two electrons in an atom can have all four quantum numbers the same.' This version of the Pauli Principle can be seen to follow from the following more general formulation: 'Systems with several electrons occur only in those states whose complete eigenfunctions (including spin) are antisymmetrical with respect to interchange of any two electrons.'

The two helium functions previously deduced must now be combined with appropriate spin functions, so that the Pauli Principle is obeyed.

$$S = 0 \qquad \underbrace{[\psi^I(1) . \psi^{II}(2) + \psi^I(2)\psi^{II}(1)]}_{\text{sym.}} . \underbrace{[\alpha(1)\beta(2) - \alpha(2)\beta(1)]}_{\text{antisym.}}$$

$$= \begin{vmatrix} \alpha(1)\psi^I(1) & \alpha(2)\psi^I(2) \\ \beta(1)\psi^{II}(1) & \beta(2)\psi^{II}(2) \end{vmatrix} - \begin{vmatrix} \beta(1)\psi^I(1) & \beta(2)\psi^I(2) \\ \alpha(1)\psi^{II}(1) & \alpha(2)\psi^{II}(1) \end{vmatrix}$$

where $\psi^I(1) = \psi^I(x_1 y_1 z_1)$, $\psi^I(2) = \psi^I(x_2 y_2 z_2)$, etc.

$\alpha(1) = $ spin function for $s = +\frac{1}{2}$ on electron 1

$\beta(1) = $ spin function for $s = -\frac{1}{2}$ on electron 1, etc.

There is only the one antisymmetric spin function given above which is able to make the total function antisymmetrical. The electron term associated with it is therefore unique, having a total spin moment, $S = +\frac{1}{2} - \frac{1}{2} = 0$. This is called a *singlet state*. It can be illustrated by a linear combination (difference) of two determinants which were first developed by Slater[8.1] (*Slater Determinants*). The one-electron functions for a specific state are arranged along the rows, while the functions for a given electron are displayed down the individual columns. Starting with the antisymmetrical eigenfunction, there are three possible symmetrical spin functions, with the components S_z in the direction of the z-axis, which may be used to give an antisymmetrical total function:

$$S_z = +1 \qquad [\psi^I(1).\psi^{II}(2) - \psi^I(2).\psi^{II}(1)][\alpha(1).\alpha(2)]$$

$$= \begin{vmatrix} \alpha(1) . \psi^I(1) & \alpha(2) . \psi^I(2) \\ \alpha(1) . \psi^{II}(1) & \alpha(2) . \psi^{II}(2) \end{vmatrix}$$

$$S_z = 0 \qquad [\psi^I(1).\psi^{II}(2) - \psi^I(2).\psi^{II}(1)][\alpha(1).\beta(2) + \alpha(2).\beta(1)]$$

$$= \begin{vmatrix} \alpha(1) . \psi^I(1) & \alpha(2) . \psi^I(2) \\ \beta(1) . \psi^{II}(1) & \beta(2) . \psi^{II}(2) \end{vmatrix} + \begin{vmatrix} \beta(1) . \psi^I(1) & \beta(2) . \psi^I(2) \\ \alpha(1) . \psi^{II}(1) & \alpha(2) . \psi^{II}(2) \end{vmatrix}$$

$$S_z = -1 \qquad [\psi^I(1).\psi^{II}(2) - \psi^I(2).\psi^{II}(1)][\beta(1).\beta(2)]$$

$$= \begin{vmatrix} \beta(1) . \psi^I(1) & \beta(2) . \psi^I(2) \\ \beta(1) . \psi^{II}(1) & \beta(2) . \psi^{II}(2) \end{vmatrix}$$

This '*triplet state*' is threefold: $S_z = 1, 0, -1$.

Each Slater determinant is antisymmetrical relative to an interchange of two electrons since a determinant changes sign when either two rows or two columns are interchanged. If two electrons were described by the same, spin-containing, one-electron function, then two rows would be identical, and the determinant would be equal to zero. The more general formulation of the Pauli Principle then leads to the narrower one. Two electrons with the same spatial eigenfunction ($\psi^{\mathrm{I}} = \psi^{\mathrm{II}}$) must have anti-parallel spin moments. If, however, the spatial eigenfunctions differ, then either parallel, ($S = \pm 1$), or antiparallel, ($S = 0$), moments are possible.

8.2 Representation of Chemical Bonding by Product Functions

If in the Schrödinger equation for the hydrogen molecule (chapter 4, Fig. 4.1) the mutual repulsion of the electrons and of the nuclei is neglected, the equation can again be separated into two equations, each of which depends on the co-ordinates of only one electron.

$$\frac{\partial^2 \psi(x_i y_i z_i)}{\partial x_i{}^2} + \frac{\partial^2 \psi(x_i y_i z_i)}{\partial y_i{}^2} + \frac{\partial^2 \psi(x_i y_i z_i)}{\partial z_i{}^2} + \frac{8\pi^2 m}{h^2}\left(E_i + \frac{e_1 Z_A e}{r_{iA}} + \frac{e_2 Z_B e}{r_{iB}}\right)$$
$$\times \ \psi(x_i y_i z_i) = 0 \quad \text{with } i = 1 \text{ or } 2.$$

In the neighbourhood of nucleus A, $\psi(x_i, y_i, z_i)$ is given by the eigen-function ψ_A of atom A; in the neighbourhood of nucleus B, it is given correspondingly by the eigenfunction ψ_B of atom B. In the space between the two nuclei, the eigenfunction to a first rough approximation is given by the sum (or difference) of the two atomic eigenfunctions. Using this formulation, the molecular function can be obtained as a product function:

$$\psi(x_1 y_1 z_1 x_2 y_2 z_2) = N[\psi_A(1) \pm \psi_B(1)].[\psi_A(2) \pm \psi_B(2)]$$
$$= N[\psi_A(1).\psi_A(2) + \psi_B(1).\psi_B(2) \pm \psi_A(1).\psi_B(2) \pm \psi_A(2).\psi_B(1)]$$

The first two terms represent functions for the case where both electrons are on atom A or atom B, respectively. The last two terms, in contrast, are for the case where the electrons are distributed over atoms A and B. Upon squaring, the mixed products between the first two members on the one hand and the last two on the other contribute a great deal of electron density to the space between the two atoms when the positive sign is chosen. In this way, the electron density is increased, the mutual repulsion of the two nuclei is diminished and bonding results. Since the product function is symmetrical relative to interchange of either electrons or nuclei, the spin function must, according to the Pauli Principle, be antisymmetric. The spin pairing in chemical bonds which is so familiar to chemists thus results from the Pauli Principle. The saturation of the spin moments contributes virtually nothing energetically to the binding. What is essential, is the increase in electron density between the nuclei.

When the negative sign is chosen, negative terms appear in the function, $\psi(x_1y_1z_1x_2y_2z_2)$, which diminish the electron density between the nuclei, increase the internuclear repulsion, and lead to antibonding states.

Following the development of atomic bonding functions by Heitler and London, we proceed from the principle that electron 1 is on atom A and electron 2 on atom B, giving the product function $\psi_A(1).\psi_B(2)$. Since, however, electrons are indistinguishable, they can be interchanged, giving the equally important product function $\psi_A(2).\psi_B(1)$. The symmetrical linear combination is then:

$$\psi(x_1y_1z_1x_2y_2z_2) = N[\psi_A(1).\psi_B(2) + \psi_A(2).\psi_B(1)]$$

The Heitler–London approximation thus considers only the third and fourth terms of the product function obtained by the molecular orbital method. This latter method therefore gives a better approximate function.

8.3 Complex Eigenfunctions

The eigenfunction of an electron, e.g., a $3d_{x^2-y^2}$ electron of hydrogen, consists of a radial component $\chi(r)$ and an angular function, the spherical harmonic $Y_2^2(\vartheta, \varphi)$.

Linear combinations can be formed from two spherical harmonics with the same l and the same λ. These will also be solutions of the Schrödinger equation, since they belong to the same energy eigenvalue, e.g., $l = 2$, $\lambda = \bar{\lambda} = 2$.

$$\frac{1}{\sqrt{2}}\cdot\frac{\sqrt{5}}{2\sqrt{\pi}}\cdot\frac{1}{2}\cdot\sqrt{3}.\sin^2\vartheta.(\cos 2\varphi \pm i \sin 2\varphi)$$

$$= \frac{1}{\sqrt{2}}\cdot\frac{\sqrt{5}}{2\sqrt{\pi}}\cdot\frac{1}{2}\cdot\sqrt{3}.\sin^2\vartheta.e^{\pm 2i\varphi}.$$

This leads to other expressions for normalized complex spherical harmonics which, just like the original functions, are orthogonal to each other (Table 8.1).

In the language of complex spherical harmonics, instead of the axial quantum number, λ, the *magnetic quantum number*, m, exists. This can take all integral values from $-l$ to $+l$; in the above example, $m = 2$ and -2.

As φ varies, the functions $e^{im\varphi}$ represent rotation about the z-axis. They can be related to a circular current in the atom, and are therefore the functions which describe the *angular momentum* and the *orbital magnetic moment* of an electron.

The absolute value of the orbital angular momentum vector $\mathbf{l}$ of an electron is given by $J = -(h/2\pi)\sqrt{l(l+1)}$, whose component in the

Table 8.1. The complex orthogonal normalized spherical harmonics
$Y_l^m(x, y, z)$ *and* $Y_l^m(\vartheta, \varphi)$

l	m	$Y_l^m(x, y, z)$	$Y_l^m(\vartheta, \varphi)$
0	0	$+\dfrac{1}{2\sqrt{\pi}}$	$+\dfrac{1}{2\sqrt{\pi}}$
1	1	$-\dfrac{\sqrt{3}}{2\sqrt{\pi}}\cdot\dfrac{1}{\sqrt{2}}(x+iy)$	$-\dfrac{\sqrt{3}}{2\sqrt{\pi}}\cdot\dfrac{1}{\sqrt{2}}\cdot\sin\vartheta\cdot e^{+i\varphi}$
1	0	$+\dfrac{\sqrt{3}}{2\sqrt{\pi}}\cdot z$	$+\dfrac{\sqrt{3}}{2\sqrt{\pi}}\cdot\cos\vartheta$
1	−1	$+\dfrac{\sqrt{3}}{2\sqrt{\pi}}\dfrac{1}{\sqrt{2}}(x-iy)$	$+\dfrac{\sqrt{3}}{2\sqrt{\pi}}\dfrac{1}{\sqrt{2}}\cdot\sin\vartheta\cdot e^{i\varphi}$
2	2	$+\dfrac{\sqrt{5}}{2\sqrt{\pi}}\cdot\sqrt{\dfrac{3}{\sqrt{2^3}}}(x+iy)^2$	$+\dfrac{\sqrt{5}}{2\sqrt{\pi}}\sqrt{\dfrac{3}{2^3}}\sin^2\vartheta\cdot e^{+i2\varphi}$
2	1	$-\dfrac{\sqrt{5}}{2\sqrt{\pi}}\cdot\sqrt{\dfrac{3}{2}}(x+iy)z$	$-\dfrac{\sqrt{5}}{2\sqrt{\pi}}\sqrt{\dfrac{3}{2}}\cos\vartheta\,\sin\vartheta\cdot e^{+i\varphi}$
2	0	$+\dfrac{\sqrt{5}}{2\sqrt{\pi}}\dfrac{1}{2}(3z^2-1)$	$+\dfrac{\sqrt{5}}{2\sqrt{\pi}}\cdot\dfrac{1}{2}(3\cos^2\vartheta-1)$
2	−1	$+\dfrac{\sqrt{5}}{2\sqrt{\pi}}\sqrt{\dfrac{3}{2}}(x-iy)z$	$+\dfrac{\sqrt{5}}{2\sqrt{\pi}}\sqrt{\dfrac{3}{2}}\cos\vartheta\,\sin\vartheta\cdot e^{-i\varphi}$
2	−2	$+\dfrac{\sqrt{5}}{2\sqrt{\pi}}\sqrt{\dfrac{3}{2^3}}(x-iy)^2$	$+\dfrac{\sqrt{5}}{2\sqrt{\pi}}\sqrt{\dfrac{3}{2^3}}\sin^2\vartheta\cdot e^{-i2\varphi}$
3	3	$-\dfrac{\sqrt{7}}{2\sqrt{\pi}}\cdot\dfrac{\sqrt{5}}{2^2}(x+iy)^3$	$-\dfrac{\sqrt{7}}{2\sqrt{\pi}}\cdot\dfrac{\sqrt{5}}{2^2}\sin^3\vartheta\cdot e^{+i3\varphi}$
3	2	$+\dfrac{\sqrt{7}}{2\sqrt{\pi}}\cdot\sqrt{\dfrac{15}{2^3}}(x+iy)^2 z$	$+\dfrac{\sqrt{7}}{2\sqrt{\pi}}\sqrt{\dfrac{15}{2^3}}\cos\vartheta\,\sin^2\vartheta\cdot e^{+i2\varphi}$
3	1	$-\dfrac{\sqrt{7}}{2\sqrt{\pi}}\cdot\dfrac{\sqrt{3}}{2^2}(x+iy)(5z^2-1)$	$-\dfrac{\sqrt{7}}{2\sqrt{\pi}}\cdot\dfrac{\sqrt{3}}{2^2}(5\cos^2\vartheta-1)\sin\vartheta\cdot e^{+i\varphi}$
3	0	$+\dfrac{\sqrt{7}}{2\sqrt{\pi}}\cdot\dfrac{1}{2}(5z^3-3z)$	$+\dfrac{\sqrt{7}}{2\sqrt{\pi}}\cdot\dfrac{1}{2}(5\cos^3\vartheta-3\cos\vartheta)$
3	−1	$+\dfrac{\sqrt{7}}{2\sqrt{\pi}}\cdot\dfrac{\sqrt{3}}{2^2}(x-iy)(5z^2-1)$	$+\dfrac{\sqrt{7}}{2\sqrt{\pi}}\cdot\dfrac{\sqrt{3}}{2^2}(5\cos^2\vartheta-1)\sin\vartheta\cdot e^{-i\varphi}$
3	−2	$+\dfrac{\sqrt{7}}{2\sqrt{\pi}}\cdot\sqrt{\dfrac{15}{2^3}}(x-iy)^2\,z$	$+\dfrac{\sqrt{7}}{2\sqrt{\pi}}\sqrt{\dfrac{15}{2^3}}\cos\vartheta\,\sin^2\vartheta\cdot e^{-i2\varphi}$
3	−3	$+\dfrac{\sqrt{7}}{2\sqrt{\pi}}\cdot\dfrac{\sqrt{5}}{2^2}(x-iy)^3$	$+\dfrac{\sqrt{7}}{2\sqrt{\pi}}\cdot\dfrac{\sqrt{5}}{2^2}\sin^3\vartheta\cdot e^{-i3\varphi}$

direction of the z-axis is: $J_z = -(h/2\pi)m$. The z-component of the magnetic moment is $M_z = -(eh/4\pi mc)m = -\mu_B m$.

Calculation with complex functions has advantages, and complex spherical harmonics are therefore frequently used. They easily illustrate the rotation of an eigenfunction about the unique z-axis.

8.4 The System of Two p-Electrons

8.4.1 *Derivation of the Product Functions*

In an atom, there may be electrons which have the same principal and angular momentum quantum number, but which differ in axial quantum number. These electrons belong to the same energy eigenvalue and are indistinguishable in a free atom.

Many-electron systems of d-electrons are the bases of transition-metal compounds. Systems of f-electrons appear in the rare earths and actinides. Even though p-electrons in chemical bonds can generally be treated as single electrons, the system of two p-electrons will be considered since the mathematical treatment is simple, and the results can be descriptively discussed.

Just as with an excited helium atom, the solution of the Schrödinger equation for two p-electrons (e.g., carbon, $1s^2 2s^2 2p^2$), neglecting electron–electron interaction is given by a product function, $\psi^I(1)\psi^{II}(2)$. Here ψ^I and ψ^{II} are any two orthogonal p-eigenfunctions with the same principal quantum number. Since there are three p-eigenfunctions with the same principal quantum number, there must be $3 \times 3 = 9$ different product functions. Any solution of the Schrödinger equation can be formed from these 9 product functions by making appropriate linear combinations.

These product functions must now be linearly combined in such a way that both symmetrical and antisymmetrical spatial functions result. These then can be further combined with antisymmetrical and symmetrical spin functions to give antisymmetrical total functions.

In order to interpret spectroscopic data for a system with several p, d, or f electrons, linear combinations must be formed so that the product functions are again distinguished by an integral total momentum and an integral angular momentum about the z-axis (see Vector Model, page 94. These integers are given for the eigenfunctions of an individual electron by the angular momentum and magnetic quantum numbers. Thus one attempts to form symmetrical and antisymmetrical linear combinations with total angular momentum quantum number, L and total magnetic quantum number, M. According to convention, the quantum numbers in many-electron systems are denoted by capital letters. The mathematical basis for the existence of these linear combinations with definite L and M is rather involved, just as is the derivation of the method for finding the proper linear combination. For the case of two p-electrons the results are given in Table 8.2. For the derivation of complex product functions, the complex spherical harmonics of Table 8.1 are used.

Table 8.2. Angular component of the product functions in a system of two non-interacting p-electrons

M L	2	1	0	-1	-2	Symmetry	Term symbol
2	(11)	$\frac{1}{\sqrt{2}}\{(10) + (01)\}$	$\frac{1}{\sqrt{6}}\{2(00) + (1-1) + (-11)\}$	$\frac{1}{\sqrt{2}}\{(0-1) + (-10)\}$	$(-1-1)$	sym.	^1D
1	—	$\frac{1}{\sqrt{2}}\{(10) - (01)\}$	$\frac{1}{\sqrt{2}}\{(1-1) - (-11)\}$	$\frac{1}{\sqrt{2}}\{(0-1) - (-10)\}$	—	anti-sym.	^3P
0	—	—	$\frac{1}{\sqrt{3}}\{(00) - (1-1) - (-11)\}$	—	—	sym.	^1S

From complex product functions, we can again build real product functions by taking the sum or difference of two functions which differ only in the sign on M. In this way the angular function $1/\sqrt{2}\,e^{im\varphi}$ is transformed into $\cos \lambda\varphi$ and $\sin \lambda\varphi$. Total axial quantum numbers Λ and $\overline{\Lambda}$ are then obtained, for which the relationship $0 \leqslant \Lambda \leqslant L$ holds. In both expressions for the product functions, Λ and M give definite symmetry properties, in particular the relationships on rotation.

The radial components are ignored in Table 8.2 since they are identical for all p-electrons in the outermost shell of an atom. This leaves then only the complex products of the spherical harmonics for two electrons. The spherical harmonics of the individual electrons are labelled only by the magnetic quantum number. In the braces, there stands first the spherical harmonic of the first electron, and in second position that of the second, i.e.:

$$\frac{1}{\sqrt{2}}\{(10) + (01)\} = \frac{1}{\sqrt{2}}\{Y_1^1(\vartheta_1\varphi_1)\cdot Y_1^0(\vartheta_2\varphi_2) + Y_1^0(\vartheta_1\varphi_1)\cdot Y_1^1(\vartheta_2\varphi_2)\}$$

The associated ψ-function for the two p-electrons in a ^1D state with $M = 1$ (ignoring electron–electron interaction) is:

$$\frac{1}{\sqrt{2}}\{\chi(r_1)\cdot Y_1^1(\vartheta_1\varphi_1)\cdot \chi(r_2)Y_1^0(\vartheta_2\varphi_2) + \chi(r_1)\cdot Y_1^0(\vartheta_1\varphi_1)\cdot \chi(r_2)Y_1^1(\vartheta_2\varphi_2)\}$$

Multiplying by the antisymmetrical spin function gives:

$$\frac{1}{\sqrt{2}}\{\underbrace{\chi(r_1)\cdot Y_1^{\,1}(\vartheta_1\varphi_1)}_{\psi^I(1)}\cdot \underbrace{\chi(r_2)Y_1^{\,0}(\vartheta_2\varphi_2)}_{\psi^{II}(2)} + \underbrace{\chi(r_1)Y_1^{\,0}(\vartheta_1\varphi_1)}_{\psi^{II}(1)}\cdot \underbrace{\chi(r_2)Y_1^{\,1}(\vartheta_2\varphi_2)}_{\psi^I(2)}\}$$

$$\times \{\alpha(1)\beta(2) - \alpha(2)\beta(1)\}$$

$$= \frac{1}{\sqrt{2}}\cdot \begin{vmatrix} \alpha(1)\chi(r_1)Y_1^{\,1}(\vartheta_1\varphi_1) & \alpha(2)\chi(r_2)Y_1^{\,1}(\vartheta_2\varphi_2) \\ \beta(1)\chi(r_1)Y_1^{\,0}(\vartheta_1\varphi_1) & \beta(2)\chi(r_2)Y_1^{\,0}(\vartheta_2\varphi_2) \end{vmatrix}$$

$$- \frac{1}{\sqrt{2}}\cdot \begin{vmatrix} \beta(1)\chi(r_1)Y_1^{\,1}(\vartheta_1\varphi_1) & \beta(2)\chi(r_2)Y_1^{\,1}(\vartheta_2\varphi_2) \\ \alpha(1)\chi(r_1)Y_1^{\,0}(\vartheta_1\varphi_1) & \alpha(2)\chi(r_2)Y_1^{\,0}(\vartheta_2\varphi_2) \end{vmatrix}$$

8.4.2 *The Vector Model*

The quantum number l is a measure of the angular momentum of an electron. The angular momentum of a two-electron system is determined from the momenta of the individual electrons by the *vector model*, which was known long before the advent of wave mechanics. In this model:

(a) The angular momentum $\mathbf{l}_i$ of individual electrons has an integral absolute value, l (in units of $h/2\pi$).

(b) The angular momentum vectors of two electrons are vectorially added so that the resultant vector $\mathbf{L}$ also has an integral absolute value.

(c) The resultant vector from two electrons is added to a third vector in the same fashion so that again the resultant vector is integral. This same condition applies to all further vector additions.

(d) Each of the angular momenta with absolute value $L(h/2\pi)$, so obtained for the entire system has associated with it an energy term. This term is designated as $S, P, D, F, \ldots$ accordingly as $L = 0, 1, 2, 3, \ldots$.

(e) The angular momentum of the system can be arranged only in those ways in which its component about the unique z-axis has the absolute value $M(h/2\pi)$ where the magnetic quantum number, M, can take any integral value from $-L$ to $+L$. This gives $2L + 1$ electron states with the same energy. Only in the vector model is the value of the angular momentum vector l or L. In the exact quantum mechanical calculation one obtains $\sqrt{l(l + 1)}$ or $\sqrt{L(L + 1)}$ instead.

For the case of two p-electrons, vectorial addition of the angular momenta $\mathbf{l}_1$ and $\mathbf{l}_2$ gives:

| $L = 2$ with 5 states | $L = 1$ with 3 states | $L = 0$ with 1 state |

According to the vector model, a fivefold D-state, a threefold P-state, and a single S-state should be expected. The S- and D-states (see table) are symmetric, relative to interchange of two electrons. They must thus be combined with the antisymmetrical spin function, which was found for the excited helium atom. These are thus singlet states, ^1D and ^1S ($S = 0$). The multiplicity of a term is equal to $2S + 1$ and is given as the upper left index of the term symbol. The symbol S, somewhat confusingly, is used in two ways:

(a) S is the symbol for $L = 0$.

(b) S is the symbol for the total spin quantum number.

The three p-states are antisymmetrical with respect to the interchange of the electrons; they can thus be considered as a triplet state with the spin components, $S_z = 1, 0, -1$.

8.4.3 *Interpretation of Product Functions*

A product function is difficult to interpret. For the case $L = 1$ and $M = 0$, it reads:

$$\frac{1}{\sqrt{2}}\{(1 \quad -1) - (-1 \quad 1)\} = \frac{1}{\sqrt{2}}\left\{\left(-\sqrt{\frac{3}{2^3\pi}}\sin\vartheta_1 e^{i\varphi_1}\sqrt{\frac{3}{2^3\pi}}\sin\vartheta_2 e^{-i\varphi_2}\right)\right.$$

$$\left.-\left(\sqrt{\frac{3}{2^3\pi}}\sin\vartheta_1 e^{-i\varphi_1}\left(-\sqrt{\frac{3}{2^3\pi}}\right)\sin\vartheta_2 e^{i\varphi_2}\right)\right\}$$

$$= -\frac{1}{\sqrt{2}}\cdot\frac{3}{2^3\pi}\{\sin\vartheta_1\sin\vartheta_2(e^{i(\varphi_1-\varphi_2)} - e^{-i(\varphi_1-\varphi_2)})\}$$

$$= (-i)\frac{\sqrt{2}\cdot 3}{2^3\pi}\{\sin\vartheta_1\sin\vartheta_2\sin(\varphi_1 - \varphi_2)\}$$

The factor $-i$ is without significance and can be ignored. The total function is zero when $\vartheta_1 = 0$ or $\vartheta_2 = 0$. That means that along the z-axis, the product function vanishes, signifying a nodal line. For $\vartheta_1 = 90°$ and $\vartheta_2 = 90°$ (i.e., in the xy-plane) the eigenfunction takes on especially large values. For $\varphi_1 = \varphi_2$, $\sin(\varphi_1 - \varphi_2) = 0$ and for $\varphi_1 - \varphi_2 = 90°$, $\sin(\varphi_1 - \varphi_2) = 1$. The eigenfunction, and therefore also the electron probability density for the two electrons, becomes largest when the φ-co-ordinates of the electrons 1 and 2 differ by $90°$. The positions of the two electrons are thus not independent of their φ-co-ordinates, although they are independent of their ϑ-co-ordinates.

When the entire electron system is rotated about the z-axis by an angle α, the value of $\sin(\varphi_1 - \varphi_2) = \sin[\varphi_1 + \alpha - (\varphi_1 + \alpha)] = \sin(\varphi_1 - \varphi_2)$ remains unaltered. The two electrons separate themselves as much as possible (right angle) relative to their mutual φ-co-ordinates. However, the product function is invariant relative to a rotation about the z-axis.

It possesses the same rotational symmetry as a p_z-electron. The eigen-function of a p_z-electron is dumb-bell shaped; that of the product function is toroidal.

Inversion through the origin of the co-ordinate system carries $\sin \vartheta$ into $\sin(180° - \vartheta) = \sin \vartheta$. Both the difference $\varphi_1 - \varphi_2$ and of course the sine of the difference, $\sin(\varphi_1 - \varphi_2)$ remain unaltered. The product function then, in contrast to a p_z-eigenfunction, is a gerade function.

According to the addition theorem for trigonometric functions, $\sin(\varphi_1 - \varphi_2) = \sin \varphi_1 \cos \varphi_2 - \cos \varphi_1 \sin \varphi_2$. The resulting product function is then:

$$(-i) \frac{\sqrt{2 \cdot 3}}{2^3 \pi} (\sin \vartheta_1 \sin \varphi_1 \sin \vartheta_2 \cos \varphi_2 - \sin \vartheta_1 \cos \varphi_1 \sin \vartheta_2 \sin \varphi_2)$$

$$= (-i) \frac{\sqrt{2 \cdot 3}}{2^3 \pi} (y_1 x_2 - x_1 y_2)$$

where x_i, y_i, z_i are the Cartesian co-ordinates of electron i on the surface of a unit sphere.

From the complex eigenfunctions for $L = 1$ and $M = +1$ and -1, two real eigenfunctions with axial quantum numbers $\Lambda = \bar{\Lambda} = 1$ can be formed by addition and subtraction.

$$\frac{1}{\sqrt{2}} \left[\frac{1}{\sqrt{2}} \{(10) - (01)\} \pm \frac{1}{\sqrt{2}} \{(0-1) - (10)\} \right]$$

$$= \frac{1}{2} \cdot \frac{3}{2^2 \pi} \left[\frac{1}{\sqrt{2}} \sin \vartheta_1 \cdot e^{i\varphi_1} \cdot \cos \vartheta_2 - \cos \vartheta_1 \cdot \frac{1}{\sqrt{2}} \sin \vartheta_2 \cdot e^{i\varphi_2} \right.$$

$$\left. \pm \cos \vartheta_1 \cdot \frac{1}{\sqrt{2}} \sin \vartheta_2 \cdot e^{-i\varphi_2} \mp \frac{1}{\sqrt{2}} \sin \vartheta_1 \cdot e^{-i\varphi_1} \cdot \cos \vartheta_2 \right]$$

$$= \frac{3}{2^3 \pi} \cdot \frac{1}{\sqrt{2}} \left[\sin \vartheta_1 (e^{i\varphi_1} \mp e^{-i\varphi_1}) \cos \vartheta_2 - \cos \vartheta_1 (e^{i\varphi_2} \mp e^{-i\varphi_2}) \cdot \sin \vartheta_2 \right]$$

$$= \frac{3\sqrt{2}}{2^3 \pi} \left[\sin \vartheta_1 \begin{Bmatrix} i \cdot \sin \varphi_1 \\ \cos \varphi_1 \end{Bmatrix} \cos \vartheta_2 - \cos \vartheta_1 \begin{Bmatrix} i \cdot \sin \varphi_2 \\ \cos \varphi_2 \end{Bmatrix} \sin \vartheta_2 \right]$$

or in Cartesian co-ordinates:

$$\text{(i)} \ \frac{\sqrt{2 \cdot 3}}{2^3 \pi} (y_1 z_2 - z_1 y_2) \quad \text{and} \quad \frac{\sqrt{2 \cdot 3}}{2^3 \pi} (x_1 z_2 - z_1 x_2).$$

The state for $\Lambda = \bar{\Lambda} = 1$ results then from the state $M = \Lambda = 0$ by interchanging the co-ordinates in the same way as the p_x and p_y electron eigenfunctions can be derived from that for the p_z electron.

In conclusion we shall demonstrate the spherical symmetry of the state $L = 0$, $M = 0$. The product function in angular co-ordinates reads:

$$\frac{1}{\sqrt{3}} \{(00) - (1-1) - (-11)\}$$

$$= \frac{1}{\sqrt{3}} \left(\frac{\sqrt{3}}{2\sqrt{\pi}}\right)^2 \left\{\cos \vartheta_1 \cos \vartheta_2 - (-1)\frac{1}{\sqrt{2}} \sin \vartheta_1 e^{i\varphi_1} \cdot \frac{1}{\sqrt{2}} \sin \vartheta_2 e^{-i\varphi_2}\right.$$

$$\left. - \frac{1}{\sqrt{2}} \sin \vartheta_1 e^{-i\varphi_1} \cdot (-1)\frac{1}{\sqrt{2}} \sin \vartheta_2 \cdot e^{i\varphi_2}\right\}$$

$$= \frac{\sqrt{3}}{2^2\pi} \left\{\cos \vartheta_1 \cos \vartheta_2 + \frac{1}{2} \sin \vartheta_1 \sin \vartheta_2 [(\cos \varphi_1 + i \sin \varphi_1)\right.$$

$$\left. \times (\cos \varphi_2 - i \sin \varphi_2) + (\cos \varphi_1 - i \sin \varphi_1)(\cos \varphi_2 + i \sin \varphi_2)]\right\}$$

$$= \frac{\sqrt{3}}{2^2\pi} \{\cos \vartheta_1 \cos \vartheta_2 + \sin \vartheta_1 \cos \varphi_1 \sin \vartheta_2 \cos \varphi_2$$

$$+ \sin \vartheta_1 \sin \varphi_1 \sin \vartheta_2 \sin \varphi_2\}$$

or in Cartesian co-ordinates:

$$\frac{\sqrt{3}}{2^2\pi} (x_1 x_2 + y_1 y_2 + z_1 z_2).$$

This expression represents nothing other than the inner product of the two vectors $x_1 y_1 z_1$ and $x_2 y_2 z_2$. Since this expression is referred to unit vectors, the expression corresponds to the direction cosines between the two vectors. The most probable state is that where the axes of the two p-states are collinear ($\cos 0° = 1$). The state where the axes are perpendicular to each other ($\cos 90° = 0$) is not observed. The position of the two vectors is otherwise free and indeterminate, so that a spherically symmetrical product function results.

In a ^1S-state, the symmetry of the individual p-electrons is completely lost, while the product function for the ^3P-state bears a close resemblance to the sum of the eigenfunctions of two p-electrons. The rotational symmetry about the z-axis of the product function $L = 1$ and $\Lambda = 0$, and the disappearance of the function along the z-axis can be visualized approximately as the superposition of the eigenfunctions for one p_x- and one p_y-electron. Much use will be made of this approximation. For example, the case of triple bonding in acetylene has already been treated as the superposition of two π-bonds from p_x- and p_y-electrons. We must not forget that p_x and p_y electrons are mutually degenerate, as are also their π-bonding systems. From the π_x and π_y bonding functions product functions should really be formed in order to obtain the correct state with rotational symmetry.

In a field free of electron–electron interaction, all functions of the terms ^1D, ^3P, and ^1S have the same energy. If now the inter-electronic interaction is gradually added, the quantum numbers and therefore the symmetry properties of the product function remain, the latter being merely deformed. In addition, the terms ^1D, ^3P, and ^1S are separated from one another in energy for the following reasons:

(a) Even without inter-electronic repulsion, the distances r_{12} between the two electrons are different for the three cases. In the ^3P-state the two electrons are better able to arrange themselves remote from one another than they can in the ^1S-state. Therefore, when inter-electronic repulsion $(\lambda_{e_1 e_2}/r_{12})$ is gradually added $(\lambda \to 1)$ the ^3P-state is energetically favoured.

(b) In a triplet state two electrons have the same spin. There thus exists the possibility of an exchange interaction, whereby energy is gained. This exchange interaction is also the principal basis for Hund's Rule. As more electrons with identical spin are available in an atom, the exchange interaction becomes greater.

8.5 The System of Two d-Electrons

According to the vector model, angular momentum quantum numbers from $L = 0$ to $L = 2 + 2 = 4$ are possible for the product functions of two d-electrons. In addition we know that there must be $5 \times 5 = 25$ orthogonal product functions since each of the five d-eigenfunctions can be coupled by multiplication with itself or with one of the other four d-eigenfunctions. In Table 8.3 these 25 functions are given.

If now one considers also the spin, then each electron has a choice among 10 states: $m = 2, -1, 0, 1, 2$, and $s = \pm\frac{1}{2}$. There are $(10 \times 9)/2! = 45$ possibilities where two electrons can be distributed and therefore there are also 45 product functions when the spin is considered.

By looking at Table 8.3, these 45 functions can be obtained, and it can be seen which product functions are symmetrical and which antisymmetrical. It is then only necessary to complete them with the appropriate spin function in order to make the total function antisymmetrical. There is only one possibility for division into singlet and triplet states as Table 8.4 shows.

Table 8.3. Angular portion of the product functions of a system of two d-electrons, without electron–electron interactions

$L\backslash M$	4	3	2	1	0	-1	-2	-3	-4
4 (^1G)	(22)	$\frac{1}{\sqrt{2}}\{(21)+(12)\}$	$\frac{1}{\sqrt{7}}\left\{\sqrt{\frac{3}{2}}((20)+(02))+2(11)\right\}$	$\frac{1}{\sqrt{7}}\left\{\frac{1}{\sqrt{2}}((2-1)+(-12))+\sqrt{3}((10)+(01))\right\}$	$\frac{1}{\sqrt{7}}\left\{\frac{1}{2\sqrt{5}}((2-2)+(-22))+2\sqrt{\frac{2}{5}}((1-1)+(-11))+3\sqrt{\frac{2}{5}}(00)\right\}$	$\frac{1}{\sqrt{7}}\left\{\frac{1}{\sqrt{2}}((1-2)+(-21))+\sqrt{3}((0-1)+(-10))\right\}$	$\frac{1}{\sqrt{7}}\left\{\sqrt{\frac{3}{2}}((0-2)+(-20))+2(-1-1)\right\}$	$\frac{1}{\sqrt{2}}\{(-1-2)+(-2-1)\}$	$(-2-2)$
3 (^3F)	—	$\frac{1}{\sqrt{2}}\{(21)-(12)\}$	$\frac{1}{\sqrt{2}}\{(20)-(02)\}$	$\frac{1}{\sqrt{5}}\left\{(10)-(01)+\sqrt{\frac{3}{2}}((2-1)-(-12))\right\}$	$\frac{1}{\sqrt{5}}\left\{\sqrt{2}((1-1)-(-11))+\frac{1}{\sqrt{2}}((2-2)-(-22))\right\}$	$\frac{1}{\sqrt{5}}\left\{(0-1)-(-10)+\sqrt{\frac{3}{2}}((1-2)-(-21))\right\}$	$\frac{1}{\sqrt{2}}\{(0-2)-(-20)\}$	$\frac{1}{\sqrt{2}}\{(-1-2)-(-2-1)\}$	—
2 (^1D)	—	—	$\frac{1}{\sqrt{7}}\{\sqrt{2}((20)+(02))-\sqrt{3}(11)\}$	$\frac{1}{\sqrt{7}}\left\{\sqrt{3}((2-1)+(-12))-\frac{1}{\sqrt{2}}((10)+(01))\right\}$	$\frac{1}{\sqrt{7}}\left\{\sqrt{2}((2-2)+(-22))+\frac{1}{\sqrt{2}}((1-1)+(-11))-\sqrt{2}(00)\right\}$	$\frac{1}{\sqrt{7}}\left\{\sqrt{3}((1-2)+(-21))-\frac{1}{\sqrt{2}}((-10)+(0-1))\right\}$	$\frac{1}{\sqrt{7}}\{\sqrt{2}((0-2)+(-20))-\sqrt{3}(-1-1)\}$	—	—
1 (^3P)	—	—	—	$\frac{1}{\sqrt{5}}\left\{(2-1)-(-12)+\sqrt{\frac{3}{2}}((01)-(10))\right\}$	$\frac{1}{\sqrt{5}}\left\{\sqrt{2}((2-2)-(-22))-\frac{1}{\sqrt{2}}((1-1)-(-11))\right\}$	$\frac{1}{\sqrt{5}}\left\{(1-2)-(-21)+\sqrt{\frac{3}{2}}((-10)-(0-1))\right\}$	—	—	—
0 (^1S)	—	—	—	—	$\frac{1}{\sqrt{5}}\{(2-2)+(-22)-(1-1)-(-11)+(00)\}$	—	—	—	—

Table 8.4. *Possible product functions of the system of two d-electrons*

Product functions	Number of functions	
	without spin	with spin
^1G	9	9
^3F	7	21
^1D	5	5
^3P	3	9
^1S	1	1
	25	45

8.6 Systems of Three and More Electrons

In order to develop the product functions for systems with 3 and more electrons, one proceeds from the Slater determinants. For three-electron systems they appear like this:

$$
\begin{vmatrix}
\alpha(1)\psi^I(1) & \alpha(2)\psi^I(2) & \alpha(3)\psi^I(3) \\
\alpha(1)\psi^{II}(2) & \alpha(2)\psi^{II}(2) & \alpha(3)\psi^{II}(3) \\
\beta(1)\psi^{III}(1) & \beta(2)\psi^{III}(2) & \beta(3)\psi^{III}(3)
\end{vmatrix}
$$

Acceptable linear combinations must then again be found in order to obtain states (ignoring electron–electron interaction) which are characterized by the quantum numbers L and M. It is quite difficult to find these linear combinations because:

(a) It is generally impossible to make a division between symmetrical and antisymmetrical spatial and spin functions. Only antisymmetrical total functions (linear combinations of Slater Determinants) can be specified.

(b) It is generally possible to form a given L-state in several ways. For example, with $3p$-electrons, a D-state can be formed according to the vector model with the two electron product function $L_{12} = 2$ or $L_{12} = 1$.

The possible quantum numbers, L, for the total angular momentum can still be easily obtained from the vector model, as can also the number of possible states.

9

Crystal Field Theory

9.1 Ionic Complexes with One *d*-Electron

9.1.1 $d_\varepsilon(t_{2g})$- and $d_\gamma(e_g)$-Electrons

Historically, an ionic complex is one which has the same number of unpaired *d*-electrons with parallel spin-momenta in the complex as in the free gaseous state. Therefore these are often called *high spin complexes*. One example is $[Ti(OH_2)_6]^{3+}$. Following up the work of Bethe[9.1] and van Vleck,[9.2] Hartmann and Ilse[6.2] were able, by studying this compound, to lay the basis for understanding the nature of bonding in these ionic complexes.

The oxygen atoms of the six water molecules octahedrally surround the Ti^{3+}-ion. If we now set up in the octahedron the co-ordinate system shown in Fig. 9.1, we observe that three of the *d*-electrons: d_{xy}, d_{yz}, d_{xz} (which we

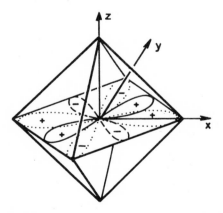

Fig. 9.1. The position of a d_{xy}- and a $d_{x^2-y^2}$-electron in an octahedral field.

shall label d_ε or t_{2g}) differ in their orientation relative to the co-ordinate axes from the remaining two electrons: d_{3z^2-1} and $d_{x^2-y^2}$ (the d_γ or e_g-group).

In the case of the t_{2g}-electrons, the greatest electron density is found in the space between the oxygen atoms, while with the e_g-group, the orbitals have their maximum extension and therefore the electrons their greatest density in the immediate vicinity of the oxygen atoms. A water molecule possesses a dipole moment. The negative side of this dipole can more closely approach the highly charged Ti^{3+} ion in the former case, while the electron clouds of the e_g-electrons would repel the water dipole. In the ground state, the complex ion will thus have one t_{2g}-electron. A definite energy Δ (otherwise designated $10Dq$) is required to raise the electron to an e_g-state. In the case of $[Ti(OH_2)_6]^{3+}$, this energy is 58 kcal/mole $= 20,300$ cm^{-1}. It is this transition, $t_{2g} \rightarrow e_g$, which brings about the violet colour of the ion. In a free, gaseous Ti^{3+}-ion, all d-electron states are mutually degenerate; they belong to the same energy eigenvalue. It is therefore impossible to specify which state an individual electron will occupy. In an octahedral field, this degeneracy is partially lifted and the d-state is *split* into two terms (Fig. 9.2).

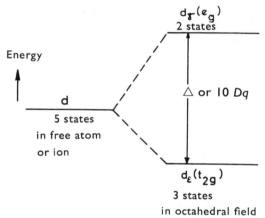

Fig. 9.2. Term splitting of the d-electrons in an octahedral field.

The term of an individual p-electron is not split in an octahedral field, since it is immaterial whether one considers a p_x- p_y- or p_z-electron. The p-electron terms are also not split in tetrahedral or cubic fields since the three axes of a Cartesian co-ordinate system are transformed into themselves by the symmetry operations of a tetrahedron or cube (Fig. 9.3). The p-electron states are, however, split in fields of lower symmetry, for example in a tetragonal field.

In contrast to p-states, the five d-states are split by tetrahedral and cubic groups again into t_{2g}- and e_g-groups. With these symmetries, however, it is the t_{2g}-electrons which come nearer to the ligand atoms and the e_g-state is the ground state when the ligand has either a negative charge or a dipole (Fig. 9.4). The energy difference between the e_g-ground state and the first excited state, containing one t_{2g}-electron, is smaller than the difference in an octahedral field, since the positions of the two types of

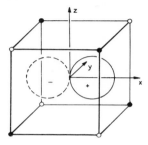

Fig. 9.3. *Position of a p_x-electron in a tetrahedral (●) and cubic (● + ○) environment.*

electrons relative to the ligand atoms are not so very different. It can be shown that the splitting in a tetrahedral field is $\frac{4}{9}$ that in an octahedral field.

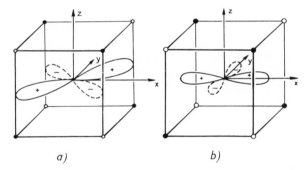

a)   *b)*

Fig. 9.4. *(a) Position of a d_{xy}- and (b) a $d_{x^2-y^2}$-electron in a tetrahedral (●) and cubic (● + ○) environment.*

The tetrahedron does not have a centre of symmetry, hence the notation 'g' and 'u', for gerade and ungerade character, has no meaning. In this case, one omits, by convention, the indices g and u in the electron notation and writes, for example, simply t_2 and e instead of t_{2g} and e_g. The gerade or ungerade character of the orbitals is in any case given by the azimuthal quantum number.

9.1.2 *Matrix Representation of the Transformation of Spherical Harmonics*
We shall examine from another point of view the splitting by an octahedral field of the fivefold degenerate terms of one d-electron in a

gaseous ion. Choosing any orthogonal and normalized system of five d-eigenfunctions, it is possible by a linear transformation to form another orthogonal and normalized system of five d-eigenfunctions:

$$\varphi_1 = a_{11}\psi_1 + a_{12}\psi_2 + a_{13}\psi_3 + a_{14}\psi_4 + a_{15}\psi_5$$

$$\varphi_2 = a_{21}\psi_1 + a_{22}\psi_2 + a_{23}\psi_3 + a_{24}\psi_4 + a_{25}\psi_5$$

$$\varphi_3 = a_{31}\psi_1 + a_{32}\psi_2 + a_{33}\psi_3 + a_{34}\psi_4 + a_{35}\psi_5$$

$$\varphi_4 = a_{41}\psi_1 + a_{42}\psi_2 + a_{43}\psi_3 + a_{44}\psi_4 + a_{45}\psi_5$$

$$\varphi_5 = a_{51}\psi_1 + a_{52}\psi_2 + a_{53}\psi_3 + a_{54}\psi_4 + a_{55}\psi_5$$

$$\text{with} \quad \begin{vmatrix} a_{11}a_{12}a_{13}a_{14}a_{15} \\ a_{21}a_{22}a_{23}a_{24}a_{25} \\ a_{31}a_{32}a_{33}a_{34}a_{35} \\ a_{41}a_{42}a_{43}a_{44}a_{45} \\ a_{51}a_{52}a_{53}a_{54}a_{55} \end{vmatrix} \neq 0$$

The transformed eigenfunctions, φ_i, represent solutions of the Schrödinger equation. It is necessary only that the coefficients of the transformation matrix be subject to definite normalization conditions, and that the five equations be linearly independent (i.e., that the determinant formed from the matrix does not equal zero).

A *symmetry operation* is a movement of a body into an *equivalent position*, that is, a position which cannot be distinguished from the original one. The symmetry operations of an octahedron are: inversion, reflection in various planes, and rotation about axes which can be arranged in certain specific ways in the octahedron. If these octahedral symmetry operations are now applied to the real d-eigenfunctions of Table 2.4, the radial component can be ignored, since this transforms into itself in all the symmetry operations. It suffices to consider the behaviour of the respective spherical harmonics. Using the co-ordinate system of Fig. 9.1, we can see that in the symmetry operations of an octahedron the three states, d_{xy}, d_{yz}, and d_{zx}, go into themselves and in the same way the two states, d_{3z^2-1} and $d_{x^2-y^2}$, go into themselves. The five-dimensional transformation matrix for spherical symmetry is thus decomposed into one three-dimensional and one two-dimensional matrix, providing we limit ourselves to the symmetry operations of an octahedron. This may be illustrated with some examples:

Let us rotate the octahedron with its associated system of spherical harmonics by $90°$ about its z-axis (Fig. 9.5). The new spherical harmonics

$\bar{Y}$, expressed relative to the new co-ordinate system $\bar{x}$, $\bar{y}$, $\bar{z}$, can be given with the help of the old spherical harmonics Y (co-ordinates x, y, z):

$$\bar{Y}_2{}^0 = \frac{\sqrt{5}}{2\sqrt{\pi}}\frac{1}{2}(3\bar{z}^2 - 1) \quad = \frac{\sqrt{5}}{2\sqrt{\pi}}\left\{1\frac{1}{2}(3z^2 - 1) + 0\frac{\sqrt{3}}{2}(x^2 - y^2)\right.$$

$$\left. + 0\sqrt{3}\,xy + 0\sqrt{3}\,yz + 0\sqrt{3}\,zx\right\}$$

$$\bar{Y}_2{}^2 = \frac{\sqrt{5}}{2\sqrt{\pi}}\frac{\sqrt{3}}{2}(\bar{x}^2 - \bar{y}^2) = \frac{\sqrt{5}}{2\sqrt{\pi}}\left\{0\frac{1}{2}(3z^2 - 1) - 1\frac{\sqrt{3}}{2}(x^2 - y^2)\right.$$

$$\left. + 0\sqrt{3}\,xy + 0\sqrt{3}\,yz + 0\sqrt{3}\,zx\right\}$$

$$\bar{Y}_2{}^{\bar{2}} = \frac{\sqrt{5}}{2\sqrt{\pi}}\sqrt{3}\,\bar{x}\bar{y} \quad = \frac{\sqrt{5}}{2\sqrt{\pi}}\left\{0\frac{1}{2}(3z^2 - 1) + 0\frac{\sqrt{3}}{2}(x^2 - y^2)\right.$$

$$\left. - 1\sqrt{3}\,xy + 0\sqrt{3}\,yz + 0\sqrt{3}\,zx\right\}$$

$$\bar{Y}_2{}^1 = \frac{\sqrt{5}}{2\sqrt{\pi}}\sqrt{3}\,\bar{y}\bar{z} \quad = \frac{\sqrt{5}}{2\sqrt{\pi}}\left\{0\frac{1}{2}(3z^2 - 1) + 0\frac{\sqrt{3}}{2}(x^2 - y^2)\right.$$

$$\left. + 0\sqrt{3}\,xy + 0\sqrt{3}\,yz - 1\sqrt{3}\,zx\right\}$$

$$\bar{Y}_2{}^{\bar{1}} = \frac{\sqrt{5}}{2\sqrt{\pi}}\sqrt{3}\,\bar{z}\bar{x} \quad = \frac{\sqrt{5}}{2\sqrt{\pi}}\left\{0\frac{1}{2}(3z^2 - 1) + 0\frac{\sqrt{3}}{2}(x^2 - y^2)\right.$$

$$\left. + 0\sqrt{3}\,xy + 1\sqrt{3}\,yz + 0\sqrt{3}\,zx\right\}$$

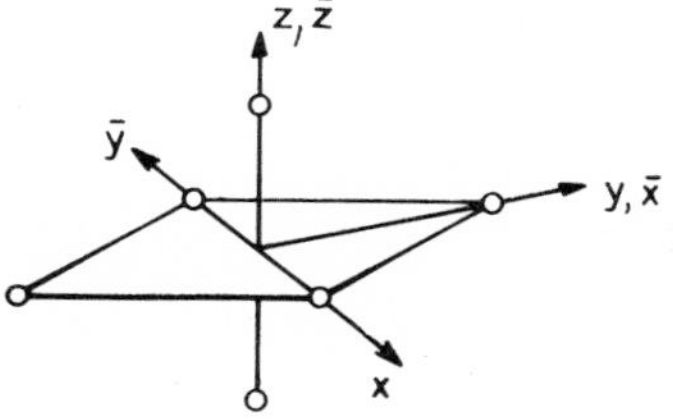

Fig. 9.5. *90° rotation of a Cartesian co-ordinate system about the z-axis.*

The transformation matrix which belongs to this rotational operation can be obtained by arranging the coefficients of every term in a table:

	$3z^2 - 1$	$x^2 - y^2$	xy	yz	zx
$3\bar{z}^2 - 1$	1	0	0	0	0
$\bar{x}^2 - \bar{y}^2$	0	-1	0	0	0
$\bar{x}\bar{y}$	0	0	-1	0	0
$\bar{y}\bar{z}$	0	0	0	0	-1
$\bar{z}\bar{x}$	0	0	0	1	0

The associated matrix then reads:

$$\begin{pmatrix} 1 & 0 & 0 & 0 & 0 \\ 0 & -1 & 0 & 0 & 0 \\ 0 & 0 & -1 & 0 & 0 \\ 0 & 0 & 0 & 0 & -1 \\ 0 & 0 & 0 & 1 & 0 \end{pmatrix}$$

Rotation about the x-axis by $90°$ gives:

$$\bar{Y}_2^{\,0} = \frac{\sqrt{5}}{2\sqrt{\pi}} \frac{1}{2} (3\bar{z}^2 - 1) = \frac{\sqrt{5}}{2\sqrt{\pi}} \left\{ -\frac{1}{2}\frac{1}{2}(3z^2 - 1) - \frac{\sqrt{3}}{2}\frac{\sqrt{3}}{2}(x^2 - y^2) \right.$$
$$\left. + 0\sqrt{3}\,xy + 0\sqrt{3}\,yz + 0\sqrt{3}\,zx \right\}$$

$$\bar{Y}_2^{\,2} = \frac{\sqrt{5}}{2\sqrt{\pi}} \frac{\sqrt{3}}{2} (\bar{x}^2 - \bar{y}^2) = \frac{\sqrt{5}}{2\sqrt{\pi}} \left\{ -\frac{\sqrt{3}}{2}\cdot\frac{1}{2}(3z^2 - 1) + \frac{1}{2}\frac{\sqrt{3}}{2}(x^2 - y^2) \right.$$
$$\left. + 0\sqrt{3}\,xy + 0\sqrt{3}\,yz + 0\sqrt{3}\,zx \right\}$$

$$\bar{Y}_2^{\,\bar{2}} = \frac{\sqrt{5}}{2\sqrt{\pi}} \sqrt{3}\,\bar{x}\bar{y} = \frac{\sqrt{5}}{2\sqrt{\pi}} \left\{ 0\frac{1}{2}(3z^2 - 1) + 0\frac{\sqrt{3}}{2}(x^2 - y^2) \right.$$
$$\left. + 0\sqrt{3}\,xy + 0\sqrt{3}\,yz - 1\sqrt{3}\,zx \right\}$$

$$\bar{Y}_2^{\,\bar{1}} = \frac{\sqrt{5}}{2\sqrt{\pi}} \sqrt{3}\,\bar{y}\bar{z} = \frac{\sqrt{5}}{2\sqrt{\pi}} \left\{ 0\frac{1}{2}(3z^2 - 1) + 0\frac{\sqrt{3}}{2}(x^2 - y^2) \right.$$
$$\left. + 0\sqrt{3}\,xy - 1\sqrt{3}\,yz + 0\sqrt{3}\,zx \right\}$$

$$\bar{Y}_2^{\,1} = \frac{\sqrt{5}}{2\sqrt{\pi}} \sqrt{3}\,\bar{z}\bar{x} = \frac{\sqrt{5}}{2\sqrt{\pi}} \left\{ 0\frac{1}{2}(3z^2 - 1) + 0\frac{\sqrt{3}}{2}(x^2 - y^2) \right.$$
$$\left. + 1\sqrt{3}\,xy + 0\sqrt{3}\,yz + 0\sqrt{3}\,zx \right\}$$

Here, the five-dimensional matrix can likewise be separated into one two-
and one three-dimensional matrix:

$$
\begin{pmatrix}
-\dfrac{1}{2} & -\dfrac{\sqrt{3}}{2} & 0 & 0 & 0 \\[2mm]
-\dfrac{\sqrt{3}}{2} & \dfrac{1}{2} & 0 & 0 & 0 \\[2mm]
0 & 0 & 0 & 0 & -1 \\[2mm]
0 & 0 & 0 & -1 & 0 \\[2mm]
0 & 0 & 1 & 0 & 0
\end{pmatrix}
$$

For each symmetry operation of the octahedron, there is one specific
matrix. If all these matrices are considered as a whole, the elements of the
matrices can have values other than zero only in those square blocks
bordered by broken lines in the above two matrices. Those fields arranged
along the diagonal of the matrix and containing the non-zero elements are
referred to as *blocks of the matrix*. The number of their constituent
columns (or rows) is called the *dimension of the block*. It is generally
mathematically provable that in all the symmetry operations of the
octahedron this splitting of the five-dimensional matrix for the d-eigen-
functions or for the second order spherical harmonics, into two- and three-
dimensional blocks is possible. By proceeding from another basis, e.g., the
complex spherical harmonics, the transformation matrices for the
individual octahedral symmetry operations would appear different. In
particular, the five-dimensional matrix would not be separable into two
component matrices, blocks of dimension 2 and 3. There are, however,
mathematical methods borrowed from group theory, which permit the
determination of the dimensions of the component matrices when the
basis functions are properly chosen. These methods have not been used
here since we have intuitively chosen acceptable basis functions.

In considering the seven spherical harmonics belonging to f-electrons
(Table 2.4), it is clear that the spherical harmonic $Y_3^{\bar{2}}$ goes into itself, with
the possible exception of the sign (Fig. 2.23d), under all symmetry
operations of an octahedron. The six remaining functions are transformed
into each other. It can be shown by group theory that there must exist
another basis system which has the property that on application of the
octahedral symmetry operations the matrix is always split into three
component matrices: 1 one-dimensional and 2 three-dimensional. These
can be obtained from the original basis functions by a linear transformation, i.e.:

$$
\tfrac{1}{2}(5x^3 - 3x) = -\sqrt{\tfrac{5}{8}} \cdot \sqrt{\tfrac{5}{8}}\,(3y^2 - x^2)x - \sqrt{\tfrac{3}{8}} \cdot \sqrt{\tfrac{3}{8}}\,(4z^2 - x^2 - y^2)x.
$$

In Cartesian co-ordinates, these new functions read:

$$\left.\begin{array}{l} \dfrac{\sqrt{7}}{2\sqrt{\pi}} \cdot \dfrac{1}{2}(5x^2 - 3)x \\[2.5ex] \dfrac{\sqrt{7}}{2\sqrt{\pi}} \cdot \dfrac{1}{2}(5y^2 - 3)y \\[2.5ex] \dfrac{\sqrt{7}}{2\sqrt{\pi}} \cdot \dfrac{1}{2}(5z^2 - 3)z \end{array}\right\} T_{1u}$$

$$\left.\dfrac{\sqrt{7}}{2\sqrt{\pi}} \cdot \sqrt{15}\, xyz \quad\right\} A_{2u}$$

$$\left.\begin{array}{l} \dfrac{\sqrt{7}}{2\sqrt{\pi}} \cdot \sqrt{15} \cdot \dfrac{1}{2}(x^2 - y^2)z \\[2.5ex] \dfrac{\sqrt{7}}{2\sqrt{\pi}} \cdot \sqrt{15} \cdot \dfrac{1}{2}(y^2 - z^2)x \\[2.5ex] \dfrac{\sqrt{7}}{2\sqrt{\pi}} \cdot \sqrt{15} \cdot \dfrac{1}{2} \cdot (z^2 - x^2)y \end{array}\right\} T_{2u}$$

It is easy to prove that the first three functions transform, under the symmetry operations of an octahedron, exactly as do the real first-order spherical harmonics (i.e., as p_x, p_y, and p_z eigenfunctions. See Fig. 2.23a.) The last three functions transform as do the t_{2g} eigenfunctions with, however, the difference that on inversion each eigenfunction of the t_{2g}-group goes into itself (gerade), while third-order spherical harmonics are ungerade. The sign of the function is altered on inversion, and so the symmetry description is t_{2u}.

The symmetry operations of an octahedron—rotations, reflections, and inversion—when applied to properly chosen spherical harmonics, generate one-, two-, and three-dimensional component matrices whose dimensions are fixed and which cannot be further reduced. The symmetry operations can be expressed as matrices. These expressions are unique; to each symmetry operation there belongs one matrix. The converse of this statement, namely, that to every component matrix there corresponds one and only one symmetry operation, is not generally true. It applies only for three-dimensional component matrices under certain conditions, as can be shown mathematically. The component matrices give a 'representation' of the symmetry.

One-dimensional matrices of a representation are labelled either 'A' or 'B', two-dimensional with 'E' and three-dimensional with 'T'. The indices 1 and 2 represent certain definite symmetry properties of the matrices, which cannot here be more fully discussed. The interested reader is referred to the book by Cotton[9.3], *Chemical Applications of Group Theory*. One differentiates between T_1 and T_2 according to whether the blocked matrices are identical with those which generate the previously given operations having basis functions x, y, and z (p_x, p_y, p_z), or xy, yz, and xz (d_{xy}, d_{yz}, and d_{xz}). The matrices are further labelled either g (gerade) or u (ungerade) according to the inversion properties of the associated basis functions.

The equivalence of a given set of eigenfunctions, e.g., the t_{2g}-eigenfunctions in an octahedral field, results from the fact that these eigenfunctions are transformed into each other by the application of the symmetry operations of the group and that no other eigenfunctions, e.g., e_g-eigenfunctions result. Group theory simplifies the methods of determining the dimensions of the irreducible matrices for a given symmetry. The discovery of the associated basis functions is then a second problem.

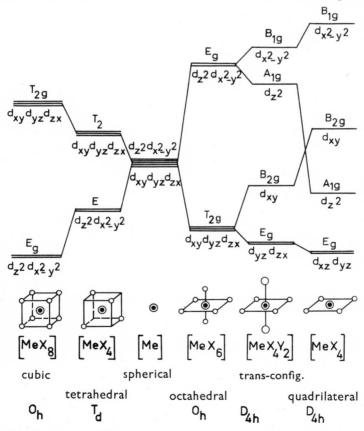

Fig. 9.6. *Term splitting of a d-electron in complex ions of various symmetries.*

Figure 9.6 shows the term splitting of one d-electron for complex ions of various symmetries.

9.2 Ionic Complexes with Several d-Electrons

The free ions of the transition metals have the electronic configurations in the gaseous state, shown in Table 9.1.

Table 9.1. Electron configurations of transition element ions

	Ti^{2+}	V^{2+}	Cr^{2+}	Mn^{2+}	Fe^{2+}	Co^{2+}	Ni^{2+}	Cu^{2+}	Zn^{2+}
Ti^{3+}	V^{3+}	Cr^{3+}	Mn^{3+}	Fe^{3+}	Co^{3+}	Ni^{3+}	Cu^{3+}		
d^1	d^2	d^3	d^4	d^5	d^6	d^7	d^8	d^9	d^{10}
^2D	^3F	^4F	^5D	^6S	^5D	^4F	^3F	^2D	^1S

Since product eigenfunctions of many-electron systems behave in an analogous fashion to the eigenfunctions of a single electron, as long as the secondary and axial quantum numbers are the same, the number of split terms for a given symmetry is given by the secondary quantum number, L. In going from a one-electron to a many-electron system with the same secondary quantum number only the gerade or ungerade character can change (e.g., in passing from one p-electron to the ^3P-state of two p-electrons). In this example, one p_z-electron makes the approach of a negative ligand to the z-axis more difficult, while a ^3P-state with $\Lambda = 0$ eases the approach since this product function disappears along the z-axis. The product function contains as factors the single electron eigenfunctions, p_x and p_y. The splitting is the same with all terms of the same secondary quantum number. The direction and magnitude of the shift in energy of the individual split term, however, can only be found if the magnitude of the product eigenfunction in the given spatial direction and the distribution of the total electron density are calculated. Figure 9.7 shows the

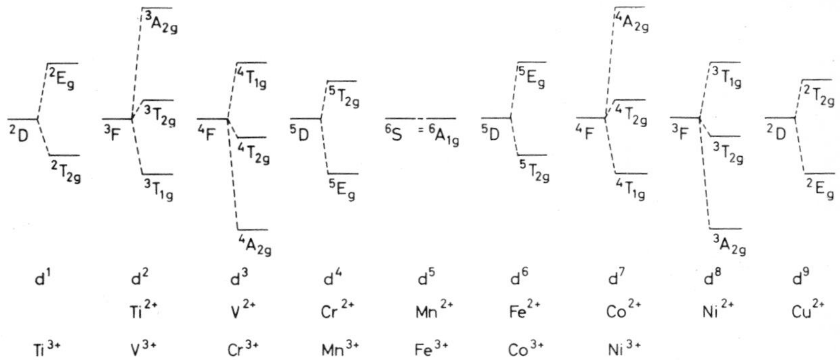

Fig. 9.7. Term splitting of d-electron systems in an octahedral field.

positions of the split terms in an octahedral field. The splitting pictures for both the d^1- and d^6-electron configurations correspond to each other. The half-filled d^5-configuration has spherical symmetry (^6S). The sixth electron then corresponds in its action on a ligand to a single d-electron. In both the d^4- and d^9-configurations, only one electron is lacking to form a spherically symmetrical state (d^5 and d^{10}). The hole in the spherical symmetrical charge distribution here corresponds to one d-electron with a positive charge and the splitting is similar to that for d^1 and d^6 but is now in the opposite direction.

The splitting of the ^3F term in V^{3+} with an electron configuration d^2 will now be discussed. In Table 8.3 the angular components of the product functions of this ^3F term are given and are ordered according to the magnetic quantum number, M. From these complex functions real functions can be formed, just as was done in the case of one-electron systems using the complex functions of Table 8.1 and arriving at the real functions of Table 2.4. The real product functions must now be linearly combined so that, as for the case of a single f-electron (see section 9.1) three functions with symmetry T_{1g}, three with T_{2g}, and one of type A_{2g} result.

The ^3F product function corresponding to the one-electron function $f_{(5z^2-3)z}$ is that with $M = 0$ in Table 8.3. $M = 0$ signifies a rotational symmetry about the z-axis. The two remaining T_{1g} functions can be obtained from this one by exchanging the co-ordinates.

The real product eigenfunctions corresponding to the one-electron functions f_{xyz} ($\bar\lambda = 2$) and $f_{(x^2-y^2)z}$ ($\lambda = 2$) are obtained by taking the sum or difference of the ^3F-product functions with $M = \pm2$. One of these functions has the symmetry A_{2g} and the other T_{2g}. The two remaining T_{2g} functions can be obtained from the latter by interchanging co-ordinates.

As with a single f-electron, the ^3F-term is split in an octahedral field into three terms: $^3T_{1g}$, $^3T_{2g}$, and $^3A_{2g}$. The direction and magnitude of the term splitting can be determined only by quantum mechanical calculations. Figure 9.7 shows the results. The $^3T_{1g}$ term is energetically favoured since a perturbation calculation shows that here the electron density distribution is especially large in the space between the ligands.

The d^8-configuration of the Ni^{2+}-ion is best considered as a spherically symmetrical d^{10}-shell from which two d-electrons have been removed. The vacancies lead then, just as with the d^2-state of V^{3+}, to an ^3F-ground term and to the same split terms. However, the displacement of the terms is in the reverse direction.

The special stability of octahedral Cr^{3+} complexes is apparent from the table. The lowest lying A_{2g} term fits especially well in an octahedral field just as does the a_{2u} term of an individual f-electron, the product function having large values in the space between the ligands. Under all symmetry operations of an octahedron, the $^4A_{2g}$-electronic configuration goes into itself; the representation is naturally one-dimensional.

With Fe^{2+} and Co^{3+} both ionic and low spin complexes are observed. How can the difference between these be explained by crystal field theory?[9.4, 9.5] The magnitude of the term splitting shown in Fig. 9.7 for Fe^{2+} or Co^{3+} is a function of the electric field strength. According to Hund's Rule, the ground state is a ^5D-term. There is, however, still a ^1I-term ($L = 6$), having a $^1A_{1g}$-term as a sub-term, which contains six t_{2g} (d_ε)-electrons. In this last state, all spin moments are compensated and it is a singlet term. Since it fits especially well in an octahedral field, its position is strongly affected by increasing field strength. When the field strength is sufficiently great it becomes energetically favoured relative to the $^5T_{2g}$-term of the ground state. There results then, according to the crystal field theory, a diamagnetic complex with the same configuration of the three free electron pairs on cobalt $((t_{2g})^6)$, which were accepted in formulating the bonding with (d^2sp^3)-hybrids.

This electrostatic model for the formation of ionic complexes rests on the following assumptions:

(a) The magnetic interaction of the spin moment with the orbital moment is small. In forming product eigenfunctions, the spin factor can, from a purely energetic point of view, be ignored as long as the total product function, with the spin factor, remains anti-symmetric. The total magnetic moment of the atom is given by the quantum number $J = L + S$ where L is the secondary quantum number given by the vector model and S is the total spin quantum number of all the electrons. This weak 'spin–orbit' coupling is called *Russel–Saunders Coupling*. With heavier atoms, especially in the third long period of the periodic system, the so-called *j-j coupling* becomes increasingly prominent. Here the spin–orbit interaction becomes stronger and can no longer be ignored. With each individual electron, there is associated a quantum number, $j = l + s$. The orbital angular momenta, l, can no longer be separately added together vectorially in order to get the azimuthal quantum number, L, for the many-electron system.

(b) The mutual interaction of the d-electrons is stronger than the influence of the crystal field, so that the product eigenfunctions of the free ions still represent good approximations. This is referred to as the *weak-field* case.

(c) The interaction between the central ion and the ligands can be approximated by an electrostatic picture.

There is a second way of looking at the formation of complex salts from an electrostatic point of view. Single-electron eigenfunctions are sought which fit in with the crystal field. In the cases of Cr^{3+} or Co^{3+}-complexes for instance these are the d_{xy}, d_{yz}, and d_{zx} electrons. The interaction of these three or six electrons with each other, leading to a $^4A_{2g}$ or $^1A_{1g}$ state respectively, can be subsequently considered by a quantum mechanical perturbation calculation. This interaction is then treated as a perturbation of the original configuration.

The influence of the crystal field is prominent in this type of calculation, being referred to as the *strong-field* method. It was developed by Y. Tanabe and S. Sugano.[9.4] In these special cases as well as in several other examples, the electron distribution derived from the product function is very similar to the sum of the electron distributions of the individual electrons. Thus the electron distribution in a ^3P-state of two electrons with $\Lambda = 0$ is similar to the sum of the electron densities of one p_x- and one p_y-electron. If the product function of a split term contains as factors only the one-electron functions which were used in the strong-field method then the electron densities obtained from the square of the one-electron functions often give a good representation of the electron distribution of the product function. Frequent use of this approximation will be made.

9.3 Jahn–Teller Effect

Up to now we have been considering a truly octahedral environment about a central atom. However, in both complex salts and in crystal lattices, distorted octahedra or tetrahedra are frequently observed. The arguments of the last chapter simplify the explanation of these distortions, which was first elucidated by Jahn and Teller.[9.6]

As an example let us examine a Cu^{2+}-ion, with the electron configuration d^9. One electron is missing from a spherically symmetrical shell with d^{10}. According to the electrostatic crystal field theory this must be an e_g-electron, either a d_{3z^2-1}- or a $d_{x^2-y^2}$-electron. In the former case, the two ligands which lie along the z-axis can come closer to the central atom than the four ligands in the xy-plane, since there is only one d_{3z^2-1}-electron to repel the ligands (Fig. 9.8). In the latter case, it is the four ligands in the xy-plane which can come closer to the central atom. Which of these two possibilities will occur cannot be theoretically predicted. Experimentally, however, one observes a large series of Cu^{2+} compounds having the four ligands in the xy-plane closer to the central atom while the two ligands along the z-axis are farther removed.

If these same considerations are applied to the electron configuration d^4 where again the atom is one electron removed from spherical symmetry (d^5), distortions would be expected as in the octahedral complexes of Mn^{3+} and Cr^{2+}, for example in MnF_3 or the ion $[MnF_6]^{3-}$.

The Jahn–Teller effect is very pronounced in octahedral complexes

9

which lack one d-electron from a spherically symmetrical electronic arrangement. It is also observed with d^7-electron configurations when, contrary to Hund's Rule, a low-spin complex has a fully occupied t_{2g}-state

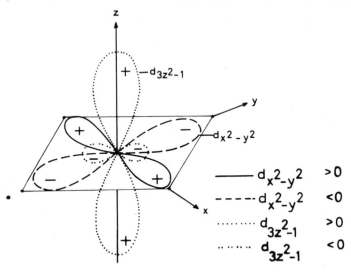

Fig. 9.8. *Orientation of a d_{3z^2-1}- and a $d_{x^2-y^2}$-electron in an octahedral complex.*

and one electron in an e_g-state, $(t_{2g})^6(e_g)^1$, as in the lattice of $NaNi^{III}O_2$ which has four short and two long Ni–O distances. Naturally, no Jahn–Teller effect is possible for configurations such as $(t_{2g})^3 = {}^4A_{2g}$ of Cr^{3+}-complexes and $(t_{2g})^6 = {}^1A_{1g}$ of the typical Co^{3+}-complexes, since here the product functions go into themselves under all symmetry operations of an octahedron. This means that the octahedral axes are equivalent. The representation is one-dimensional (A).

A single t_{2g}-electron (for example in Ti^{3+}) should also give a Jahn–Teller effect. Since, however, this eigenfunction has large values only in the space between the ligands, the effect is so weak that it has not yet been observed by X-ray structure analysis.

In tetrahedral complexes a t_2-electron should have a stronger Jahn–Teller effect than an e-electron since the former approaches more closely to the ligands.

10

Molecular Orbital Theory of
Complexes—Ligand Field Theory

10.1 σ-Bonding in Octahedral Complexes Containing One
d-Electron

The electrostatic crystal field theory has the great advantage that quantum mechanical perturbation calculations are possible and term splittings can be mathematically estimated. Since, however, the electrons in the space between two atoms are subject to the nuclear charges of both atoms, it must be possible to apply the theories of Heitler and London (Valence Bond Theory) and of Hund and Mullikan (Molecular Orbital Theory). Atomic bonding functions have already been used in the consideration of low-spin complexes. More general is the molecular orbital theory which will now be expanded to cover the so-called ionic complexes. Its disadvantage is that quantum-mechanical calculations cannot be carried out; only symmetry considerations and qualitative results are possible.

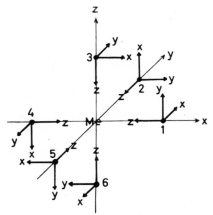

Fig. 10.1. Co-ordinate systems of the central atoms and of the ligands used to describe the molecular functions of an octahedral complex.

As an exercise, several examples of molecular orbitals by a *linear combination of atomic orbitals* (LCAO method) will be constructed here. A metal ion, Me, from the first long period forms the centre of an octahedral complex. The atomic orbitals $4s_{Me}$, $4p_{Me}$, and $3d_{Me}$ are available for the valence electrons. The ligands have only *s*- and *p*-orbitals in their outermost shell. In the ligand atoms, the co-ordinate systems will be arranged according to the convention that the *z*-direction points toward the central atom and the positive *x*- and *y*-axis are as given (Fig. 10.1).

A $4s_{Me}$-orbital can mix with the *s*-orbitals of the ligands as well as with their p_z-orbitals to form a bonding and an antibonding molecular orbital. The p_z-orbitals overlap better with the $4s_{Me}$-orbitals than do the *s*-orbitals. A still better overlap can be obtained using (sp_z)-hybrid orbitals on the ligands. The degree of hybridization depends on the bond strength. The molecular orbitals, using the p_z-orbitals, and the normalization factors, N_{Me} and N_L, for the metal and ligand functions respectively, reads:

$$a_{1g}:\quad \Psi_{\sigma,s} = \frac{1}{\sqrt{2}}\left\{N_{Me}\cdot s_{Me}\ (\pm)\ N_L\frac{1}{\sqrt{6}}(p_{z,1}+p_{z,2}+p_{z,3}+p_{z,4}\right.$$

$$\left. +\ p_{z,5}+p_{z,6})\right\}$$

The sign for the antibonding function is enclosed in parentheses. The normalizing factors for the bonding function are somewhat smaller, and for the antibonding function somewhat greater than 1. Further molecular

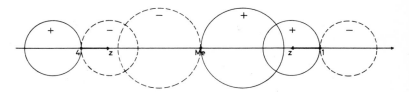

Fig. 10.2. Schematic representation of a $\Psi_{\sigma,p}$-molecular function in an octahedral complex.

functions of the σ-type can be obtained using the p_{Me}-orbitals and the p_z-orbitals (or hybrid orbitals) of the ligands (Fig. 10.2):

$$\Psi_{\sigma,p_x} = \frac{1}{\sqrt{2}}\left\{N_{Me}\cdot p_{x,Me}\ (\pm)\ N_L\frac{1}{\sqrt{2}}(p_{z,1}-p_{z,4})\right\}$$

$$t_{1u}:\quad \Psi_{\sigma,p_y} = \frac{1}{\sqrt{2}}\left\{N_{Me}\cdot p_{y,Me}\ (\pm)\ N_L\frac{1}{\sqrt{2}}(p_{z,2}-p_{z,5})\right\}$$

$$\Psi_{\sigma,p_z} = \frac{1}{\sqrt{2}}\left\{N_{Me}\cdot p_{z,Me}\ (\pm)\ N_L\frac{1}{\sqrt{2}}(p_{z,3}-p_{z,6})\right\}$$

From the $3d$-orbitals of the metal, only those from the symmetry group e_g can take part in σ-bonding:

$$\Psi_{\sigma,\,d_{x^2-y^2}} = \frac{1}{\sqrt{2}}\left\{ N_{Me} \cdot d_{x^2-y^2,\,Me} \; {(\pm)} \; N_L \frac{1}{\sqrt{4}}\left(p_{z,\,1} + p_{z,\,4} - p_{z,\,2} - p_{z,\,5}\right)\right\}$$

e_g:

$$\Psi_{\sigma,\,d_{3z^2}} = \frac{1}{\sqrt{2}}\left\{ N_{Me} \cdot d_{3z^2-1,\,Me} \; {(\pm)} \; N_L \frac{1}{\sqrt{6}}\left(\sqrt{2}\,p_{z,,\,3} + \sqrt{2}\,p_{z,\,6}\right.\right.$$

$$\left.\left. - \frac{1}{\sqrt{2}}p_{z,\,1} - \frac{1}{\sqrt{2}}p_{z,\,2} - \frac{1}{\sqrt{2}}p_{z,\,4} - \frac{1}{\sqrt{2}}p_{z,\,5}\right)\right\}$$

These six molecular orbitals correspond, in the approximation method with atomic bonding functions, completely to Pauling's (d^2sp^3)-hybrid functions, since both contain the same atomic orbitals of the metal atom: s_{Me}, $p_{x,\,Me}$, $p_{y,\,Me}$, $p_{z,\,Me}$, $d_{x^2-y^2,\,Me}$, and $d_{3z^2-1,\,Me}$.

Figure 10.3 shows schematically the term scheme of bonding (b) and antibonding (a) molecular orbitals with σ-symmetry along the inter-atomic bonding line. On the left side of this diagram stand the term levels of

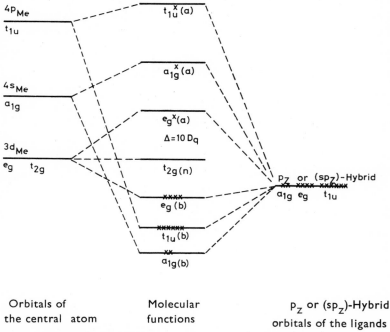

Fig. 10.3. *Combination of the orbitals on the central atom with those on the ligands to form σ-molecular functions, and their term schemes.*

the central atom or ion with the electronic configurations specified relative to octahedral symmetry using the strong field method. On the right side stands the term level of the ligand electrons which take part in σ-bonding. These are the p_z-functions, which, however, can be hybridized more or less with s-functions. For each ligand this is only one function. In order to form a molecular function linear combinations are then formed whose symmetry is given as: a_{1g}, $e_g(2x)$, and $t_{1u}(3x)$. In the middle of the diagram, the term levels of these molecular eigenfunctions are given schematically along with their symmetries. The six bonding molecular orbitals a_{1g}, $t_{1u}(3x)$, and $e_g(2x)$ have the lowest term levels and are occupied in all octahedral complexes from Ti to Zn with six electrons. These complexes differ in the position, and especially in the occupation, of the higher lying terms.

If a Ti^{3+} complex is considered the $3d$-electron is a t_{2g}-electron either d_{xy}, d_{yz}, or d_{xz}. For reasons of symmetry, it cannot take part in σ-bonding and will therefore appear as a non-bonding electron (n). When the complex is irradiated with light, the electron can be raised to an e_g-state ($d_{x^2-y^2}$ or d_{z^2}), making σ-bonding possible. Since the bonding states are fully occupied, the electron goes into the antibonding e_g^*-state. The energy difference $e_g^* - t_{2g}$ is, as in the crystal field theory, $\Delta = 10D_q$. With further excitation, the a_1^* and the t_{1u}^*-states can be occupied. These, however, no longer contain $3d_{Me}$-functions as components, but rather $4s_{Me}$ and $4p_{Me}$.

10.2 π-Bonding in Octahedral Complexes

The theory of bonding in octahedral complexes (according to Pauling) in the case of the $[Co(CN)_6]^{3-}$-ion requires that π-bond systems must also be considered in the formation of molecular functions. Let us start with a single-electron case, a Ti^{3+}-complex. The t_{2g}-electron is a d_{xy}, a d_{yz}, or a d_{zx}-electron. In choosing a state at random, the molecular function symbolized in Fig. 10.4 can be formed. Analytically it reads:

$$\Psi_{\pi, d_{xy}} = \frac{1}{\sqrt{2}}\left\{ N_{Me} \cdot d_{xy, Me} \; (\pm) \; N_L \frac{1}{\sqrt{4}}(p_{x,1} + p_{y,2} + p_{x,5} + p_{y,4}) \right\}$$

Correspondingly:

t_{2g}:

$$\Psi_{\pi, d_{yz}} = \frac{1}{\sqrt{2}}\left\{ N_{Me} \cdot d_{yz, Me} \; (\pm) \; N_L \frac{1}{\sqrt{4}}(p_{x,2} + p_{y,3} + p_{x,6} + p_{y,5}) \right\}$$

$$\Psi_{\pi, d_{zx}} = \frac{1}{\sqrt{2}}\left\{ N_{Me} \cdot d_{zx, Me} \; (\pm) \; N_L \frac{1}{\sqrt{4}}(p_{x,3} + p_{y,1} + p_{x,4} + p_{y,6}) \right\}$$

The three bonding π-states are occupied by three p-electron pairs of the ligands. For the single t_{2g}-electron of the metal atom there remain available the three mutually degenerate t_{2g}^*, antibonding, molecular functions. The electron is free to enter any of these three states.

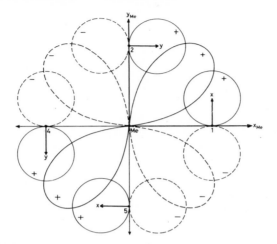

Fig. 10.4. *π-bonding systems from a d_{xy}-orbital on the central atom and p-orbitals on the ligands.*

If the electron is excited, it goes into the first antibonding e_g^*-state with σ-symmetry. The transition $t_{2g}^* \rightarrow e_g^*$ again corresponds to $10Dq = \Delta$.

A 4p-function on the metal can also enter into π-bonding. Its strength is, however, much weaker, since the overlap of the functions is poorer (Fig. 10.5).

$$\Psi_{\pi, p_z} = \frac{1}{\sqrt{2}} \left\{ N_{Me} \cdot p_{z, Me} (\pm) N_L \frac{1}{\sqrt{4}} (p_{x,2} + p_{y,1} - p_{x,4} - p_{y,5}) \right\}$$

t_{1u}:

$$\Psi_{\pi, p_y} = \frac{1}{\sqrt{2}} \left\{ N_{Me} \cdot p_{y, Me} (\pm) N_L \frac{1}{\sqrt{4}} (p_{x,1} + p_{y,3} - p_{x,6} - p_{y,4}) \right\}$$

$$\Psi_{\pi, p_x} = \frac{1}{\sqrt{2}} \left\{ N_{Me} \cdot p_{x, Me} (\pm) N_L \frac{1}{\sqrt{4}} (p_{x,3} + p_{y,2} - p_{x,5} - p_{y,6}) \right\}$$

Of the many-electron systems the cases of Cr^{3+}- and Co^{3+}-complexes will be considered. The electron configuration on the metal atom is $d^3 = {}^4A_{2g}$ or $d^6 = {}^1A_{1g}$ respectively. According to the strong-field method the associated product functions can be treated as the sum of three individual functions belonging to the symmetry class t_{2g}. Each of these functions can then be combined with p-functions on the ligands in the manner given above to form bonding and antibonding molecular eigen-functions having the same symmetry:

$$\Psi_{\pi, d_{xy}}, \quad \Psi_{\pi, d_{yz}}, \quad \Psi_{\pi, d_{xz}}.$$

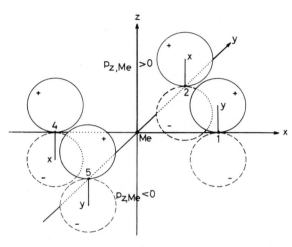

Fig. 10.5. The p-orbitals on four ligands which can take part in π-bonding with a p_z-orbital on the central atom.

In Cr^{3+}-complexes each antibonding molecular function is occupied by one electron and in the typical Co^{3+}-complex by an electron pair.

11

The Seven Crystal Systems

Since the following sections are mainly concerned with a discussion of the structure of crystalline substances, a few words about the co-ordinate systems used to describe the positions of the atoms in a crystal lattice will not be out of place. All crystals belong to one of the seven systems described below.

If we take, for example, an arrangement of two different kinds of atoms, such as is found in NaCl (Fig. 11.1), it is appropriate to place the origin of our co-ordinate system in the centre of any given atom (e.g., a Cl-atom)

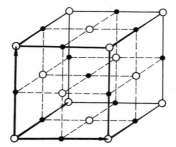

Fig. 11.1. Co-ordinate system used to describe the rock salt lattice: ○ Cl, ● Na.

and to draw three perpendicular lines to the nearest neighbouring sodium atoms to form the axes of the co-ordinate system. The distance between two identical points along each of the axes is chosen as the unit of length of that axis. This distance is referred to as the *identity period*. In the NaCl-lattice this corresponds to the shortest distance between two chlorine (or sodium) atoms. In this case, the unit of distance, designated by the letter a, is identical along all three axes. The co-ordinate system is thus determined when we specify that all three axes are mutually perpendicular and when we specify the lattice parameter, a (normally in Ångstrom Units, Å, $1\,\text{Å} = 10^{-8}$ cm). In papers published before about 1950 one frequently finds lattice parameters given in Siegbahn or KX units ($1\,\text{KX} = 1\cdot00202$ Å). This unit, however, is no longer in use.

Such a co-ordinate system, in which all three axes are perpendicular to each other and whose unit of length (*a*) is identical for all three axes, is called *cubic* (Fig. 11.2a). It corresponds to a Cartesian co-ordinate system.

If it is necessary to choose one axis (*c*) having a unit of length different from the other two (*a*), this system is called *tetragonal*, provided that all axes are mutually perpendicular (Fig. 11.2b).

The *hexagonal* system is characterized by two axes which have the same length (*a*) and form an angle of 120° with each other. The third axis, with length (*c*), is perpendicular to the plane formed by the other two axes (Fig. 11.2c).

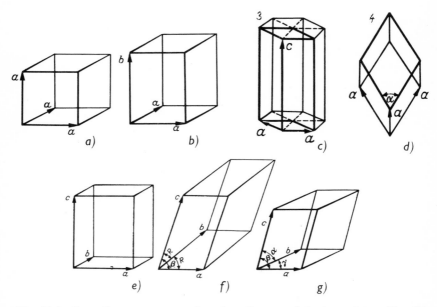

Fig. 11.2. Co-ordinate system used to describe crystal lattices: (a) cubic, (b) tetragonal, (c) hexagonal, (d) rhombohedral, (e) orthorhombic, (f) monoclinic, (g) triclinic.

That system in which all axes have the same length (*a*), but are not perpendicular to each other (interaxial angle α ≠ 90°), is called *rhombohedral* or *trigonal* (Fig. 11.2d). The rhombohedral system is used, for example, to describe a cube which has been extended or compressed along a body-diagonal.

That crystal system in which all axes are mutually perpendicular, but in which the units of length along the three axes are different (*a, b, c*) is called *orthorhombic* or simply *rhombic* (Fig. 11.2e).

The *monoclinic* system is derived from the orthorhombic. Here again all three axes have different lengths (a, b, c). However, while the b-axis is perpendicular to both a and c, the a-axis makes an angle $\beta \neq 90°$ with c in the ac-plane (Fig. 11.2f).

Finally, the *triclinic* system has three axes, all with different lengths (a, b, c). The angles (α, β, γ) which these axes make with each other may also vary (Fig. 11.2g).

In Table 11.1 are given for each of the seven crystal systems, those factors which must be specified in order completely to describe the system of axes. These factors are called the *lattice parameters*. Table 11.1 also gives those values which are fixed once the crystal system is specified.

Table 11.1. Lattice parameters which must be specified and resulting parameters

Figure	Crystal system	Necessary specifications	Resulting parameters		
11.2a	Cubic	a	$a = b = c$	$\alpha = \beta = \gamma = 90°$	
11.2b	Tetragonal	a, c	$a = b$	$\alpha = \beta = \gamma = 90°$	
11.2c	Hexagonal	a, c	$a = b$	$\alpha = \beta = 90°$	$\gamma = 120°$
11.2d	Rhombohedral	a, α	$a = b = c$	$\alpha = \beta = \gamma$	
11.2e	Orthorhombic	a, b, c		$\alpha = \beta = \gamma = 90°$	
11.2f	Monoclinic	a, b, c, β		$\alpha = \gamma = 90°$	
11.2g	Triclinic	$a, b, c, \alpha, \beta, \gamma$			

If one takes the three vectors which represent the unit translations in the three co-ordinate directions and completes the parallelepiped determined by these lines, a body is obtained having the property, that if it were infinitely repeated, it could completely fill all space. Such a parallelepiped is called a *unit cell*.

The positions of the individual atoms within a unit cell can now be simply described by their co-ordinates. Thus, the origin is located at the position 0 0 0, i.e., $x = 0, y = 0, z = 0$. Moving out a unit length along each of the three axes we arrive at: 1 0 0, 0 1 0, and 0 0 1. In a NaCl crystal, the Na atoms in the ac-plane have the co-ordinates: $\frac{1}{2}$ 0 0, 0 0 $\frac{1}{2}$, 1 0 $\frac{1}{2}$, and $\frac{1}{2}$ 0 1.

A direction in a crystal is identified by a vector whose origin is the origin of the co-ordinate system and which points in the desired direction. This vector is labelled by the co-ordinates of its end point which are, by convention, enclosed in brackets, [...]. The direction of a body diagonal of a unit cell is then [111] or [1 −1 1] etc. (Fig. 11.3). Instead of [1 −1 1] one normally writes [1$\bar{1}$1].

The orientation of a plane in a crystal lattice is given by the reciprocals of the co-ordinates of the intercepts of the plane with the axes. A plane with intercepts on the axes at $\frac{1}{3}$ 1 $\frac{1}{2}$, is labelled (312) (Fig. 11.3). Parentheses are the symbols for a plane. In describing the orientation of a given plane one reduces the values to the lowest terms. That is, instead of (426), one would write (213). The three numbers in parentheses, generally referred to as *hkl*,

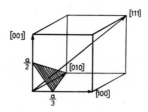

Fig. 11.3. The direction vectors: $[100]$, $[010]$, $[001]$, *and* $[111]$; *and the* (312)-*plane in the cubic system.*

are called the *Miller Indices* of a plane. The limiting planes of any cell are characterized by the symbols: (100), (010), and (001), since the intercept on two of the axes is ∞ ($1/\infty = 0$).

12

Crystal Structures of the Elements (A-Types)

12.1 Structures of the Metallic Elements

The elements which are between the alkali and the zinc group on the long form of the periodic table, crystallize mostly in the following three lattice types.

12.1.1 *The Body-centred Cubic Structure, W-type (A2-type)*

The corners and the body centre of the unit cell are occupied (Fig. 12.1). The unit cell contains a total of two atoms. The atom in the body centre belongs exclusively to the unit cell while the eight atoms on the corners are each shared by seven other unit cells adding 8/8, or 1 atom to the unit cell. The number, Z, of atoms per unit cell is thus $Z = 2$. Since the atoms in the corners of the cell are identical, it suffices in describing the cell to give the co-ordinates of the atom at the origin and that in the body centre (0 0 0, and $\frac{1}{2}\frac{1}{2}\frac{1}{2}$).

In this lattice type crystallize:

Alkali metals	Li,	Na,	K,	Rb, Cs
Heavy alkaline earths	*Ca*,	*Sr*,	*Ba*	
Actinides	*U*,	*Np*,	*Pu*	

Elements of the
- 4th sub-group   *Ti*, *Zr*, *Hf* above 882, 870, 1750°C,
- 5th sub-group   V, Nb, Ta   respectively, and
- 6th sub-group   Cr, *Mo*, W

Also Fe up to 906°C (α-iron) and from 1404°C to the melting point at 1530°C (δ-iron).

Fig. 12.1. Body-centred cubic structure.

The italicized elements are also found in other crystalline modifications. Substances which crystallize in the same lattice type are referred to as *isotypic*.

Structures of the elements are frequently called *A-types*.

12.1.2 *The Face-centred Cubic Structure, Cu-type (A1-type)*

The corners and face centres are occupied by atoms in this type of cubic unit cell (Fig. 12.2). The unit cell contains four atoms, 8/8 on the corners and 6/2 on the face centres. The most important metals which crystallize in this type are: *Ca*, *Sr*, Al, *γFe* (906°–1404°C), *βCo*, *Ni*, Rh, Pd, Ir, Pt, Cu, Ag, Au, Pb, the meaning of the italics being as before.

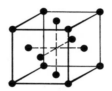

Fig. 12.2. Face-centred cubic structure.

The face-centred cubic lattice is also called the cubic close-packed lattice. In a close-packed plane of rigid spheres, each sphere is surrounded by six other spheres arranged in the form of a regular hexagon (Fig. 12.3).

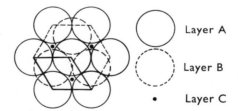

Layer A

Layer B

Layer C

Fig. 12.3. Structure of a close-packed layer of atoms and their superposition in a cubic close-packed arrangement of spheres.

If a second layer (B) is now laid over the first layer (A), the second layer (indicated by broken lines in Fig. 12.3) fits into the depressions formed between the spheres in layer A. Because of the size of the spheres, only half of the depressions can be occupied. A third layer, C (represented by ● in Fig. 12.3) can now be placed over B (or under A) in such a way that the new layer lies directly over (or under) the previously unoccupied depressions in layer A. If this sequence of layers, A B C A B C . . ., is continued, one arrives at a face-centred arrangement (Fig. 12.4a and b). From these diagrams, one can see how layers follow one after the other in the direction of a space diagonal of the cubic unit cell. It is inherent in the symmetry of a cubic lattice that a face-centred cubic lattice can be decomposed into layers in four different ways, namely along the sets of planes which are perpendicular to one of the four body diagonals.

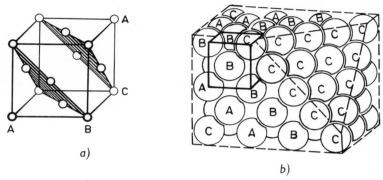

a)

b)

Fig. 12.4. *Structure and sequence of layers* (ABC) *in a close-packed cubic arrangement of spheres, (a) layers perpendicular to* $[111]$, *(b) perpendicular to* $[1\bar{1}1]$.

The application of high pressure transforms the structure of several elements from body-centred cubic to the more closely packed face-centred class. Caesium, for example, becomes face centred cubic at 41 kbar pressure (Cs_{II}, $a = 5.984$ Å). At 42.5 kbar, the lattice constant suddenly drops further (Cs_{III}, $a = 5.800$ Å).[12.1] A pressure of 10^6 dyn/cm² is called 1 *bar*, which corresponds to 1.019716 kg/cm², or 0.986924 atmosphere.

12.1.3 *Hexagonal Close Packing, Mg-type (A3-type)*

If for the superposition of close-packed layers of spheres, only two of the possible positions are used, for example A B A B . . ., then instead of every fourth, every third layer lies above the first (Fig. 12.5a). Cubic symmetry is lost and there results a lattice best described by a hexagonal system. The unit cell contains two atoms at the positions: 0 0 0, and $\frac{2}{3} \frac{1}{3} \frac{1}{2}$. In order to show the relationship between cubic and hexagonal close-packing, Fig. 12.5b is drawn so that the body diagonal of the cubic cell $[111]$ is vertical.

The most important representatives of hexagonal close-packing are:

the light alkaline earths Be, and Mg
Most of the rare earths
Ti, Zr, Hf, Tc, Re, Ru, Os, αCo, as well as Zn and Cd;
under high pressure the transformation of Ti and Zr from the low-temperature hexagonal into the high-temperature body-centred cubic form is only slightly altered toward lower temperatures (with Zr -2.4°C/kbar).[12.2]

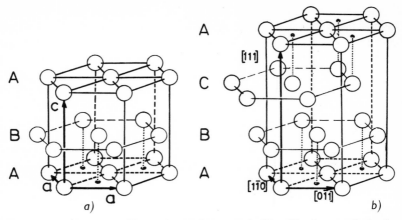

Fig. 12.5. *Arrangement of layers in (a) hexagonal, (b) cubic close-packed spheres (displayed analogously to (a)).*

Fig. 12.6 shows how the three lattice types which we have discussed are distributed over the periodic system.

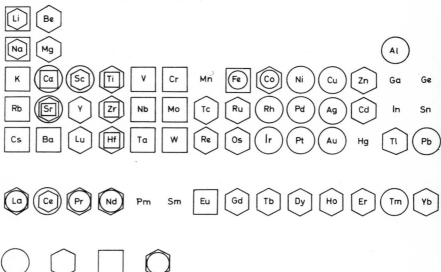

Fig. 12.6. *Occurrence in metals of the cubic close-packed (A1), hexagonal close-packed (A3), and body-centred cubic (A2) structures, as well as those with a regularly alternating layer sequence ABC and AB (A1–A3). Where an element can exist in more than one form, the largest symbol represents the most stable form at room temperature.*

If the structural building blocks were rigid spheres, then the ratio of the two axis lengths, c/a, would be 1·633. In general, the ratio is close to this ideal value. The ratio is, however, smaller with Be ($c/a = 1·5848$) and with a series of rare earths ($c/a \approx 1·57$). It is appreciably greater with Zn ($c/a = 1·856$) and Cd ($c/a = 1·885$). In Be, the distance between nearest neighbour atoms within a layer ($r_2 = 2·2679$ Å) is greater than the separation between the atoms of two adjacent layers ($r_1 = 2·2235$ Å). The ratio of the two distances, $r_2/r_1 = 1·015$. Here and in the remainder of this book r_1 refers to the shortest interatomic distance in a crystal (the nearest-neighbour distance), r_2 is the next-nearest neighbour distance, and so on. With Zn and Cd, it is the atoms within a layer which are closer together, the differences here being almost 10 per cent (Zn: $r_2/r_1 = 1·093$; Cd: $r_2/r_1 = 1·099$). From this we can conclude that in the first case (Be) the chemical bonding between layers is strong while in the second case (Zn and Cd) it is stronger within the layers and therefore the atoms are forced more closely together.

It is also possible for cubic close-packing to be so distorted that some of the 12 neighbours stand closer to the central atom than do the rest. Indium, for example, has a tetragonally distorted face-centred lattice with lattice parameters $a = 4·588$ Å and $c = 4·958$ Å. There are thus 4 neighbours at 3·24 Å, and 8 at 3·33 Å ($r_2/r_1 = 1·03$).

12.2 The Atomic Radii of Metals: Metallic Bonding

Half the distance between two nearest-neighbour metal atoms is appropriately the definition of the atomic radius. In the following Fig. 12.7 the experimentally-determined atomic radii are given for metal atoms in co-ordination number 12. If the metal crystallizes in a body-centred crystal (CN 8) the observed atomic radius is increased by 3 per cent, an empirical value applied to compensate for the transition from 12 to 8 co-ordination. If the metal in question does not crystallize in any of the three lattices described above, the radii for CN 12 are frequently obtained from inter-atomic separations in alloys.

The large atomic radii of the alkali metals are striking, being almost twice as large as their ionic radii (see later). The radii of the alkaline earths are smaller, and atomic radii continue to decrease as one proceeds across the periodic table until Group VI (chromium) after which the radii remain fairly constant.

This is due to the fact that in any period of the periodic system the extension of the atom decreases as the atomic number increases (see chapter 3, section 2). In addition, the bonding forces in the alkali metals are very weak, since these metals have only one valence electron per atom. The bonding forces then increase with increasing numbers of valence

10

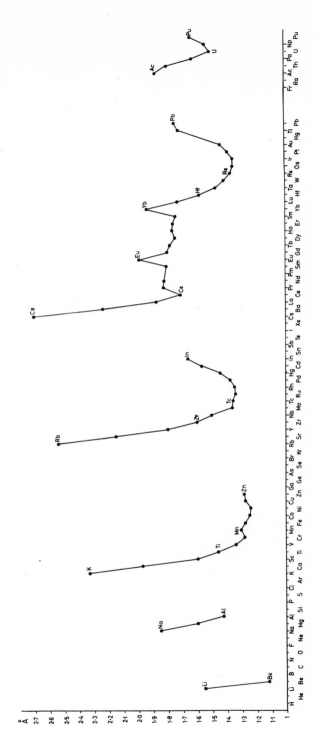

Fig. 12.7. *Atomic radii for co-ordination number 12.*

electrons until for the chromium group and beyond, the forces remain relatively constant. According to Pauling,[12.3] d-electrons added beyond this point no longer take part in the bonding and the inter-atomic distances therefore remain fairly constant. After leaving the transition metals, the number of valence electrons evidently again decreases. Thus with the copper group, the atomic radii slowly increase. It must be emphasized that the elements of the copper group also have small atomic radii so that they cannot be mono- or divalent in the metallic state. Several valence electrons must be present.

These considerations about the bonding energy are also reflected in the melting points of the metals. The alkalis have the lowest melting points while the highest are found in the chromium group (Fig. 12.8).

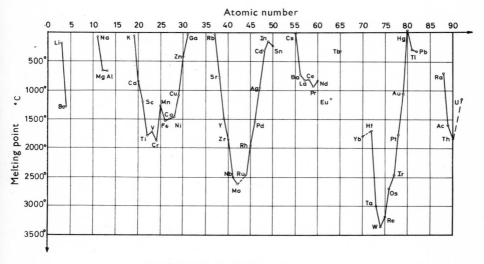

Fig. 12.8. Melting points of metals.

Much discussion has taken place about the bonding forces in typical metals. Nevertheless, it is not possible even today to derive theoretically the structure for any metal.

Drude postulated that a metal consists of positive ions embedded in a mobile free-electron gas. Many physical properties of metals such as their high thermal and electrical conductivity, strong reflectivity for light, and their plasticity, can, in principle, be explained by this assumption. However, it is not possible to derive the crystal structure. This theory ignores the fact that valence electrons must be describable by eigenfunctions which increasingly resemble atomic eigenfunctions when the valence electrons approach close to the nucleus.

Pauling[12.3] attempted to apply the concept of mesomerism to bonding in metallic crystals. Since the typical metal is characterized by a large number of possible eigenfunctions and relatively few electrons to occupy them, these electrons are more or less free to enter into several possible quantum states and are able to bond in several different ways with the neighbouring atoms. In the case of lithium with one valence electron to four orbitals, i.e., one 2s- and three 2p-states, chemical bonding can be described formally, according to the scheme shown in Fig. 12.9. There is an abundance of such bonding possibilities, a linear combination of which

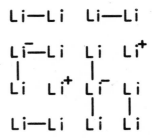

Fig. 12.9. Schematic representation of one bonding possibility in a lithium crystal.

represents, according to the assumption of mesomerism, the true bonding state.

It is certainly better in this case to use the concept of molecular orbitals. It is possible from the s- and p-atomic orbitals of the alkali metals to form a large number of molecular orbitals which extend over the entire lattice. Their mathematical description is complex and cannot be treated here. There results a multiplicity of energy levels for the valence electrons, lying very close together, which form the so-called *valence band*.

In an electric field, an electron can migrate since empty molecular orbitals are available in profusion, the number of valence electrons being substantially smaller than the number of atomic functions from which the molecular functions are formed. The valence band is therefore only partially filled, and the electrical conductivity of the alkali metals is very high. In general, the electrical conductivity decreases as one goes across the periodic table from the alkaline metals to the alkaline earths, to the aluminium group, and on to the chromium group.

The frequent occurrence of body-centred lattices in the titanium, vanadium, and chromium groups is surprising. Ganzhorn[12.4] and Dehlinger[12.5] have related this to the symmetry of the d-eigenfunctions.

The four (d^3s)-hybrid functions using the t_{2g} d-functions are:

$$\varphi_1 = \frac{1}{\sqrt{4}} (\psi_s + \psi_{d_{xy}} + \psi_{d_{yz}} + \psi_{d_{zx}})$$

$$\varphi_2 = \frac{1}{\sqrt{4}} (\psi_s - \psi_{d_{xy}} + \psi_{d_{yz}} - \psi_{d_{zx}})$$

$$\varphi_3 = \frac{1}{\sqrt{4}} (\psi_s + \psi_{d_{xy}} - \psi_{d_{yz}} - \psi_{d_{zx}})$$

$$\varphi_4 = \frac{1}{\sqrt{4}} (\psi_s - \psi_{d_{xy}} - \psi_{d_{yz}} + \psi_{d_{zx}})$$

They have large values in the directions of the four body diagonals of a cube and are thus principally suited to form bonds with eight atoms which surround a central atom cubically (Fig. 12.10).

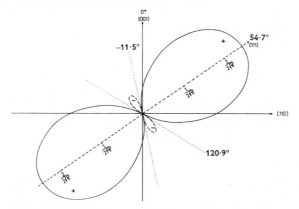

Fig. 12.10. Polar diagram of a $(d_\varepsilon^{\ 3}s)$-hybrid function.

In the vanadium and chromium groups, in addition to the d_ε-electrons (t_{2g}) there are also one or two d_γ-electrons (e_g) available. The orbitals of the latter are directed to the corners of an octahedron so that they avoid the atoms in the corners of the cube and appear suited to form bonds with six octahedrally arranged neighbours in the second co-ordination sphere. If still further electrons are added, the relationships become increasingly complex and can no longer be visualized.

12.3 Structures of Non-metals and Semi-metals

12.3.1 *The Noble Gases*

The noble gases neon, argon, krypton, and xenon crystallize in the cubic close-packed structure while helium crystallizes with hexagonal close-packing.

Only weak van der Waals' forces operate between the noble gas atoms. Because of this, their melting points are unusually low while the interatomic distances are relatively large (van der Waals' distance). Half the distance between two identical atoms is referred to as the atomic radius. As a rule, the atomic radii of the noble gases in the solid state are somewhat larger than the so-called Goldschmidt radii of the isoelectronic halide ions, when they are built into NaCl-type lattices (see later). Because of the reduction in nuclear charge on going from a noble gas atom to a halide ion, the electron cloud expands. Since, however, according to the ionic model, the forces between the atoms in a NaCl-type lattice are stronger, the building blocks of the lattice are more strongly pressed together whereby the expansion is to some extent compensated.

The compounds N_2, CO, HCl, HBr, CH_4, PH_3, AsH_3, H_2S, and H_2Se also crystallize in a cubic close-packed lattice just below their melting point. At low temperatures this high-temperature form changes into another packing. The high cubic symmetry of the high-temperature form is understandable when one remembers that the molecules rotate in the lattice.

12.3.2 The Halogens

Chlorine,[12.6, 12.7] bromine,[12.6, 12.8] and iodine[12.6, 12.9] crystallize in a simple orthorhombic structure (A14-type), Fig. 12.11a, b, c. For example, iodine molecules form layers arranged one over the other in such a way that the upper iodine molecule lies in the depressions formed by the molecules in the lower layer. This layering makes the tabular form of the crystals understandable.

A comparison of inter-atomic distances (Table 12.1) shows immediately that the structure consists of diatomic molecules. Each atom has only one nearest neighbour at a distance $r_1 = 2.67$ Å. From Fig. 12.11c it is plainly visible how the molecules are ordered into layers so that all atoms lie at the

Table 12.1. Inter-atomic distances in halogen crystals

Atom positions	Chlorine		Bromine		Iodine	
	Inter-atomic distance Å	$\frac{r_x}{r_1}$	Inter-atomic distance Å	$\frac{r_x}{r_1}$	Inter-atomic distance Å	$\frac{r_x}{r_1}$
X_1–X_2	1·98	1	2·27	1	2·67	1
X_2–X_3	3·32	1·65	3·31	1·46	3·57	1·34
X_3–X_4	3·82	1·93	3·79	1·67	4·05	1·52
Between layers	3·74–3·97	1·89–2·00	3·99–4·14	1·76–1·82	4·35–4·50	1·63–1·98

points of intersection of two groups of lines. Within these layers the inter-atomic distances $r_2 = 3.57$ Å and $r_3 = 4.05$ Å are smaller than the distances between next nearest neighbour atoms on different double layers, $r_4 = 4.35$ Å–4.50 Å. The distance r_4 is about twice the Goldschmidt ionic radius of iodine ($2 \times 2.20 = 4.40$) and can be associated with a van der Waals' radius. The weak bonding forces between molecules in adjacent layers is reflected in the easy cleavability of the crystals parallel to the planes of the layers. The cohesion of molecules within a layer is stronger and raises the question (which will be answered later) of explaining the bonding forces which bring about the shortened distances, r_2 and r_3.

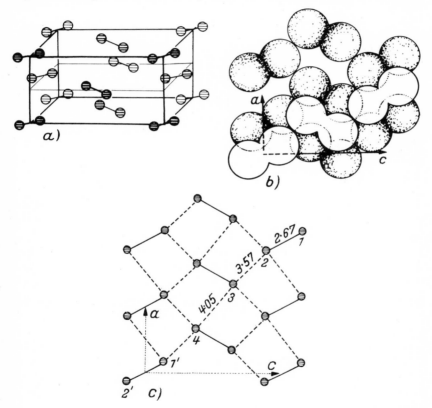

Fig. 12.11 (a) Unit cells of the halogens Cl, Br, and I. (b) Packing of I_2-molecules into layers. (c) Atomic positions and distances within one layer of the iodine crystal.

12.3.3 The Chalcogens

Oxygen forms a molecular lattice with an intramolecular distance of 1.208 Å.

Five crystalline modifications of sulphur are known. The first is rhombic sulphur (α-form), stable at room temperature, which transforms enantiotropically into the monoclinic crystalline form (β-sulphur) at 95·6°C. There further exist, as thermodynamically unstable forms, a second monoclinic, first discovered by Muthman, and a recently discovered orthorhombic,[12.10] as well as a rhombohedral modification. The stable rhombic and the two monoclinic forms contain as a structural element the S_8 ring, while the rhombohedral and the unstable rhombic contain the S_6 and S_{12} rings respectively.

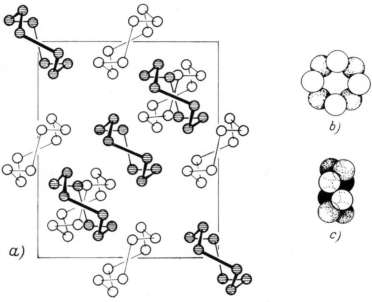

Fig. 12.12. (a) 'Roll of coins' packing of S_8-rings in the crystal of rhombic sulphur, (b) and (c) S_8-rings in basal and lateral views.

In the rhombohedral modification, bent six-membered rings lie one over the other like coins in a roll (distance S–S is 2·057 Å; bond angle S–S–S is 102·2°).[12.11] Each such roll is surrounded by six others at a van der Waals' distance of 3·501 Å, as with a dense packing of spheres in a plane.

In the orthorhombic form, bent S_8-rings are also superposed like in a coin roll (S–S distance is 2·05 Å, bond angle, S–S–S is 108°) (Fig. 12.12). [12.12, 12.13] These 'coin rolls' are arranged in layers parallel beside one another and cross-wise over one another. The upper layer is shown in Fig. 12.12a by a heavier shading. The shape of the S_8-molecule is shown in Fig. 12.12b and c in both horizontal and vertical projections. In the lattice of monoclinic β-sulphur[12.14] and of the S_{12}[12.15] likewise puckered rings are present with similar atomic distances and angles.

Two red, monoclinic modifications of selenium are known. The structural elements of both modifications are puckered Se_8-rings, just as observed with rhombic sulphur (S_8).[12.16, 12.17] The positions of these rings relative to one another are difficult to describe. The shortest inter-atomic distance within a ring is 2·34 Å. The distance between neighbouring atoms in adjacent rings differs from atom to atom since not all atoms of a given ring have the same surroundings. The average distance is $\bar{r}_2 = 3·80$ Å, so that $r_2/r_1 = 1·62$. The average bond angle is 105·3° and the average dihedral angle (see later) is 102°.

The stable form of selenium is the hexagonal modification, which is isotypic with hexagonal tellurium. It is possible to replace any number of selenium atoms in hexagonal selenium with tellurium atoms and vice versa. Therefore, the two phases form a complete series of *solid solutions*.

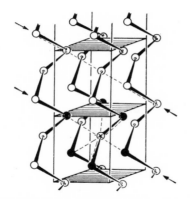

Fig. 12.13. Structure of hexagonal Se and Te. The one atom (⊗) surrounded by an octahedron (●) is brought forward. Mesomeric chains are designated by broken lines (−−−) and by arrows (→).[12.17a]

In the selenium lattice, each atom, in accordance with its valence, is bonded to two neighbours: $r_1 = 2·374$ Å (Fig. 12.13, Table 12.2). Further coupling here does not, however, lead to rings but instead to chains which extend throughout the crystal, and which lie parallel to one another forming spirals along the c-axis. Each selenium atom on a given chain has four neighbours from three other chains at a distance $r_2 = 3·426$ Å. This distance is smaller than one would expect for a normal van der Waals' distance. The result is that each atom is surrounded by six others arranged in a distorted octahedron (Fig. 12.13). In this figure, the chosen atom is designated ⊗ while the six neighbours are marked ●. Geometrically, the selenium lattice is like a distorted rock-salt lattice, where again any chosen atom (e.g., Cl) is octahedrally surrounded by six other atoms (Na).

In the transition from hexagonal selenium to hexagonal tellurium, the packing becomes even more like that in rock salt. The bond angle within the chain approaches 90°, and the distance r_2 approaches r_1 ($r_2/r_1 = 1.199$).

Table 12.2. Inter-atomic distances and bond angles in the crystal structures of Se, Te, and Po

	Bond angle	r_1 (Å)	r_2 (Å)	$r_2:r_1$	Reference
Se (hexagonal)	102° 50′	2·374	3·426	1·443	12.18
Te (hexagonal)	101° 46′	2·878	3·451	1·199	12.18
Po (cubic-α)	90°	3·359	3·359	1·000	12.19, 12.20

The rock-salt structure is finally reached in the cubic modification of polonium (α-Po). Here Po-atoms take both the sodium and chlorine positions, resulting in a cubic structure having a smaller unit cell in which only the corners are occupied. A lattice such as this in which only the cell corners are occupied is called *primitive*.

12.3.4 *Elements of the Nitrogen Group*

As previously mentioned, nitrogen forms a molecular lattice. Phosphorus has several modifications. White phosphorus consists of tetrahedral P_4-molecules (P–P distance 2·21 Å) both in the liquid and solid state (Fig. 12.14). The abnormal bond angle, 60°, makes this phosphorus

Fig. 12.14. Geometry of the P_4-molecule.

modification unstable. By heating white phosphorus to 180°C, the bonds in the molecules are split and polymerization takes place. Amorphous phosphorus results, in which individual phosphorus atoms, keeping as far as possible the normal valence angle, are irregularly cross-linked with each other. Each phosphorus atom is pyramidally surrounded by three others at a distance of 2·24 Å, the valence angle being 102°.[12.21] If red phosphorus is heated to 450°, a slow crystallization to so-called Hittorf's phosphorus results. The micelles are poorly developed and only at 550°C do small crystallites develop. The atoms are also interlaced with one another in Hittorf's phosphorus. In this case, however, the interlacing is regular.[12.22]

Two planar chains of P-atoms (Fig. 12.15a, b: atoms 1–8, and 9–16) are interconnected to form a $\vee$-shaped groove. The free valencies on the edges of the groove are saturated by further P-atoms (atoms 17–20) so that a tube of pentagonal cross-section is formed. In this way P_8-groups (atoms 5, 6, 7, 13, 14, 15, 19, and 20) which are arranged as in As_4S_4, and

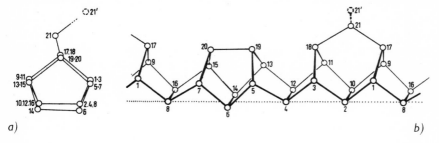

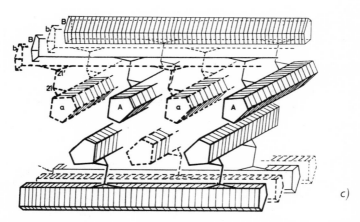

Fig. 12.15. *Tubes in the structure of violet phosphorus: (a) Projection of one tube parallel to its axis (end view); (b) parallel perspective; (c) schematic representation of the structure. The tubes are represented by pentagonal prisms; in parts of the upper layer only one edge is drawn to show the linkage of the two halves of a double layer via atoms 21 and 21'.*

P_9-groups (atoms 1, 2, 3, 9, 10, 11, 17, 18, and 21) arise. These latter couple pairs of layers together, via atoms 21, so that the axes of the tubes in the two layers form an angle of almost 90° (Fig. 12.15c). Thus double layers are formed from layers of parallel tubes lying crosswise over one another. The tubes marked a on the one half of the double layer are bound only with those marked b on the other while those marked A are connected only to those marked B. Thus a double layer is formed which consists of two interlocking systems not connected by any chemical bonds. The filling by one sub-lattice of the vacancies in another is observed only rarely, e.g., in the structures of Cu_2O (chapter 17, section 5), $NbF_{2.5}$ (chapter 27, section 2), and of some borates (chapter 26, section 14). These double layers are stacked together so that each tube is above a gap between two tubes of the layer below. They are held together only by van der Waals' forces. The mean bond length is 2·219 Å and the bond angle is 100·9°.

The relatively complicated structure of Hittorf's phosphorus is probably due to the difficulty of satisfying all three of the pyramidal valencies of phosphorus, while retaining the normal valence angle of something over 100°. From the complexity of the structure one can see why a glassy product is obtained first when white phosphorus is heated. In this glassy product the P_8-, P_9-, and P_2-groups are not arranged in so ordered a fashion.

When Hittorf's phosphorus is heated to over 600°, the network is no longer stable. It breaks up, and under these conditions there appear, on melting, P_4-molecules having the abnormal valence angle of 60°.

In addition to the above, there is also black phosphorus, which crystallizes with an orthorhombic cell. It is formed from double layers, the structure of which is given in Fig. 12.16a.[12.23, 12.24] Figure 12.16b shows the packing of double layers in the crystal projected onto the (100)-plane.

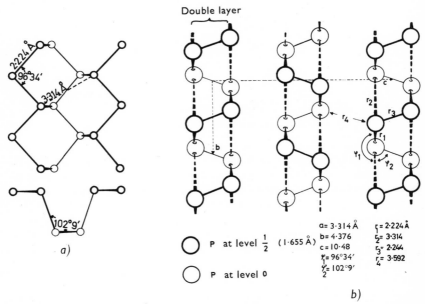

Fig. 12.16. *Structure of black phosphorus: (a) Double layer in a top and side view. The atoms which lie above in the basal view are identified by darker outlines. Mesomeric chains are indicated by broken lines (– – –). (b) Projection on the (100) plane.*

The double layers consist of parallel chains lying one over the other. The third valency of each P-atom forms a bond with the neighbouring chain. The valence angle within the chain is $96° 34'$. The shortest distance between neighbouring atoms on different chains of the same half of a double layer is $3\cdot314$ Å ($r_2/r_1 = 1\cdot49$). It is thus substantially smaller than the van der Waals' distance between the layers, $r_4 = 3\cdot592$, $r_4/r_1 = 1\cdot61$. It is no surprise then that this modification is black in the same way as are hexagonal Se and Te, in which a shortened inter-atomic distance is also observed.

Arsenic forms three crystalline modifications: yellow arsenic, which is analogous to white phosphorus, rhombic arsenic,[12.25, 12.26] which corresponds to black phosphorus, and a rhombohedral modification, which is found also in antimony and bismuth. The structure of the last-named modification is given in Fig. 12.17. The trivalence of the elements As, Sb, and Bi leads to a planar network of puckered six-membered rings.

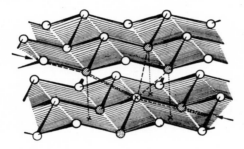

Fig. 12.17. The rock-salt-like packing of the double layers in the crystal of rhombohedral arsenic. The one atom ($\otimes$) surrounded by an octahedron (◍) is brought forward. The three weak bonds of the one atom are indicated by broken lines ($- - -$) and arrows ($\rightarrow$).

There are three possibilities for the superposition of such double layers, so that a low lying atom of the upper double layer lies in the depressions formed between three upper atoms of the lower double layer. In the crystal only that type of packing is observed in which the atoms lie on approximately straight lines which are nearly perpendicular to each other, so that a distorted NaCl structure results (Fig. 12.17). The distance, r_2, between nearest neighbour atoms on different double layers is again substantially smaller than one would expect for van der Waals' packing. As the atoms become heavier in the series arsenic, antimony, and bismuth, the heavy atoms, antimony and bismuth, show a smaller difference between inter-atomic distances and a smaller valence angle relative to the lighter arsenic, as Table 12.3 shows.

Table 12.3 also contains the results for that form of phosphorus which crystallizes in the same structure type as rhombohedral arsenic. This form is prepared by compressing black phosphorus at a pressure of 83 kbar. At 111 kbar, this modification transforms reversibly into a primitive cubic form in which each phosphorus atom is octahedrally surrounded by six others at a distance of 2·377 Å.[12.27] Antimony, too, forms a primitive cubic modification (a = 2·96 Å) at a pressure of 85 kbar. When antimony is subjected to still higher pressure, 100 kbar, it transforms into a hexagonal close-packed form having an Sb–Sb distance of 1·64 Å.[12.29]

Table 12.3. *Inter-atomic distances and bond angles in elements with the rhombohedral* As *type structure*

	Bond angle	r_1 (Å)	r_2 (Å)	$r_2:r_1$	Reference
Phosphorus (83 kbar)	104° 30′	2·13	3·27	1·53	12.27
Phosphorus (111 kbar)	90°	2·377	2·377	1	12.27
Arsenic	97°	2·51	3·15	1·25	
Antimony	95° 35′	2·908	3·355	1·154	12.28
Antimony (85 kbar)	90°	2·96	2·96	1	12.29
Bismuth	95° 29′	3·071	3·529	1·149	12.30

If arsenic vapour is condensed on a cooled surface, yellow arsenic results. If now the surface on which yellow arsenic is condensing, is warmed to 100–200°C, glassy modifications result.[12.31] In these, As atoms are irregularly joined together in a network. The inter-atomic distance is 2·94 Å and the bond angle 100°.[12.32]

So-called explosive antimony consists of irregular networks of antimony packed one over the other. These networks appear to be structurally related to those in black phosphorus. The extent of the nets is limited. The free valencies on the antimony atoms along the periphery are saturated by chlorine.[12.32]

Yellow antimony consists of an amorphous network of antimony atoms in which part of the valencies is saturated by hydrogen.[12.33] It does not, therefore, correspond to yellow arsenic, but rather to the weakly coloured amorphous network of arsenic with hydrogen described in the literature as solid arsenic hydride with the approximate formula AsH or to the solid phosphorus hydride with the approximate composition P_2H.

Bismuth exists at room temperature in the above-mentioned rhombohedral modification. Even when bismuth vapour is condensed on a surface cooled with liquid helium (4°K), polymerization appears to take place immediately, forming an amorphous network which is superconducting to 6°K and is stable to 14°K. At 20°K one can already observe the rhombohedral phase.[12.34]

12.4 An Explanation of the Structures of the Elements of the V, VI, and VII Principal Groups

As we have seen earlier, in the hybridization of s- and p-eigenfunctions, the coefficients are continuously variable. It is possible, given the observed valence angles in rhombohedral arsenic, antimony, and bismuth to calculate back and determine what coefficients must be chosen. The hybrid functions, φ_1 for a bonding electron, and φ_4 for the free electron pair are:

As

$$\varphi_1 = \frac{1}{\sqrt{4}} (0{\cdot}64\psi_s + 1{\cdot}09\psi_{p_x} + 1{\cdot}09\psi_{p_y} + 1{\cdot}09\psi_{p_z})$$

$\vartheta = 96° \, 30'$

$$\varphi_4 = \frac{1}{\sqrt{4}} (1{\cdot}67\psi_s - 0{\cdot}64\psi_{p_x} - 0{\cdot}64\psi_{p_y} + 0{\cdot}64\psi_{p_z})$$

Sb and Bi

$$\varphi_1 = \frac{1}{\sqrt{4}} (0{\cdot}62\psi_s + 1{\cdot}10\psi_{p_x} + 1{\cdot}10\psi_{p_y} + 1{\cdot}10\psi_{p_z})$$

$\vartheta = 95° \, 30'$

$$\varphi_4 = \frac{1}{\sqrt{4}} (1{\cdot}69\psi_s - 0{\cdot}61\psi_{p_x} - 0{\cdot}61\psi_{p_y} + 0{\cdot}61\psi_{p_z})$$

One can see that the bonding functions are made up principally of p-components, while the free electron pair has more s-character. The values of the orbitals on all atoms and also of the 4s- and 4p-orbitals on arsenic have been calculated.[12.34a] From these the bonding function φ_1 of arsenic was derived. This is shown in Fig. 12.18a by contour lines.[4.7] One can observe how in the space within a double layer, orbitals which overlap have large values while in the space between double layers, smaller values of the orbitals are observed. In Fig. 12.18b there are represented the values of the bonding functions along the bonding line of the three arsenic atoms as well as their summed function. Because the calculations are tedious, in this figure the normalization factors necessary for a determination of the molecular orbital have been ignored. Within a double layer there is a plateau which is about twice as high as in the space between double layers.

We may assume that each of the three valence electrons on a given As atom can take part in bonding on each of two sides. One bonding direction is preferred because of the greater electron probability density on one side of the atom. The preferred direction is that bonding within the double layer. The other, between the double layers, is unfavourable and weak. The atom pairs are arranged obliquely to the double layers, approximately in the direction of the lattice vectors: [100], [010], and [001]. Along one such line one can formulate according to the ideas of mesomerism two bonds:[12.35]

As—As   As—As   As—As ⟷
                    As   As —— As   As —— As   As

In the first, the bonding within the layers is observed and in the second, which is less probable, the unfavoured, weak bonding between the layers. The bonding mechanism is completely analogous to that in conjugated organic double-bonded systems. The essential difference is only that in arsenic we are looking at a mesomeric σ-bonding system, while in conjugated organic compounds a mesomeric π-bonding system is superimposed on the simple σ-bonds.

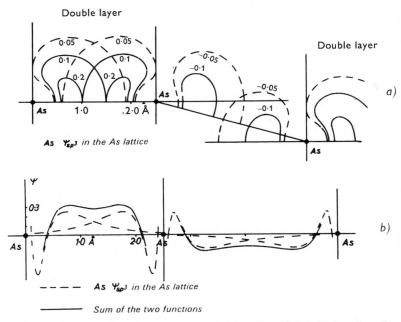

Fig. 12.18. Structure of rhombohedral As (a) overlap of hybrid functions for a mesomeric chain, (b) values of the hybrid functions along the bonding line of atoms in a mesomeric chain and their summed functions.

Conjugated organic systems are coloured. Graphite is black and even shows metallic conductivity within the layers. [12.36] Completely analogously, the rhombohedral modifications of arsenic, antimony, and bismuth are metallic. As with graphite, the metallic conductivity of these elements can be explained by saying that no energy is necessary to remove an electron from a given atom since the mesomeric system can supply electrons to smear out the remaining positive charge over many atoms.

All valence electrons in one of the above-mentioned lattice lines are coupled together. This coupling would be better still if the bonding functions were pure p-functions and both bonding directions were of equal strength.

It must be mentioned that as in the chlorine molecule, π-bonds are also possible in three directions, between the valence electron pairs with predominantly p-character and empty d_ε-quantum states.

In the crystal of black phosphorus, it is only those bonding functions which run parallel to the double layer and which are associated with the smaller bonding angle of $96°\ 34'$, that have predominantly p-character and the possibility of forming a mesomeric bonding system. There remains then for the other electrons (in the third bonding function and in the free electron pair) a greater s-component.

In order to explain the crystal structure of the chalcogens, it is first necessary to make several observations. If a series of three atoms in the lattice is considered, these define a plane which in Fig. 12.19 stands

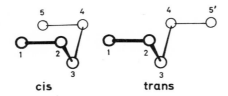

Fig. 12.19. *cis-* and *trans-coupling of S-atoms.*

perpendicular to the plane of the paper. A fourth and fifth atom can now be added on one side of the plane or they can be divided so that one is on one side and the other on the other side. Following O. Foss, the first position is called the *cis-* and the second the *trans-*arrangement.[12.37] The first coupling leads to ring systems: S_8, S_6, and Se_8, the second to the chain-type molecules such as hexagonal Se and Te. The planes defined by atoms 123 and 234 form an angle with one another, the so-called *torsion-* or *dihedral-angle* which is in the range of $90°–100°$.

If the atoms were coupled only by σ-bonds, one would expect free rotation about the inter-atomic bond. It seems probable that π-bonding between p-electron pairs and free d_ε-states on neighbouring atoms brings about the *cis-* and *trans-*configurations.

As O. Foss has shown by means of several structural studies, *cis-* and *trans-*coupling is characteristic of all compounds with sulphur chains, such as the salt-like polysulphides and the sulphanes with the general formula $R—S_x—R$.[12.37] *Trans-*coupling appears to be favoured by heavier elements.

In a sulphur melt, the dissociation and recombination of bonds lead to an equilibrium between rings of various sizes, where the proportion of S_8 is about 90 per cent. This can be seen from the melting point depression of monoclinic sulphur under long-term heating. The remainder consists of S_6-rings and other, principally low-molecular, rings up to S_{30}.[12.38] High

11

molecular weight rings cannot occur because of the tendency of the element to favour *cis*-bonding. With increasing temperature, the probability of *trans*-coupling increases. Bulky molecules result, making it very difficult to achieve dense packing when their concentration is high. Above a critical temperature, 160°C, the entire system goes into a state where *trans*-coupling is preferred. The melt suddenly becomes highly viscous and a parallel orientation of molecules or of parts of molecules results. This parallel orientation favours the formation of large extended ring molecules over the low molecular weight rings (Fig. 12.20).

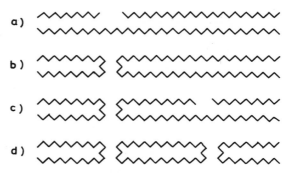

Fig. 12.20. Schematic representation of the formation of large rings by parallelization of molecular parts.

If a bond in a chain dissociates thermally (a), the radical ends can either recombine or can react with neighbouring chains, e.g., such that two folded chains result (b). The same process can take place at another position (c) and lead to an extended high-molecular ring (d).[12.39]

The concentration of radical ends is determined by the extent of thermal dissociation, and the average molecular size by the probability of a radical end reacting with an atom of the same folded chain. In a strongly heated sulphur melt, approximately 40 per cent of the sulphur is in the form of low-molecular rings. The remainder consists essentially of high-molecular rings with an average ring size of 5000 atoms.[12.39]

Since selenium, as a heavy atom, prefers *trans*-coupling there is a tendency for the atoms in the melt, at all temperatures, to arrange themselves in more or less long spirals which have to be, to some extent, parallel to each other, in order to fill the space. In equilibrium there are formed, at all temperatures, primarily large rings with an average molecular size of about 500 atoms, in equilibrium with smaller molecular rings[12.40].

With organic high polymers, one observes macromolecular rings when either through steric effects (e.g.

$$\left[-OOC-\!\!\!\left\langle\!\!\!\bigcirc\!\!\!\right\rangle\!\!\!-COO-CH_2-CH_2- \right]_n$$

or hydrogen bonding (e.g., the polyamides) the compounds are forced to assume a parallel orientation in the melt.[12.39, 12.41]

As previously pointed out, the relatively dense packing of spiral chains in hexagonal selenium and tellurium to form an NaCl-type structure is surprising. From the bond angle of $102° 50'$ in hexagonal selenium the hybrid functions can be calculated. If one chooses the bisector of the bond angle as the negative x-axis the results are:

$$\left.\begin{array}{l} \varphi_1 = \dfrac{1}{\sqrt{3}}\left(0{\cdot}74\psi_s - 0{\cdot}98\psi_{p_x} - \sqrt{\dfrac{3}{2}}\,\psi_{p_y} \right) \\[3mm] \varphi_2 = \dfrac{1}{\sqrt{3}}\left(0{\cdot}74\psi_s - 0{\cdot}98\psi_{p_x} + \sqrt{\dfrac{3}{2}}\,\psi_{p_y} \right) \end{array}\right\} \text{Bonding functions}$$

$$\varphi_3 = \frac{1}{\sqrt{3}}\,(1{\cdot}38\psi_s + 1{\cdot}04\psi_{p_x}) \quad \text{Free electron pair.}$$

The second free electron pair is then described by a p_z-orbital. In contrast to the symmetrical (sp^2)-hybrid function, these bonding functions have more p-character while the one free electron pair has more s-content. Nevertheless, the coefficients do not differ from unity as much as they do in the series arsenic, antimony, and bismuth. The superposition of φ_1- and ψ_{p_z}-functions in the structure of hexagonal selenium is illustrated in Fig. 12.21a, b.

The bonding in the backward direction is weak and the relative shortening of the shortest distance between atoms in neighbouring chains is small in comparison to one van der Waals' distance.

Why are the coefficients of the hybrid functions in selenium closer to 1 than with the previously discussed functions of arsenic, antimony, and bismuth? This can be explained by examining the position of the atoms and their associated orbitals along one axis of the distorted octahedron pictured in Fig. 12.13. Along this axis there alternate an atom pair and a single selenium atom whose p_z-electron pair lies approximately in the direction of this straight line. If one formulates the bonding possibilities:

	Chain I	Chain II	Chain III
I	Se————Se	Se	Se————Se $\longleftrightarrow$
	(−)	(+)	
II	Se Se———	———Se	Se————Se $\longleftrightarrow$
		(+)	(−)
III	Se————Se	Se———	———Se Se

they are possible only by forming ionic structures. To electrically charge an atom, however, requires energy.[5.2, 5.3] Formulae II and III are therefore less probable and have only a small weight. Favouring of the p-component by bonding such as that in Formulae II and III is thus very slight.

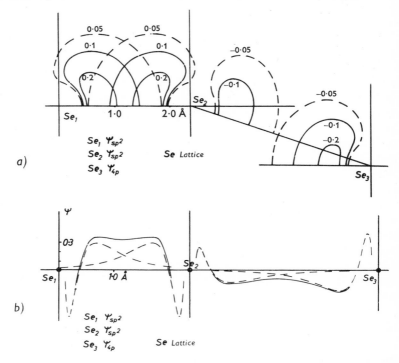

Fig. 12.21. Structure of hexagonal Se *(a) overlap of the hybrid functions and p-orbitals for a mesomeric chain, (b) values of hybrid functions and of p-orbitals along the bonding line of atoms in a mesomeric chain and their summed functions.*

In order to discuss the structure of iodine, bromine, and chlorine, we must look back at Fig. 12.11 and Table 12.1. The axes of the two p-orbitals of the valence electrons can be directed toward the two previously mentioned sets of straight lines, while the axis of the third p-orbital stands perpendicular to the layer. One p-orbital on each iodine atom is occupied by only one electron and therefore. acts to couple two atoms into a molecule (Formula I). For simplicity, hybridization with s-orbitals will be neglected. All other p-orbitals are occupied by an electron pair. There are also other possible electron distributions in which an electron wanders from an electron pair to a p-state, which previously was only singly occupied. The lone non-bonding electron pairs now are in different positions and bonds result between the original molecules, approximately as illustrated in Formula II.

Atom No.	1	2	3	4	1'	2'
I	I——I	I	I	I——I	$\longleftrightarrow$
II	$I^{(-)}$ I———$I^{(+)}$	I	I	I	$\longleftrightarrow$
III	$I^{(-)}$ I	$I^{\underline{(+)}}$———$I^{(+)}$	I	$I^{(-)}$

Since charged atoms are produced, this formula is unfavourable relative to Formula I. Another distribution is shown in Formula III. The participation of Formulae II and III, according to the doctrine of mesomerism, makes possible the shortening of the inter-atomic distance r_2 to 3·57 Å. Formula III shows the relationship to the π-bonding system of butadiene in which the inter-atomic distance between central carbon atoms is smaller than would be expected for single bonding. Since in Formula III atoms with the same charge stand next to one another, their participation in the structure is relatively small. The inter-atomic distance I_{3-4} is larger, 4·05 Å.

As the distance between two atoms is shortened, the π-bonding between free d_ε-states of one atom and p-electron pairs on another appears more pronounced and the effect described above becomes stronger.

The shortening of the inter-atomic distance in bromine is not so pronounced, as can be easily verified by comparing the ratios of the inter-atomic distances, r_x/r_1 in Table 12.1. In the case of chlorine, the distance r_2 is only slightly shortened, $r_2/r_1 = 1·68$. In the case of the halogens, the mesomeric phenomena are more pronounced as the atoms become heavier, just as in the earlier discussed series. This generalization will often be observed.

Structures in which there exist clearly defined groups which are strongly bound within themselves and which therefore can be considered as molecules are called *molecular structures*. It should be especially emphasized that the molecular concept can be applied to the structures just described even though there are stronger forces operable between these molecules than those which correspond to van der Waals' bonding. In dealing with high molecular weight crystalline compounds, one refers to *chain structures* when there is a one-dimensional coupling of the atoms (e.g., hexagonal selenium), to *layer structures* if there is a two-dimensional atomic coupling (e.g., rhombohedral arsenic) and to a *three-dimensional* network when the coupling is in all spatial directions (e.g., diamond). If it is possible in a structure to collect all the atoms into co-ordination polyhedra which are interpenetrating, one speaks of *co-ordination structures* (e.g., body-centred cubic or face-centred cubic metal structures).

12.5 Elements of the Carbon Group

Two crystalline modifications of carbon are known: graphite and diamond. Diamond is thermodynamically stable only under high pressure.

Graphite forms a distinct layer structure (Fig. 12.22a). Within a layer, each atom is surrounded by three nearest neighbours at a distance of 1·418 Å; the bond angle is 120°. Thus, just as in benzene, regular hexagons are formed. The packing of the layers occurs in such a way that one-half of the carbon atoms lie always above or below the centre of a hexagonal

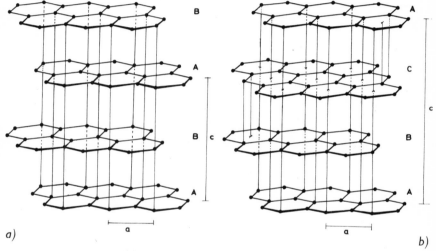

a)

b)

Fig. 12.22. Structure of hexagonal (a) and rhombohedral (b) graphite.

ring of the two neighbouring layers. The second half of the C-atoms lie above or below one another. This can be visualized by considering that these halves of the atoms lie continuously over one another throughout the crystal as Fig. 12.22a shows. The layer sequence is A B A B and the symmetry is hexagonal. If the second possibility of superposition (Fig. 12.22b) were realized, the sequence would be A B C A B C and the structure could be indexed as rhombohedral. The rhombohedral form is rare and is never observed as a single phase; the layering remains at least in part A B A B.[12.42]

The interlayer distance in hexagonal graphite is very large; $c/2 = 3·354$ Å.[12.43] Forces between the layers must therefore be very weak, while the bonding forces within a layer are very strong. This explains the easy cleavage of graphite parallel to the (001) plane.

If an attempt is made in the usual way to assign a structural formula to the layer which represents a giant molecule, a formula as shown in Fig. 12.23a is obtained. A great number of such structural formulae are possible, which differ only in the positions of the double bonds. If any given C—C bonding picture is chosen out of these possibilities, one-third of all

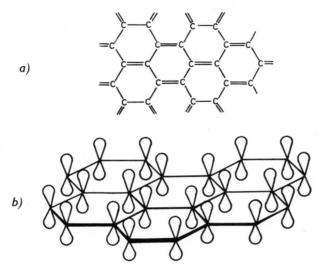

a)

b)

Fig. 12.23 (a) Example of one mesomeric form in a carbon layer of graphite. (b) The pπ-electron system of a carbon layer in graphite.

possible structures will have double bond, and two-thirds single bond character. All structures are mesomeric with one another and the real state is a superposition of all possible structures so that each bond can be formulated as $1\frac{1}{3}$ bond. The C—C bond length here (1·418 Å) fits in very well in the series of distances observed for single bonds (1·544 Å) (paraffins), double bonds (1·334 Å) (olefins), triple bonds (1·206 Å) (acetylenes) as well as the $1\frac{1}{2}$ bonding in benzene (1·39 Å) (Fig. 12.24).

The nature of single bonding in a graphite layer is described by the quantum state of an (sp^2)-hybrid. The corresponding three functions are directed to the three axes of an equilateral triangle and have large values in one axis direction.

Mesomerism or resonance comes about in that the fourth electron on each carbon atom is described by a p-orbital, the axis of which stands perpendicular to the plane of the layer (Fig. 12.23b). The function can laterally overlap with the three neighbouring p-functions. The p-electron has a choice of three p-electrons on the neighbouring atoms with which it can enter into a bond. The lateral extension of a p-function is essentially greater than may appear from the symbol, $\big\rangle$. The true

extension is represented in Fig. 5.1. Here is a mesomerism which extends over an entire layer. Thus, graphite is black and shows metallic conductivity within a layer. The electrical conductivity perpendicular to the layer is diminished[12.36] by a factor of 10^5. Between the layers there are only weak van der Waals' forces as is apparent from the large interlayer distance. The weakness of this bond permits the layers to slide over one another easily.

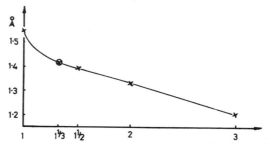

Fig. 12.24. C—C *distances in simple and multiple bonds.*

Because of this, graphite can be used as a lubricant, as for example, in the bearing surfaces of a high vacuum apparatus.

In the diamond lattice (Fig. 12.25a), one-half of the atoms form a face-centred cubic lattice. The other half can be obtained by a translation of the original lattice in the direction of the body diagonal by $\frac{1}{4}\frac{1}{4}\frac{1}{4}$. In this way, one-half of the octants, obtained by dividing the unit cell into cubes with edges equal to $a/2$, are body-centred and each C-atom is tetrahedrally surrounded by four other atoms. The inter-atomic distance of 1·5445 Å agrees quite well with the C—C distance in aliphatic compounds. The diamond structure is thus apparently held together by the same strong bonding forces as are responsible for the structure of aliphatic C-compounds. The diamond is, therefore, unusually hard. In addition, silicon, germanium, and grey tin also crystallize in the diamond structure, the A4-type.

In all these structures, a tetrahedral configuration is forced upon the atoms by the valence angles despite the voids which this leaves, for example, in the middle of the unit cell. The structure gives the impression of a framework. The 12-co-ordinate structures which would be expected for atoms of the same size would lead to hexagonal or cubic close packing and a substantially better filling of space.

The cleavability of diamond along the octahedral plane (111), depends on the fact (Fig. 12.25b) that along this plane relatively few bonds need be broken. Three-quarters of all bonds lie in the hatched, wavy planes.

If an electron is removed from a bonding pair by absorption of energy (light radiation or heat), substances which crystallize in the diamond

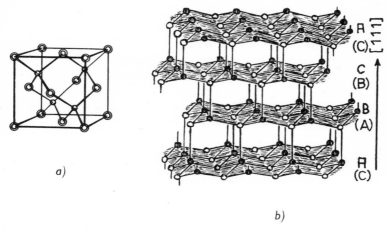

Fig. 12.25. (a) Diamond structure: ◎ first sub-lattice, ○ second sub-lattice. (b) Combination of the carbon atoms in diamond into puckered double-layers perpendicular to a cube diagonal [111].

structure become electrical conductors. A free electron (*n-conduction*) results, along with a positive electron defect which also wanders by accepting electrons from neighbouring electron pairs (*hole conduction, p-type conduction*):

$$
\begin{array}{ccccc}
& & e^{(-)} & & e^{(-)} \\
\text{Ge} \quad \text{Ge} & & \text{Ge} \quad\quad \text{Ge} & & \text{Ge} \quad \text{Ge} \\
\cdot\cdot \quad\quad \cdot\cdot & & \cdot\cdot \;(+)\; \cdot\cdot & & \cdot\cdot \quad \cdot\cdot \;(+) \\
\text{Ge}:\text{Ge}:\text{Ge}:\text{Ge} \longrightarrow \text{Ge}:\text{Ge} \quad\cdot\quad \text{Ge}:\text{Ge} \longrightarrow \text{Ge}:\text{Ge}:\text{Ge} \quad\cdot\quad \text{Ge} \\
\cdot\cdot \quad\quad \cdot\cdot & & \cdot\cdot \quad\quad \cdot\cdot & & \cdot\cdot \quad \cdot\cdot \\
\text{Ge} \quad \text{Ge} & & \text{Ge} \quad\quad \text{Ge} & & \text{Ge} \quad \text{Ge}
\end{array}
$$

Electrical conductivity in a chemically pure, stoichiometric semiconductor is called *intrinsic* conductivity. It consists here of both electronic conduction and hole conduction.

In contrast to metals, electrical conductivity in these materials increases strongly with temperature, since the reactions $C:C \rightarrow C^{(+)}C + e^- + 160$ kcal/mole (Si = 25, Ge = 17, and Sn = 2 kcal/mole) involve a dissociation energy. The dissociation process is therefore strongly temperature-dependent, following approximately an exponential law. The dissociation energy in the case of carbon is too high to be reached by thermal excitation. However, it can be achieved by X-ray irradiation. The energy to transfer an electron from the valence band into the so-called *conduction band* is designated as the *width of the forbidden zone* or the *energy gap*.

Silicon and germanium form, to a slight extent, mixed crystals with the neighbouring elements in the periodic system, for example, phosphorus or arsenic which have 5 valence electrons, aluminium and gallium with 3 instead of the 4 per atom of germanium or silicon. Since the substituting elements normally crystallize in a structure type other than that of diamond, the mixed crystal formation is referred to as *heterotypic*. The addition of impurities to a crystal is called '*doping*' in semiconductor technology. In this way it is possible to create a greater number of free electrons or holes leading to an appreciable increase in conductivity,

$$e^{(-)} \qquad\qquad e^{(-)}$$

Ge Ge	Ge Ge		Ge Ge	Ge Ge
.. ..	.. ..		.. ..	.. ..
Ge : Ge : P$^{(+)}$: Ge $\longrightarrow$	Ge : Ge : P$^{(+)}$: Ge	Ge : Al $\cdot$ Ge : Ge $\longrightarrow$	Ge : Al$^{(-)}$: Ge$^{(+)}$Ge
.. ..	.. ..		.. ..	.. ..
Ge Ge	Ge Ge		Ge Ge	Ge Ge

n-Conductivity

Hole (+) captured by P-atom

e$^-$ mobile

p-Conductivity

Hole (+) mobile

e$^-$ captured by Al-atom

and resulting in either purely electronic conductivity (n) or pure hole conductivity (p). Here the conductivity is no longer strongly temperature-dependent since the concentration of free electrons or holes is not determined by the temperature but rather by the concentration of added material.[12.44, 12.45]

Why is diamond a good insulator, and colourless, while graphite is a metallic conductor and black? The answer lies in the differences in bonding in these two materials.

The valence electron on the carbon atom of an aliphatic compound, or in diamond is characterized by an (sp^3)-hybrid state. Such an (sp^3)-hybrid function has large values in the direction of tetrahedral axes while in the opposite direction its values are smaller (Figs. 4.3 and 4.6). The bonds are strong, since two such hybrid orbitals on neighbouring C-atoms can overlap very well. The bonding electron pair is essentially localized between the two atoms and interacts only very weakly with electron pairs on neighbouring atoms; the backward direction of each such tetrahedral axis points into a void (e.g., the void in the body centre of the unit cell of diamond).

If an electron is dissociated from an electron pair, the remaining positive charge cannot be distributed over the entire structure since the electrons of the neighbouring pairs cannot be shifted back. The dissociation energy is thus substantially greater than in a mesomeric system such as graphite. If a p_z-electron is removed from a graphite orbital, electrons can flow in from three sides and the positive charge is then distributed over a large region of the carbon layer.

Under a pressure of 200 kbar, silicon slowly takes on the structure type of white tin (see below). When the pressure is released a cubic structure results, in which the silicon atoms have a distorted tetrahedral environment. The coupling is such that the filling of space is 10 per cent more efficient than in the diamond-type structure. If this structure is warmed to 200–600°C, it slowly assumes the wurtzite structure (see later).[12.46, 12.47] Under a pressure of 120 kbar, germanium also assumes the white-tin type structure.[12.47]

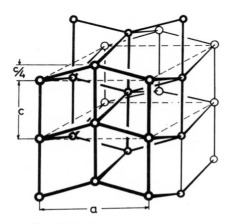

Fig. 12.26. Structure of tetragonal tin.

Lead forms a face-centred cubic structure just as do many other metals. Metallic tin crystallizes in a tetragonal unit cell in which the corners and the body centre are occupied by one-half of the atoms (Fig. 12.26). By translating this partial structure in the direction of an a-axis by $a/2$ and simultaneously in the c-direction by $c/4$, the remaining half of the atoms is reached. The surroundings of each atom is a distorted octahedron with four nearest neighbours at 3·016 Å and two somewhat further removed at 3·175 Å.

In the direction of the c-axis, p_z-orbitals can overlap very well as can also hybrid functions which have in addition some d_{3z^2-1} character. The shift of the four ligands perpendicular to the common (001)-plane with the central atom is frequently observed in compounds of Sn(II), Pb(II), Sb(III), Bi(III), the rare earths, and the actinides. This shift can be brought about by partial hybridization between p_x and d_{zx}, as well as p_y and d_{yz} and in compounds of the rare earths and actinides with a small amount of mixing of $f_{(5z^2-3)x}$ and $f_{(5z^2-3)y}$. From the bonding angle in tetragonal tin,

the coefficients of the linear combinations can be calculated. There result:
$\lambda = 0.995$ and $\sqrt{1 - \lambda^2} = 0.1$ so that the hybrid functions read:

$$\varphi_1 = 0.995\psi_x + 0.1\psi_{d_{zx}}$$

$$\varphi_2 = 0.1\psi_x - 0.995\psi_{d_{zx}}$$

$$\varphi_3 = 0.995\psi_y - 0.1\psi_{d_{yz}}$$

$$\varphi_4 = 0.1\psi_y + 0.995\psi_{d_{yz}}$$

In Fig. 12.27a is illustrated the hybrid function φ_1 in the zx-plane of the crystal. Figure 12.27b shows the same hybrid with $\lambda = \sqrt{1 - \lambda^2} = \cos(45°) = 0.707$, and therefore with the same proportion of p_x and $d_{zx}-$ functions. In addition to tin, germanium (over 120 kbar) and silicon (over $ca.$ 200 kbar) also crystallize in this structure.

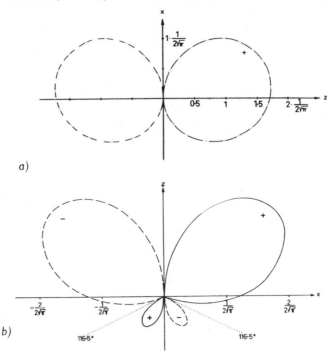

Fig. 12.27. $(p_x d_{zx})$-hybrid with (a) $\lambda = 0.1$, (b) $\lambda = \cos 45°$.

AlSb, above 120 kbar, GaSb at 90 kbar, and InSb also assume this structure.[12.47] It is assumed that the tin positions on the lattice are alternately occupied by Sb and by Al, Ga, or In.

White tin above 314°C and a pressure of 39 kbar transforms into a body-centred tetragonal structure, ($a = 3 \cdot 68$ Å, $c = 3 \cdot 48$ Å) having two atoms in the unit cell (co-ordinates 000, and $\frac{1}{2} \frac{1}{2} \frac{1}{2}$)[12.48] In this structure type the following hybrid functions fit in well: (a) ($p_z d_{3z^2 - 1}$) for the bonding of two neighbours in the direction of the c-axis, (b) the hybrid functions listed above, φ_1 to φ_4 with $\lambda \approx \cos(45°)$. These are directed toward the body diagonal of a cube which has been shortened by about 10 per cent in the c-axis direction.

13

Basic Structures of AB-Compounds (B-Types)

Especially in the older literature, structures were divided into types according to their stoichiometric composition using the following scheme:

Type	Compound	Example
A	Elements	Mg
B	AB	NaCl
C	AB_2	CaF_2
D	A_nB_m	Al_2O_3
E	More than two atoms without pronounced complex formation	$BaTiO_3$
F	Containing complexes with 2 or 3 atoms	$NaNO_2$
G	Containing complexes with 4 atoms	Na_2CO_3
H	Containing complexes with 5 atoms	Na_2SO_4
L	Alloys	Amalgams
M	Mixed Crystals	NaCl/AgCl
S	Silicates	Al_2SiO_5

13.1 Caesium Chloride Structure, CsCl (B2-type)

Both Cs and Cl atoms form primitive cubic sub-lattices, which are shifted relative to one another in the direction of the body diagonal by a translation of $\frac{1}{2}\frac{1}{2}\frac{1}{2}$. A body-centred cubic ordering results in which each atom is cubically surrounded by eight others (Fig. 13.1). Substances which crystallize in this structure type are:

(a) CsCl, CsBr, CsI.
(b) NH_4Cl, NH_4Br, NH_4I in their first low temperature forms below 184°, 138°, and −18° respectively.

(c) TlCl, TlBr, and in the red modification TlI also TlSb.

(d) MgTl, CaTl, CaCd, CaHg, LiTl, LiHg, LiAg (Zintl phases of the MgTl-type).[13.1]

(e) A large number of rare earth alloys, REX where X = Mg, Al, Cu, Ag, Au, Zn, Cd, Hg, In, Tl, Rh, Ir, Pd, Pt, as well as ScRu, ScCo, and ScNi.[13.2]

(f) Alloys of the β-brass type such as CuZn, AgZn, AuZn. The intermetallic compounds of groups (d), (e), and (f) have a certain phase width, which is especially wide in the β-brass group.

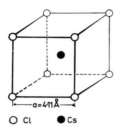

O Cl   ● Cs

Fig. 13.1. CsCl-*structure.*

(g) CsCN, CsSH, and TlCN, high-temperature forms with rotation of the anion.

(h) Under high pressure, the alkali halides with the exception of lithium salts. The transition for rubidium salts takes place at from 4 to 6 kbar, and for potassium and sodium salts at from 10 to 20 kbar.[13.3, 13.4, 13.5]

13.2 Rock-salt Structure, NaCl (B1-type)

This structure type is very widespread. The Na and Cl atoms, each taken alone, form face-centred cubic sub-lattices (Fig. 11.1). One sub-lattice can be generated from the other by a translation of $\frac{1}{2}$ 0 0. Each unit cell contains four sodium and four chlorine atoms. It is impossible to associate any given chlorine atom with a given sodium atom. Quite to the contrary, each sodium atom is octahedrally surrounded by six chlorine atoms and each chlorine atom similarly by six sodium atoms. The following are among the compounds which crystallize in this structure:

(a) Alkali halides (with the exception of CsCl, CsBr, and CsI).

(b) NH_4Cl, NH_4Br, and NH_4I in their high-temperature forms over 184°, 138°, and −18° respectively.

(c) Alkali hydrides.

(d) Alkaline earth chalcogenides (except Be-salts and MgTe).

(e) Transition metal oxides: TiO, VO, MnO, FeO, NiO.

(f) Nitrides and carbides of the Ti- and V-groups: TiN, TiC, VC, as well as CrN.

(g) LaN, LaP, LaAs, LaSb, LaBi, LaS, LaSe, LaTe, as well as many corresponding rare earth and actinide compounds; EuO,[13.2] UO, PuO, and AmO.

(h) AgF, AgCl, AgBr, CdO, and above 3·3 kbar also AgI.[13.3]

(i) PbS, PbSe, PbTe, SnTe, SnAs, as well as GeTe in the high-temperature form.

(j) RbAu and CsAu.[13.6]

(k) Under high pressure (pressures given in parentheses in kbar): AlP, AlAs, GaP, InP (133), InAs (102)[12.46, 13.7] ZnO (100),[13.8] CdS (33), CdSe (32), CdTe (36),[13.9] InTe (28 at 150° and 13 at 670°C),[13.10] CuI (16).[13.11]

(l) High-temperature forms of compounds such as: CaNH, KSH, KSeH, $RbNH_2$, and KCN.

Substances which crystallize in the same structure are called *isotypic*.

13.3 Derivatives of the NaCl-type Structure

It is not essential that the sodium positions of an NaCl-lattice be always occupied by the same type of atom. Oxides having a mixture of monovalent and tervalent metals crystallize easily in an NaCl-type structure just as do the oxides of bivalent metals. In cases such as this, one differentiates in principle between various modes of occupation of the metal sub-lattice.

(a) The metal atoms can be statistically distributed so that the symmetry of the rock-salt structure superficially remains. Examples include: γ-$LiTlO_2$, α-$NaTlO_2$,[13.12] $NaEuO_2$, Na_2CeO_3, Na_3UO_4, and Na_4MeO_5 with Me = U, Np, Pu, Am,[13.13] $LiBiS_2$,[13.14] $NaBiS_2$, $KBiS_2$,[13.15] $LiYS_2$, $NaLaS_2$,[13.12] and the high-temperature forms of $AgBiS_2$, $AgBiSe_2$,[13.16] and $AgSbTe_2$.[13.17]

(b) The two metal atoms can occupy alternately the planes ABCABC... of the face-centred metal sub-lattice, as they follow one after the other along a body diagonal (Fig. 12.4). The crystal is then rhombohedral, since it is either compressed or expanded parallel to the [111] direction. Examples are: $LiNiO_2$,[13.18] $AgBiS_2$, and $AgBiSe_2$[13.16] at intermediate temperatures, and $TlSbTe_2$ as well as $TlBiTe_2$.[13.19]

(c) More frequently those planes are alternately occupied which follow one after the other along a cube edge. This edge then becomes a unique axis and the crystal takes on tetragonal symmetry. Examples are $LiMe^{III}O_2$ where Me^{III} = Fe, In, Tl, and the rare earths[13.14] (Fig. 28.1a, left side).

Substitution can also take place in other ways. In Li_3SbO_4 and Li_3NbO_4 there are three monovalent atoms and one pentavalent atom. Both compounds are looked upon as derivatives of the rock-salt structure. Nevertheless, the distribution of lithium and antimony or niobium atoms among the sodium positions is so complex[13.20] that we shall not discuss it here more fully.

The rock-salt structure is also frequently stable when the number of metal atoms is less than the number of non-metallic atoms. Some of the metal positions are then unoccupied and remain empty. Such a *vacancy* is designated in chemical literature by a square, ($\square$). As an example one may mention the compound, Mg_6MnO_8 which can be better written as $Mg_6Mn\square O_8$.[13.21] The vacancies and the tetravalent manganese atoms bring about a slight displacement in the positions of the oxygen atoms. Another example is the complete, heterotypic mixed crystal formation between $LiCl$ and $MgCl_2$. With each added Mg atom a vacancy is created in the Li-sub-lattice of LiCl. The mixed crystals can thus also be described by the formula, $Li_{1-x}Mg_{x/2}\square_{x/2}Cl$ where $0 \leqslant x \leqslant 1$. The $MgCl_2$ structure itself can thus be looked upon as a derivative of the rock-salt structure and can be formulated, $Mg\square Cl_2$. It crystallizes in the $CdCl_2$-type structure (see later).

13.4 Zinc Blende Structure, ZnS (B3-type)

If, in the diamond lattice (Fig. 12.25), half of the carbon atoms which belong to one face-centred ordering, are replaced by zinc, and the other half by sulphur, the zinc blende structure results. Here zinc is tetrahedrally surrounded by four sulphur atoms and correspondingly each sulphur atom is tetrahedrally surrounded by four zinc atoms (Fig. 13.2a). If the

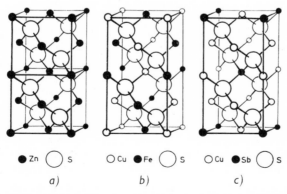

● Zn ○ S   ○ Cu ● Fe ○ S   ○ Cu ● Sb ○ S

a)   b)   c)

*Fig. 13.2. (a) Structure of zinc blende, ZnS. (b) Structure of chalcopyrite, $CuFeS_2$.
(c) Structure of famatinite, Cu_3SbS_4.*

sulphur or the zinc atoms are considered along a plane perpendicular to a body diagonal, [111], the ordering of the planes on each sub-lattice is ABCABC (Fig. 12.25b). This must be so, since each sub-lattice by itself has face-centred cubic ordering.

13.5 Wurtzite Structure, ZnS (B4-type)

The wurtzite structure results when the tetrahedra in the layers of the zinc blende structure illustrated above are rotated by 60° around the [111] direction relative to one another. It is then again possible to have each atom tetrahedrally surrounded by four atoms of the other type. If the zinc and sulphur sub-lattices are considered separately, the ordering is geometrically that in a hexagonal close-packed structure; the sequence of layers is ABAB... (Fig. 13.3a, b). It is interesting that in the zinc blende

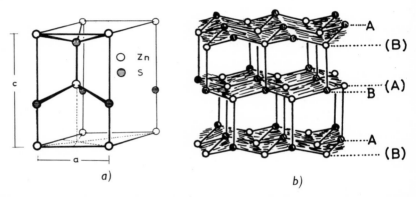

a)   *b)*

Fig. 13.3. (a) Hexagonal unit cell of wurtzite. (b) Division of the wurtzite crystal into layers perpendicular to the c-axis.

structure, six-membered rings occur only in the so-called chair form within a layer while in the wurtzite structure, both chair- and boat-form rings (in the direction of the c-axis), are found. The two structures are very closely related. They are thus referred to as *homoeotectic*, meaning structures having similar construction principles. For example, this term refers to binary compounds of the general type, $A_m B_n$ in which atom A has the same number of nearest A and B neighbours and atom B the same number of nearest A and B neighbours. Two structures which obey this principle are homoeotectic. Examples of homoeotectic structures are: (a) cubic and hexagonal close packing, (b) the zinc blende and wurtzite structures, (c) layer structures of the cadmium halogenide type, and (d) Laves phases (see later).

Table 13.1 lists several compounds which crystallize in either the zinc blende or wurtzite structures. One can see that in all cases eight electrons are available per atom pair just as in the diamond structure. The cationic and anionic components of these compounds with only few exceptions are symmetrically placed relative to the carbon group in the periodic system (*Grimm–Sommerfield Rule*).

Exceptions to this rule include MnS, MnSe, MnTe, NH_4F, and CuH which crystallize in these structures, and AgF, AgCl, AgBr (NaCl-type structures) and the gold halides which do not show these tetrahedral structures.

Table 13.1. *Inter-atomic distances in several zinc blende and wurtzite structures*

Compound	Distance (Å)	Compound	Distance (Å)
AgI	2·815	CuI	2·620
CdTe	2·807	ZnTe	2·642
InSb	2·805	GaSb	2·640
SnSn	2·810	$\frac{1}{2}$(Ge + Sn)	2·630
CuBr	2·460	MgTe	2·76
ZnSe	2·447	AlSb	2·657
GaAs	2·448	$\frac{1}{2}$(Si + Sn)	2·581
GeGe	2·450	CuCl	2·346
AlP	2·360	ZnS	2·345
SiSi	2·352	GaP	2·360
		$\frac{1}{2}$(Ge + Si)	2·401
BeO	1·645		
BN	1·565	AlN	1·87
CC	1·544	β-SiC	1·887

Most of the compounds listed in Table 13.1 crystallize in the zinc blende structure. The wurtzite lattice is favoured when the non-metallic atom is small and strongly electronegative, as in the compounds BeO, ZnO, AlN, and GaN.

A surprising observation is that the inter-atomic distance remains relatively constant when the compounds are composed of elements from the same period of the periodic system (compare, e.g., AgI, CdTe, InSb, and Sn).

13.6 Derivatives of the ZnS Structures

Since substances having diamond-like structures are unusually important for semiconductor technology, these substances have been extensively studied during the last two decades. Here only the essential structural principles will be referred to. These tetrahedral structures have been extensively treated in monographs by E. Parthé[13.22] and N. A. Goryunova.[13.23]

The zinc blende type structure with a statistical distribution of metallic atoms over the Zn-positions is observed in compounds such as: $CuSi_2P_3$, $CuGe_2P_3$,[13.24] $Cu_2Me^{IV}P_3$ where Me^{IV} = Ge, Sn and X = S, Se, Te.[13.25]

If two zinc atoms are replaced in an ordered fashion by one tervalent and one monovalent atom, both of which prefer a tetrahedral configuration, the structure of chalcopyrite is obtained (Fig. 13.2b). The copper atoms can be replaced by silver and the iron atoms by aluminium, gallium, indium, and sometimes thallium.[13.26] Other combinations are also possible, for example:

$$Me^{II}GeP_2 \quad \text{where } Me^{II} = Mg, Zn, Cd$$

$$ZnMe^{IV}As_2 \quad \text{where } Me^{IV} = Si, Ge, Sn.^{13.24}$$

If two iron atoms in chalcopyrite are replaced by one Cu^I and one Sb^V-atom, the structure of famatinite, Cu_3SbS_4, is obtained (Fig. 13.2c). The distribution of metal atoms over Zn-positions here is characteristic also for other representatives of the same formula type. Substitution can proceed still further. Derivatives are also known, having statistical (e.g., $AgInS_2$) and ordered (e.g., Cu_3AsS_4) distributions of metal atoms over the Zn-positions of the wurtzite structure. In addition, since mixed crystal formation is easily possible in these structures, the scope for variation is very wide.

In tetrahedral structures, vacancy formation is easy when it is required by the stoichiometry. Thus γ-Ga_2S_3 = $Ga_2\square S_3$ crystallizes in a zinc blende type structure with a statistical distribution of gallium atoms over the zinc positions. In the same way, β-Ga_2S_3 crystallizes in the wurtzite type with a statistical distribution of gallium over the zinc positions.[13.27] An ordered distribution of gallium atoms is observed in α-Ga_2S_3.[13.28] In these compounds, the number of electrons is such that each S-atom is surrounded by four electron pairs which are either in common with neighbouring Ga-atoms or are lone electron pairs, belonging only to sulphur. The same holds also for other representatives of this type, such as $HgGa_2Te_4$[13.29] (zinc blende, statistical distribution), $ZnAl_2S_4$[13.29] (wurtzite), the high temperature forms of Cu_2HgI_4 and Ag_2HgI_4[13.30] and others with sometimes still more complex distributions of the metal atoms.

The zinc blende structure with vacancies in the metal sub-lattice is also formed by selenides and tellurides of the rare earths, such as Sc_2Se_3, Er_2Se_3, Lu_2Se_3, Er_2Te_3, and Y_2Te_3. With the lighter element, sulphur, a defect structure is formed in Yb_2S_3, which again derives from the wurtzite structure.[13.2, 13.31]

14

Explanation of the Basic AB Structures

14.1 Model of the Ionic Structure

The chemist has long been accustomed to describing the typical salt as an ionic structure since many of the properties of a salt can be considered and explained by accepting the existence of positively and negatively charged atoms or atomic groupings. Thus, historically, the ionic model was developed, especially by V. M. Goldschmidt[14.1] and L. Pauling[5.3] and it was successful in explaining the crystal structure of many salt-like compounds. Nevertheless, the ionic model represents only an approximation. It is, however, very useful since it is simple and lends itself to mathematical treatment. Application of the ionic model has proceeded historically in the following manner.

14.2 Ionic Radii

X-ray analysis permits accurate measurement of the distances between atoms in a crystal. One of the first tests of this method is to see whether one can assign definite radii to the ions (assumed to be spherical) in a crystal. If this is the case, then the difference of the inter-atomic distances between a cation and an anion must remain the same if either the anion or the cation is replaced.

NaF	2·315 Å	KF	2·673 Å	NaF	2·315 Å	NaCl	2·8199 Å
NaCl	2·8199 Å	KCl	3·1464 Å	KF	2·673 Å	KCl	3·1464 Å
	0·505 Å		0·473 Å		0·358 Å		0·3265 Å

From these examples, the assumption appears to hold true at least to some extent. Landé, in 1920, first compared inter-atomic distances in several Mg- and Mn-chalcogenides which crystallize in the rock salt type structure.

MgO	2·1056 Å	MnO	2·2224 Å	0·12 Å difference
MgS	2·6017 Å	MnS	2·6118 Å	
MgSe	2·726 Å	MnSe	2·724 Å	Anions in contact

In the oxides, the radius of the Mn-ion is approximately 0·12 Å greater than is that of the Mg-ion. Despite that, the sulphides and selenides of these two elements have the same inter-atomic distances. Landé explained this by saying that in the sulphides and selenides the anions touch one another. The small difference between the radii of Mg^{2+} and Mn^{2+} thus lies within the variation permitted for the filling of space between anions by cations. The ionic radii of S^{2-} and Se^{2-} are thus known; namely, they are simply equal to half the distance between two neighbouring anions.

Wasastjerna, in 1923, derived from the optical properties of alkali fluorides and alkaline earth oxides a method of apportioning the inter-atomic distance between the metal ion and anion. The theoretical basis of this derivation is no longer tenable. For the radii of F^- and O^{2-} he found 1·33 and 1·32 Å respectively which fortunately aided V. M. Goldschmidt[14.1] in deriving other atomic radii from known inter-atomic distances in crystals, so that the sum of the ionic radii so obtained agree reasonably well with observed inter-atomic distances. Extended by newer results, these radii are reproduced in Fig. 14.1 and Table 14.1.[14.2] They apply for co-ordination number 6 and octahedral surroundings. For other co-ordination numbers, such as 8 in the CsCl-type structures, the inter-atomic distance and also the ionic radius is altered. The curve of Fig. 14.2 was obtained from experimental values and gives an average value of the change in the atomic or ionic sizes with the co-ordination number. The 12-co-ordinate radius serves as the reference point for the curve. As experience shows, Goldschmidt radii are only approximate. Even with the same co-ordination number a variation is observed in the radius with different lattice types.[14.3]

The following regularities in the ionic radii can be derived from Fig. 14.1 and Table 14.1.

(a) Within a given group of the periodic system, e.g., the alkali or alkaline earth metals, the ionic radius increases with increasing atomic number. This is understandable, since with increasing atomic number more and more electrons are built into the atom.

(b) Within a given period of the periodic system the ionic radius decreases with increasing atomic number (i.e., with increasing positive charge). This comes about for two reasons. First, with increasing nuclear charge, electrons are drawn more closely to the nucleus. Second, the attractive force between two oppositely charged ions increases quadratically with ionic charge according to Coulomb's law. Thus, for example, the ions in MgO are bound together four times as strongly as in LiF. An exception to this rule is observed in going from the monovalent halides to doubly charged anions. There, only small differences are observed in the ionic radii. The increase in size of the anion with lower atomic number is extensively compensated by the stronger attractive forces between more highly charged ions.

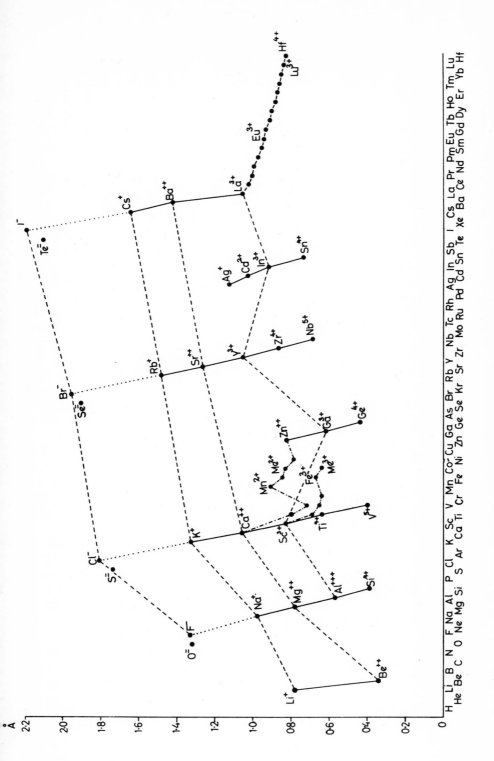

Fig. 14.1. Goldschmidt ionic radii.

Table 14.1. Ionic radii for co-ordination number 6

1+	2+	3+	4+	5+	1+	2+	3+	4+	2−	1−
Li	Be								O	F
0·78	0·34								1·32	1·33
0·60	0·31								1·40	1·36
0·60	0·44								1·76	1·36
Na	Mg						Al	Si	S	Cl
0·98	0·78						0·57	0·39	1·74	1·81
0·95	0·65						0·50	0·41	1·84	1·81
0·95	0·82						0·72	0·65	2·19	1·81
K	Ca	Sc	Ti	V	Cu	Zn	Ga	Ge	Se	Br
1·33	1·06	0·83	0·64	0·4		0·83	0·62	0·44	1·91	1·96
1·33	0·99	0·81	0·68	0·59	0·96	0·74	0·62	0·53	1·98	1·95
1·33	1·18	1·06	0·96	0·88	0·96	0·88	0·81	0·76	2·32	1·95
Rb	Sr	Y	Zr	Nb	Ag	Cd	In	Sn	Te	I
1·49	1·27	1·06	0·87	0·69	1·13	1·03	0·92	0·74	2·11	2·20
1·48	1·13	0·93	0·80	0·70	1·26	0·97	0·81	0·71	2·21	2·16
1·48	1·32	1·20	1·09	1·00	1·26	1·14	1·04	0·96	2·50	2·16

Cs	Ba		Lu	Hf	Ta	Au	Hg	Tl	Pb
1·65	1·43		0·84	0·82	0·68		1·12	1·05	0·84
1·69	1·35		0·93	0·81	0·73	1·37	1·10	0·95	0·84
1·69	1·53					1·37	1·25	1·15	1·06

	La	Ce	Pr	Nd	Pm	Sm	Eu	Gd	Tb	Dy	Ho	Er	Tm	Yb
3+	3+	3+	3+	3+	3+	3+	3+	3+	3+	3+	3+	3+	3+	3+
	1·06	1·03	1·01	1·00	0·98	0·96	0·95	0·94	0·92	0·91	0·89	0·88	0·87	0·86

Ca	Sc	Ti	V	Cr	Mn	Fe	Co	Ni	Cu	Zn
2+		2+	2+	2+	2+	2+	2+	2+	2+	2+
1·06		0·80	0·72		0·91	0·85	0·83	0·79		0·83

First row: Goldschmidt radii.[14.1]

Second row: Actual Pauling crystal radii.[5.3]

Third row: Univalent Pauling radii.[5.3]

Radii of the rare earths after Templeton and Dauben.[14.2b]

Radii of the transition metals after von Santen and von Wieringen[14.2d] and, in part, Hush and Pryce.[14.2e]

(c) With one and the same element, the ionic radius decreases with increasing positive charge, for example:

$$Ti^{2+}\ 0.80, \quad Ti^{3+}\ 0.69, \quad Ti^{4+}\ 0.64\ \text{Å}.$$

(d) The ionic radius is smaller with transition elements than with elements of the comparable principal group. Compare:

$$K^+\ 1.3\ \text{Å}, \quad Rb^+\ 1.5\ \text{Å}, \quad Ca^{2+}\ 1.0\ \text{Å}, \quad Sr^{2+}\ 1.2\ \text{Å}$$

$$Cu^+\ 0.9\ \text{Å}, \quad Ag^+\ 1.2\ \text{Å}, \quad Zn^{2+}\ 0.8\ \text{Å}, \quad Cd^{2+}\ 1.0\ \text{Å}.$$

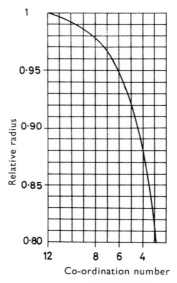

Fig. 14.2. *Average alteration of atomic and ionic radii with change in co-ordination number.*

The newly added *d*-electrons belong to the outermost shell of the ions. The shielding of the nuclear charge is therefore of necessity smaller than that which corresponds to an increase in nuclear charge by ten units. The addition of *d*-electrons must therefore lead to a diminution in the ionic radius.

(e) On this same basis the radii of rare earth and actinide ions decrease regularly with increasing atomic number. Indeed, the so-called *lanthanide contraction* is of such a magnitude that those elements immediately following the rare earths (hafnium, tantalum, and tungsten) have nearly the same ionic radii as their lighter homologues, zirconium, niobium, and molybdenum.

(f) On the basis of rules (a) and (b), two cations which are diagonal to one another in the periodic table have almost the same ionic radius. This diagonal relationship is especially pronounced in the first two periods. Thus Li^+ and Mg^{2+} have the same ionic radius, 0·78 Å. The ionic radii of Na^+ and Ca^{2+} already show a slight difference (Na^+ 0·98 Å, Ca^{2+} 1·06 Å). As a result of this relationship, lithium can often replace magnesium, and sodium can replace calcium in salt-like crystals. The chemical similarity between beryllium and aluminium as well as between boron and silicon is also (see later) partially determined by this diagonal relationship.

If the Goldschmidt or the actual crystal radii of Pauling are applied to AB-compounds with the zinc blende or wurtzite structure, the sum of the radii no longer gives the inter-atomic distance. In addition, the rule that in an isoelectronic series the inter-atomic distance becomes essentially smaller with increasing valence, no longer holds. To eliminate this problem, Pauling[5.3] derived the so-called 'tetrahedral or covalent radii' which do apply to the above-named structure types. See Table 14.2.

Table 14.2. Covalent tetrahedral radii (acc. to L. Pauling)

	Be	B	C	N	O	F
	1·06	0·88	0·77	0·70	0·66	0·64
	Mg	Al	Si	P	S	Cl
	1·40	1·26	1·17	1·10	1·04	0·99
Cu	Zn	Ga	Ge	As	Se	Br
1·35	1·31	1·26	1·22	1·18	1·14	1·11
Ag	Cd	In	Sn	Sb	Te	I
1·52	1·48	1·44	1·40	1·36	1·32	1·28
	Hg	Tl				
	1·48	1·45				

14.3 Derivation of Co-ordination Numbers

The assumption of somewhat constant ionic radii can be used to deduce the co-ordination polyhedra in an ionic lattice. The space between a series of anions must be filled by a cation. If the cation is smaller, it is possible for it to pull a part of the anions toward it and gain energy in the process. The structure must then change. If the cation is larger than the cavity, the anions can separate and move apart without requiring the crystal structure to collapse. The 'small cation boundary' is thus relatively sharp in contrast to the 'large cation' case.

Because of electrostatic attraction (Fig. 14.3), a cation, depending on the size ratios, can be surrounded by:

   (a) three anions, forming an equilateral triangle with the cation at the centre,

(b) four anions in a tetrahedral arrangement,

(c) six anions which surround the cation octahedrally,

(d) eight anions, grouped cubically about the cation.

It is scarcely possible for 12-co-ordination to occur in ionic structures, since in this case at least some nearest-neighbour ions would have like

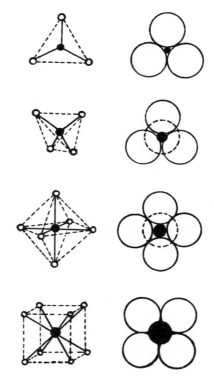

Fig. 14.3. The usual polyhedra for co-ordination numbers 3, 4, 6, and 8.

signs. From geometric considerations, the radius ratio, r_{cation}/r_{anion} should determine the co-ordination number. If the anions touch one another, the following relationship holds for an octahedral arrangement, when R_A and R_K refer to the radius of the anion and cation respectively (Fig. 14.4a):

$$(R_A + R_K)^2 = 2R_A^2$$

so that

$$R_K/R_A = 0.414$$

For an NaCl-structure the following relationship must hold, according to the electrostatic model with spherical ions: $R_K/R_A \leqslant 0.414$. With the anion as central ion, one obtains $R_A/R_K \leqslant 0.414$, or for both possibilities,

$$0.414 \leqslant R_K/R_A \leqslant 1/0.414.$$

Similarly, one obtains for cubic ordering, such as in the CsCl-structure (Fig. 14.4b):

$$(R_A + R_K)^2 = 3R_A{}^2$$

$$R_K/R_A = 0.732$$

A CsCl-structure can thus be stable only if $0.732 \leqslant R_K/R_A \leqslant 1/0.732$.

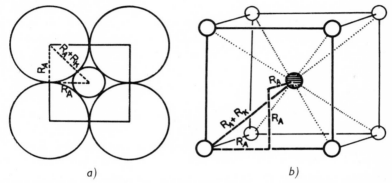

Fig. 14.4. Radius ratios with anion–anion contact for (a) octahedral, (b) cubic arrangements.

Limiting ratios for individual co-ordination numbers are summarized in Table 14.3.

Table 14.3. Radius ratios and co-ordination numbers

Co-ordination no.	Configuration	Radius ratio	Examples		
3		0.15	BN-type	BN	(0.15)
4		0.22	ZnS-type	MgTe	(0.37)
				BeO	(0.26)
6		0.41	NaCl-type	LiI	(0.35)
				CaS	(0.61)
				SrS	(0.73)
8		0.73	CsCl-type	CsCl	(0.91)
				CsI	(0.75)
(12)		1.0	(closest sphere packing)		

Even with a radius ratio over 0·732, the NaCl-lattice is strongly preferred over the CsCl-lattice (see also Table 14.4). Thus, the radius rule alone cannot determine co-ordination number or structure type.

Table 14.4. Radius ratios of several compounds with the rock-salt structure

LiF	0·59	NaF	0·73	KF	1·00	RbF	1·11	CsF	1·25
LiCl	0·43	NaCl	0·54	KCl	0·74	RbCl	0·82		
MgO	0·59	CaO	0·80	SrO	0·96	BaO	1·10		

The fact that in LiI the radius ratio $R_K/R_A = 0.35$, falls below the prescribed boundary (0·41) for octahedral ordering clearly shows that the electrostatic model does not rigorously hold. Figure 14.5 gives the relative sizes of the ions in the alkali halides structures.

14.4 Lattice Energy

The ionic model also permits calculation of the energy which would be freed when a gram atom of cation (e.g., Na^+) and a gram atom of anion (e.g., Cl^-) condense from the gaseous state to form a crystal. If two ions of charge ze infinitely far from one another are brought together to a distance r_{12}, the potential energy of this ion pair is:

$$+\frac{z_1 z_2 e^2}{r_{12}} \quad \text{(Energy added to system is positive).}$$

The ions approach until the outermost regions of their electron sheaths sufficiently interpenetrate. Then a repulsive force takes over. This force increases very rapidly as the inter-atomic distance becomes still smaller. There is thus an equilibrium distance determined by an equilibrium between these two forces. The repulsive force arises from mutual repulsion of the two atomic nuclei, the positive charges becoming more poorly shielded from one another with increasing penetration. From the compressibility of a salt, this force is estimated to be approximately proportional to $1/r^{n+1}$, where $n = 9$ for ions of medium weight. In order to overcome the repulsive force, an energy of $+(b_{12}e^2)/r_{12}^n$, (b_{12} is a constant) is required. Altogether, to bring the two ions 1 and 2 together, from infinity to a distance r_{12}, an energy of:

$$V_{12} = \frac{z_1 z_2 e^2}{r_{12}} + \frac{b_{12} e^2}{r_{12}^n} \quad \text{is required.}$$

For the approach of a third ion to ions 1 and 2, corresponding expressions, V_{13} and V_{23} are obtained. If a mole of such ionic crystal is now formed, all such expressions, V_{nm} must be summed. This summation is

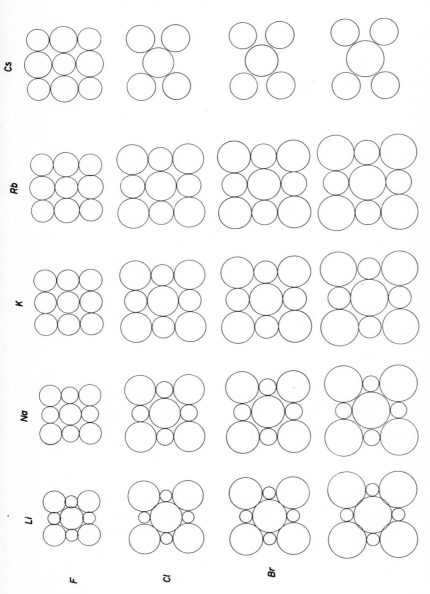

Fig. 14.5. Sizes of the ions in alkali halides, represented on a (100)-plane of the rock-salt and a (110) plane of the CsCl structure. Radii are according to Goldschmidt.

generally not simple and was originally carried out by Madelung[14.4] for a series of lattice types. He obtained for the lattice energy:

$$U = \sum_{m,\,n} V_{nm} = -\frac{Ae^2z^2N_L}{R} + \frac{Be^2N_L}{R^n}.$$

In this formula:

R = the cation–anion distance in the crystal.

A = the so-called *Madelung Constant*. It specifies the factor by which the attractive energy in a crystal is greater than that energy which is freed when the mole of ion pairs whose inter-ionic distance equals R, is formed in the gaseous state. In Table 14.5 some Madelung factors are given.

B = an experimentally determined constant.

n = a constant whose magnitude can be estimated from the compressibility (~ 9).

Table 14.5. Madelung factors based on the shortest cation–anion distance

Structure type	A	Distance used
NaCl	1·747565	Na–Cl
CsCl	1·762675	Cs–Cl
ZnS blende	1·638055	Zn–S
ZnS wurtzite	1·641322	Zn–S
CaF_2	5·038785	Ca–F
Cu_2O	4·442475	Cu–O
$CaTiO_3$	24·774936	Ti–O

Naor[14.5] has shown that it is possible to calculate the Madelung factors in more complex structures by means of a linear relation between the Madelung constants of simpler structures. For example, the following relationship holds for the fluorspar structure type (see later):

$$A_{CaF_2} = A_{CsCl} + 2A_{\text{Zinc blende}}$$

$$5\cdot0388 = 1\cdot7627 + 2 \times 1\cdot6380$$

Depending on the value adopted for the repulsive potential, various expressions are obtained for the final sum in the above-mentioned equation. The lattice energy can be experimentally determined with the help of the *Born–Haber* cycle[14.6] (Fig. 14.6). The given gaseous ion is converted into a monatomic gas. Here the ionization energy, I, of the metal atom is freed, while the electron affinity, E, of the non-metal must be supplied. In condensing the gaseous metal to a solid metal, the heat of sublimation, S, is set free. The transition of the monatomic non-metallic gas to a diatomic molecule gives up $\frac{1}{2}D$, one-half the dissociation energy. If now the metal and non-metallic element are allowed to react, a crystal is formed giving up the heat of reaction, Q. The following equation then describes the total process:

$$U = I - E + S + \tfrac{1}{2}D + Q.$$

All values on the right side are known, although the electron affinity can be determined up to now in only a few cases. If calculated and observed lattice energies are compared, only with alkali halides is sufficiently good agreement of 1–2 per cent obtained. Even with the alkaline earths, greater discrepancies are observed and with heavy metal compounds (AgCl,

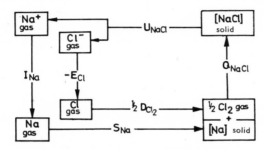

Fig. 14.6. Diagram of the Born–Haber Cycle.

PbSe), the discrepancy can easily be 10 per cent and more. The ionic model can give a good representation of the true bonding state only for alkali halides.

14.5 Univalent Radii

Pauling has derived theoretically the distribution of the distance between anion and cation into two ionic radii. The radial component of the eigenfunction for valence electrons contains the expression,

$$\frac{Z_{eff}r}{a_0 n}$$

With n constant, i.e., in an isoelectronic series such as O^{2-}, F^-, Ne, Na^+, Mg^{2+}, the same value of the orbital is observed when the product $Z_{eff}r = C_n$ is a constant. The effective nuclear charge, Z_{eff}, is equal to the true nuclear charge, Z, diminished by a shielding constant, S, which remains the same in a given isoelectronic series, $Z_{eff} = Z - S$. In the neon series, $S = 4.52$. The relative radius (R_1) of the ions is then given by the expression: $R_1 = C_n/(Z - S)$.

If, for example, the observed inter-ionic distance in an NaF-crystal is

13

divided between the two ions, the following equations are applied:

$$R_{Na^+} = C_n/(11 - 4.52), \quad R_{F^-} = C_n/(9 - 4.52) \quad \text{and} \quad R_{Na^+} + R_{F^-} = 2.31.$$

The solution of these simultaneous equations gives

$$C_n = 6.11, \quad R_{Na^+} = 0.95, \quad \text{and} \quad R_{F^-} = 1.36 \text{ Å}.$$

In a similar way, C_n and the radii for the other alkali and halide ions can be obtained. The sizes of multivalent ions such as O^{2-} and Mg^{2+} can now be calculated with reference to the sizes of the isoelectronic ions R_{F^-} and R_{Na^+}, since the C_n's are fixed. These radii are referred to as *univalent radii*. Multivalent ions would show these radii in a crystal structure if they had the co-ordination number 6, and if the attractive forces corresponded to those of singly charged ions. The contraction, brought about by the higher ionic charge, can be calculated from the equation for the lattice energy. The real inter-ionic distance (R) is fixed by the condition that the first derivative of the lattice energy with respect to distance becomes zero.

$$\frac{dU}{dR} = 0 = \frac{Ae^2 z^2 N_L}{R^2} - \frac{nBe^2 N_L}{R^{n+1}}$$

from which:

$$\frac{Az^2}{R^2} = \frac{nB}{R^{n+1}}.$$

This equation can also be used to calculate B when R is known:

$$B = \frac{Az^2 R^{n-1}}{n}.$$

This factor is required to calculate the lattice energy. Here, however, the equation is applied to determine the dependence of R on the charge, z. Therefore, the equation is written first for $z = 1$, and then for any z and the two equations are divided by one another:

$$\frac{ARz_1^2{}^2}{A1^2 R_z^2} = \frac{nBR_1^{n+1}}{nBR_z^{n+1}}$$

giving

$$R_z = R_1 z^{-2/n-1}.$$

The real radii can thus be easily calculated from univalent radii, R_1. In Table 14.1 and Fig. 14.7 univalent radii and the calculated, real radii for co-ordination number 6 are depicted. These latter are only slightly different from Goldschmidt radii. However, the numbers given for the higher valent ions do not have a real meaning; they are merely for approximate calculations of atomic distances. This is because the ionic model is a good approximation only for monovalent ions.

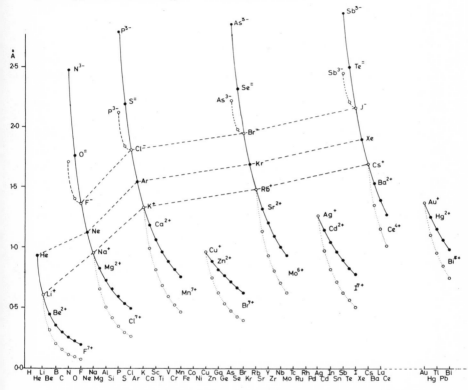

Fig. 14.7.   Univalent radii (•) and real (∘) radii for co-ordination number 6, according to Pauling[5.3]

Zachariasen[14.2h] later checked the univalent radii, compared them to experiment and obtained still better values for them. He also derived applicable formulas for the case where the crystal is made up of ions having different charges. However, both the ionic radii of Goldschmidt and those of Pauling and Zachariasen are inexact and have limited region of validity.[14.2a−h, 14.3]

14.6 Interpretation of Physical Properties by the Ionic Model

It is possible to understand several physical properties of salt-like compounds by using the ionic model. If, in the equation for the lattice energy U, the expression

$$B = \frac{Az^2 R^{n-1}}{n}$$

is inserted, there results

$$U = -\frac{Ae^2 z^2 N_L}{R}\left(1 - \frac{1}{n}\right).$$

The second term in the parentheses amounts to only about 10 per cent of the lattice energy (since $n \sim 10$) and can be ignored to a first approximation.

(a) The lattice energy becomes smaller with increasing inter-ionic distance, R. U is proportional to $1/R$.

$$\text{LiF: } R = 2\cdot01 \text{ Å}, \quad U = 240 \text{ kcal/mole}$$
$$\text{CsI: } R = 3\cdot95 \text{ Å}, \quad U = 126 \text{ kcal/mole}.$$

(b) The lattice energy is especially strongly dependent on the magnitude of the ionic charge. U is proportional to z^2.

$$\text{LiF: } \quad R = 2\cdot01 \text{ Å}, \quad z = 1, \quad U = 240 \text{ kcal/mole}$$
$$\text{MgO: } R = 2\cdot10 \text{ Å}, \quad z = 2, \quad U = 940 \text{ kcal/mole}.$$

(c) If the lattice energy is high, the crystal will generally be hard and will melt only at high temperatures. Table 14.6 and Fig. 14.8 confirm these generalizations.

Table 14.6. Hardness, melting point, and solubility of crystals as a function of the inter-ionic distance and ionic charge

Crystal	Distance Me–X (Å)	Hardness (Mohs' scale)	M.P. °C	Solubility (g/100cc)
MgO	2·106	6·5	2800	0·0006
CaO	2·405	4·5	2580	
SrO	2·580	3·5	2430	
BaO	2·762	3·3	1923	
MgS	2·602	5·0		
CaS	2·845	4·0		
BaS	3·194	3·0		
CaSe	2·96	3·2		
CaTe	3·173	2·9		
NaF	2·310	3·2	990	4·0
ScN	2·22	7–8		insol.
TiC	2·159	8–9	3140	insol.

Figure 14.8 illustrates how well potassium and rubidium halides follow these rules. With the sodium, and especially the lithium salts, the anions are in contact and so departures from the rules occur. Likewise, the caesium salts show irregularities on going from NaCl-type to the CsCl-type structure (CsCl, CsBr, CsI).

When a crystal is dissolved in water, on the one hand the lattice energy, U, must be added in order to decompose the crystal into ions. On the other hand the hydration energy, L, is given up. This latter energy results from

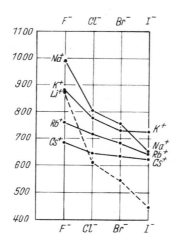

Fig. 14.8. Melting points (°C) of the alkali halides.

the reaction of the ion with water. The difference $U - L$ is difficult to estimate because of the very large difference in hydration energies of various ions. Further, since this is not the only factor determining the solubility of a salt in water, it is possible only in very special cases to expect that a high lattice energy will result in low solubility. Such a case occurs, for instance, when the lattice energy increases appreciably with increasing ionic charge. The last column in Table 14.6 shows this. In this context, nitrates ($z = 1$) are all easily soluble, sulphates ($z = 2$) frequently less soluble, while phosphates, with the exception of the alkali phosphates, are all very slightly soluble in water. In addition to charge, the symmetry of ions also has considerable influence on solubility. Thus, chlorates are generally more easily soluble than perchlorates. The pyramidal structure of the ClO_3^- ion prevents a highly symmetrical ordering of anions and cations, which would be favourable for the lattice energy.

14.7 Quantum Mechanical Explanation of Bonding

As can be observed, the ionic model is exceptionally useful, nevertheless, it is only an approximation, which becomes more nearly correct as the charges or, more accurately, the effective nuclear charges, on the ions decrease. In the following section, a quantum mechanical analysis of the chemical bonding in salts will be given. In order to get a picture of the density distribution of valence electrons in AB-compounds, the series CC,

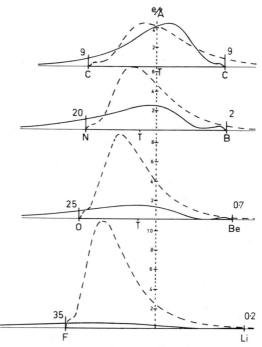

Fig. 14.9. Distribution of the electron density/Å (per spherical shell) of atoms in the ground state in the crystals of C, BN, BeO, and LiF.

——— *Electron density of the right atom*

– – – – *Electron density of the left atom*

T = *tetrahedral radii according to Pauling*

BN, BeO, and LiF will be considered. The electron densities of the free atoms in the ground state have been calculated according to the method of Hartree and Fock. In Fig. 14.9, the density is drawn to show how it is distributed over individual spherical shells which one can draw around an atomic nucleus. The shape of the curve corresponds to the function $4\pi r^2 \chi^2(r)$. The inter-atomic distance corresponds to that in the crystal. It is apparent how a significant portion of the valence electrons is concentrated in the space between the undistorted C-atoms in the diamond structure. The electron clouds penetrate each other. As previously seen, the bonding electrons are in (sp^3)-hybrid states. Each of the two valence electrons of a pair thus belongs as much to the hybrid on one atom as to that on the other. If we pass over to BN, the effective nuclear charge on the one atom, N, increases, while that on the other, B, decreases. The hybrid function on the one atom, N, contracts, that on the other, B, expands. Thereby the valence electron cloud wanders from the boron to the nitrogen atom and becomes concentrated there.

The electron cloud of the undistorted, free boron atom is of such a size that 20 per cent of it lies outside the spherical shell, the radius of which corresponds to the B–N distance. With BeO and LiF, this process continues. In BN and in BeO, the valence electrons are represented, just as in carbon, by (sp^3)-hybrid functions. On the free, undistorted metal atom, these orbitals are so extended that in the crystal they penetrate deeply into the domain of the neighbouring non-metallic nuclei. The essential difference in the bonding here compared to that in diamond is the result of the different effective nuclear charges, the (sp^3)-hybrid functions differing strongly in their spatial extension. Just as before, there exists an exchange interaction between valence electrons which simultaneously occupy the orbitals of both atoms. Since the boron atom brings with it only three valence electrons, while nitrogen brings five, the four hybrid functions on boron are more weakly occupied than are those on nitrogen. In the valence state of boron, three valence electrons are distributed over four hybrid functions, while in nitrogen there are five electrons. In proceeding from the assumption that, to a certain approximation, the atomic orbitals exhibit the same electron occupation as in the bound state, the molecular bonding function made up of (sp^3)-hybrid functions reads, for example:

$$\Psi = N\left\{ \sqrt{\frac{3}{4}} \cdot \frac{1}{\sqrt{4}} \left(\psi_{s,\,B} + \psi_{px,\,B} + \psi_{py,\,B} + \psi_{pz,\,B} \right) \right.$$
$$\left. + \sqrt{\frac{5}{4}} \cdot \frac{1}{\sqrt{4}} \left(\psi_{s,\,N} + \psi_{px,\,N} + \psi_{py,\,N} + \psi_{pz,\,N} \right) \right\}$$

From the assumption that atoms in a crystal remain as far as possible neutral, it is apparent that a displacement in the probability density of the valence electron pair toward the non-metallic atom results. It is not necessary and, indeed, not fitting to invoke a so-called ionic component of bonding[5.3] and to make this responsible for the concentration of the valence electron cloud about the non-metallic atom.

In LiF with the rock-salt structure, the valence electrons are not in (sp^3)-hybrid states but occupy unhybridized s- and p-quantum states, since these fit in with the symmetry of the lattice. Since this is the case, there is a difference here relative to other members of the isoelectronic series. The difference in effective nuclear charge is even greater in LiF than in the compounds previously considered so that the electron cloud on the non-metallic atom (F) is concentrated within a very small space, while that on the metal (Li) is strongly expanded. It practically interpenetrates the fluorine atom. Thirty-five per cent of the total 2s-electron density of the undisturbed lithium atom even lies outside the spherical shell previously defined. Here again, the valence electrons show an exchange interaction. The electrons can occupy s- and p-orbitals on either the fluorine atom or on the lithium atom. However, the influence of the lithium nucleus is weak. Its orbitals become completely altered upon entering the domain of the highly charged fluorine nucleus. Only in the neighbourhood of the lithium nucleus, where the nuclear force of fluorine is extensively shielded, does the influence of the lithium orbital become noticeable.

Just as in a free Li-atom, a spherical shell can be drawn around the nucleus within which the two 1s-electrons principally lie, and outside which the valence electron is mainly localized. If one considers this outer shell to be associated with the fluorine atom alone, the ionic model with Li^+ and F^- is arrived at.

The electron density distribution in a crystal can be determined by X-ray diffraction. Figures 14.10a and b show the measured electron density distribution along the line between two neighbouring carbon atoms in the diamond lattice, and between Li and F in the LiF-crystal.[14.7] It is seen that the electron density between atoms in LiF drops off more sharply than in diamond.

In LiF the measured electron density corresponds both to the superposition of the calculated (Hartree–Fock Method)[14.8] local electron densities of the two free atoms, Li and F, as well as to that of the two ions, Li^+ and F^-. As one can infer from Fig. 14.10b, this result comes from the fact that the 2s-electron of the free Li-atom is far removed from the nucleus in that space which is occupied by the F-atom. The position of the minimum in electron density does not completely agree with the distribution of ionic radii which Goldschmidt and Pauling have accepted (compare section 14.2).

In a crystal, the space which is available for a lithium atom is limited. The extension of the 2s- and 2p-orbitals on the lithium atom is reduced. Mathematically, it can be shown that the 2s- and 2p-orbitals of lithium have, under these conditions, especially large values at a distance of about 0·6 Å from the nucleus. The increase in measured electron density relative to that calculated (disregarding compression) at 0·6 Å from the lithium nucleus is due to this effect.[14.9]

Interesting relations can be found in the PbS-group ((i), section 13.2).[12.35]

Since lead is bivalent, the 6s-orbital is occupied by an electron pair and cannot take part in bonding. Lead then makes only its two 6p-electrons available for bonding. The sulphur atom has four 3p-electrons. Together there are then six p-valence electrons per atom pair, just as there are in the

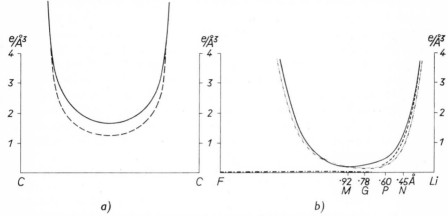

a)

b)

Fig. 14.10. Measured electron density along the bonding line between (a) two C atoms in the diamond structure, (b) one Li and one F atom in the LiF-crystal.

———— *measured electron density*[14.7]

— — — *superposition of the electron densities of two C atoms and of Li and F respectively*

··· ··· ··· *superposition of the electron density of Li⁻ and F⁻.*

—·—·—· *electron density of the 2s-electrons of the Li atom.*

------- *calculated electron density of Li⁺, taking thermal motion into account*

N: nodal surface of the 2s-electron in the Li-atom

M: minimum of the measured electron density.

G and P: ionic radius of Li⁺-ion according to Goldschmidt and Pauling, respectively.

group As, Sb, Bi. The compounds are isoelectronic to these elements. The rock-salt structure of PbS is traceable to a mesomeric σ-bonding system of p-electrons, the axes of which are directed along the lattice directions [100], [010], and [001] (Fig. 14.11). Using the language of a chemical

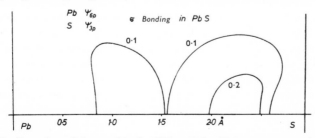

Fig. 14.11. Branches of the p-orbitals of Pb and S which are connected together in the PbS structure.[4.7]

structural formula, mesomerism along one such line can be described:

Pb————S   Pb————S   Pb————S ←→

————Pb   S————Pb   S————Pb   S————.

Since here no hybridization with s-states takes place, both formulas have equal weight. Metallic conductivity would be expected. PbS is, however, a semiconductor, because the high nuclear charge on sulphur combined with its low quantum number $n = 3$, leads to a concentration of the six valence electrons on this atom. This brings about a definite localization of the electrons. If one electron is split off a sulphur atom, the remaining positive charge cannot be so effectively smeared over several atoms as when the atoms are identical. A certain amount of hybridization and therefore a preference for one bonding direction over the other, as in arsenic, obviously does not weaken the coupling of the valence electrons among themselves as greatly as do the differences in effective nuclear charge. As discussed in the case of As, π-bonding must be assumed between empty d_ε-states on lead and filled p-states on sulphur.

The strength of the mesomeric bonding system in PbS makes itself apparent also in other ways besides the semiconducting properties and the black colour. PbS is practically insoluble and in addition, the distance between the Pb and S atoms in the crystal is 3 per cent shorter than the sum of the Goldschmidt radii would predict. Further, the mesomeric bonding system permits deviations from stoichiometry, which can amount to ± 0.1 per cent Pb in PbS,[14.10] and $+2$ per cent Te in SnTe. At 600°C the composition can vary from $Sn_{49.9} Te_{50.1}$ to $Sn_{48.9} Te_{51.1}$.[14.11] SnAs appears to be an alloy-like substance with a wide composition range.

The Sr–S distance in SrS (3.01 Å) is comparable to the inter-atomic distance in PbS (2.97 Å). SrS, however, is colourless and is an electrical insulator. This comes about for the following reasons:

The lowest lying quantum state available for bonding in Sr is the $5s$-state. This is spherically symmetrical, not directed toward the bonding partners, and therefore poorly suited for bonding. The transfer of the two valence electrons of Sr into a valence state, in this case the p-quantum states, requires an excitation energy of approximately 100 kcal/mole, so that ionization $Sr^x \rightarrow Sr^{2+} + 2e^-$ requires only about 280 kcal/mole more energy compared with the 517 kcal/mole required to ionize lead, $Pb \rightarrow Pb^{2+} + 2e^-$. The p-orbitals of Sr in the valence state are therefore widely extended and are immersed deeply in the domain of the sulphur nucleus, just as we observed in the case of Li in LiF. The p-orbitals of Sr can, therefore, develop no marked mesomeric bonding system as in PbS, their influence being weak.

The lead atoms in PbTe can be replaced at higher temperatures by cadmium (up to 20 per cent at 860°) or indium (up to 35 per cent at 650°).

Similar substitutions can occur in SnTe.[14.12] It can thus be assumed that the p-orbitals on cadmium or indium can take on the role of the p-orbitals of lead or tin. The phases, CdTe, $In_{1-x}Ag_xTe$ with $x = 0 \rightarrow 0.2$, $InTe_{1-x}As_x$ with $x = 0.33 \rightarrow 0.5$, and SnAs[14.13] which crystallize, at least under high pressure, in the NaCl-type structure, show metallic conductivity, and at low temperatures are (CdTe excepted) actually superconductors. It is certain that metallic conductivity comes about because the extent of s-orbital occupation on the metal atoms can vary and with it the occupation of the mesomeric σ-bonding system of the p-electrons. In CdTe with the zinc blende structure, and thus with localized (sp^3)-hybrid bonds, the width of the forbidden energy gap is 1.4 eV $= 32$ kcal/mol.[14.14]

The studies of Geller[14.15] suggest that superconductivity can result when the bonding system (here of p-electrons) leaves over unpaired electrons in s-states. The spherical symmetry of this atomic state appears to be essential for the undisturbed motion of electrons (compare section 18.4).

The compounds of the rare earths with an element of the N- or O-group have the rock-salt structure. Besides the p-orbitals on the metal the s- and the d_γ-functions (compare (d^2sp^3)-hybrid) contribute to the mesomeric σ-bonding system with the p-orbitals on the non-metals. This σ-bonding system is strongly developed when the metal atoms are tervalent, since a high valence causes a contraction of the bonding orbitals of the metal. A high electrical conductivity results. If the third valence electron, on the other hand is in the $4f$ shell as, for example, in SmX and EuX where X $=$ S, Se, Te, the lattice constant is large and these compounds are comparable with the corresponding compounds with Ca, Sr, and Ba. By applying pressure (25–40 kbar for EuTe and 30–45 kbar for SmTe), a $4f$ electron can be raised into the valence shell and the lattice constant drops about 5 per cent.[14.16] The electron presumably goes into a d_ε-orbital which must be spread out more. Bonding between the metal atoms then occurs (compare later NbO, Fig. 14.15b) along with metallic properties.[14.17] In the other rare earth, the preference for the $4f$ shell for the third valence electron is not so large, so that in the compounds REX where X $=$ S, Se, Te, the denser, metal-like phase with one electron per metal atom in the d_ε-conduction band can be prepared without the use of external pressure.[14.18]

The NaCl-type structure of CrN is obviously caused by the strong tendency of tervalent chromium to form octahedral complexes. According to the crystal field theory, the three d_ε-electrons here build a ^4F-term, which fits well into the symmetry of an NaCl-type structure. The three-electron system has small values of the product function in the direction of the six corners of an octahedron. The N atoms can therefore come close to the Cr nucleus. The (d^2sp^3)-hybrid functions on chromium and *p*-functions on nitrogen are available for bonding. In addition, π-bonds can be assumed as in the cyanocomplexes of tervalent cobalt, with, however, the difference that for each such bond, not two but only one electron is available. On the other hand, the *p*-functions on N contain more electrons than the *p*π-functions on the carbon of the CN-group.

The octahedral surroundings of C and N are characteristic of many carbides and nitrides. Plainly this is a result of the orientation of the *p*-orbitals of these elements. The explanation of the NaCl-type structure of TiC is relatively easy to see.

On the Ti-atom there are available for bonding:

(a) Three (d^2s)-hybrid functions, directed toward the axes of a Cartesian co-ordinate system.

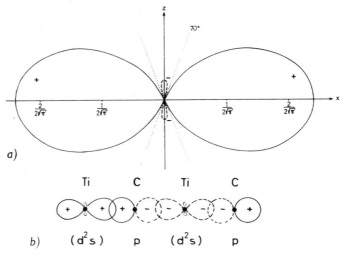

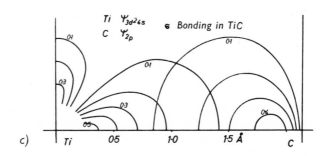

Fig. 14.12. *σ-bonding system in TiC.*[4.7] *(a) Polar diagram of a (d^2s)-hybrid. (b) Mesomeric σ-bonding system along a* [100]*-straight line. (c) Overlap of the* (d_y^2s)*-hybrid on Ti and the p-orbital on carbon.*

$$\varphi_1 = \frac{1}{\sqrt{3}}\left(\psi_s + \sqrt{2}\,\psi_{d_{3z^2-1}}\right) \qquad \text{Hybrid in } z\text{-direction}$$

$$\varphi_2 = \frac{1}{\sqrt{3}}\left(\psi_s - \frac{1}{\sqrt{2}}\,\psi_{d_{3z^2-1}} - \sqrt{\frac{3}{2}}\,\psi_{d_{x^2-y^2}}\right) \qquad \text{Hybrid in } y\text{-direction}$$

$$\varphi_3 = \frac{1}{\sqrt{3}}\left(\psi_s - \frac{1}{\sqrt{2}}\,\psi_{d_{x^2-y^2}} + \sqrt{\frac{3}{2}}\,\psi_{d_{x^2-y^2}}\right) \qquad \text{Hybrid in } x\text{-direction}$$

Since each of the three hybrid functions is directed just as much toward the positive as the negative side of the associated co-ordinate axis, it is possible to form a mesomeric σ-bond system with the p-electrons of the carbon atom.

(b) The three d_ε-orbitals of titanium. These can form a mesomeric, π-bonding system with the p-electrons of carbon (Fig. 14.13a). For the sake of clarity, only the π-bonding system in the [100] direction is given in Fig. 14.13a. The same d-function can naturally also take part in a second bond in the [010] direction. These π-bonds can be of some consequence

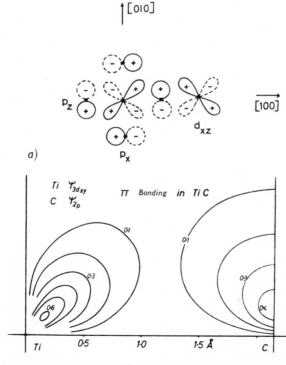

Fig. 14.13. π-bonding system in TiC.[4.7] (a) Mesomeric π-bonding system along a [100]-direction. (b) Overlap of a d_ε-orbital on Ti and a p-orbital on carbon.

since, as Fig. 14.13b shows, the d-functions are quite extended and the p-functions of carbon meet the d-functions where the latter still have appreciable values.

(c) Both the σ- and π-bonding systems are decidedly mesomeric so that the black colour and high electrical conductivity of the compound are not surprising. In addition, the composition can vary from $Ti_1C_{0.22}$ to Ti_1C_1.[14.19] In Ti_1C_1, all positions in the NaCl-type lattice are occupied, while in the carbon-poor compounds, some of the non-metal sites are unoccupied. The high melting point, 3137°C, shows that the bonding system is very stable. The substance is extraordinarily hard (8–9 on the Mohs Scale), since the bonding directions are fixed and the atoms cannot be slid over each other as they can in a typical metal.

In the bonding system described above, several electrons are added when compounds are formed with elements of the groups following Ti and C (e.g., V or N). Since all d- and s-quantum states of the metal and all p-functions of the non-metals are required for bonding, further electrons disturb the bonding system. They require space and the system is altered, vacancies being formed in the lattice. In TiN, 4 per cent of all the lattice points are unoccupied and in TiO, 15 per cent. Vacancy formation is very much dependent on the composition. Thus in the system Ti/O, those rock salt-type phases between $TiO_{0.60}$ and $TiO_{1.35}$ show the following defect structures:[14.19, 14.20]

Composition	%-vacancies in sub-lattice	
	Titanium	Oxygen
$Ti_1O_{0.69}$	4	34
$Ti_1O_{1.00}$	15	15
$Ti_1O_{1.12}$	19	9
$Ti_1O_{1.25}$	23	4
$Ti_1O_{1.33}$	26	2

TiN, ZrN, and TaC with the NaCl-type structure are superconductors with relatively high transition temperatures: 5·5, 9·5, and 9·4°K respectively. The lone s-electrons on the metal atoms cannot take part in the bonding system discussed for TiC because all these bonding states are occupied. Instead of going into energetically unfavoured antibonding states, these s-electrons surely interact in forming bonds among themselves and may also partly occupy the empty $3s$-orbitals of the non-metallic atom, e.g., N. Thus, a special band is formed from spherically symmetric s-orbitals.

Vacancy formation in NbO is regular. The body centre and the corners of the cubic unit cell are unoccupied, Fig. 14.14. Here each atom is surrounded, not by six, but by four other atoms in a square arrangement. In the atoms of the second long period, the d-levels lie energetically deeper than in the first long period. This can be recognized in the number of atoms which have the electron configuration $4d^x5s^1$ as opposed to $3d^{x-1}4s^2$.

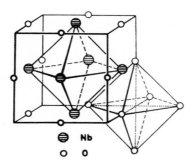

Nb
O

Fig. 14.14. Structure of NbO.

Thus the d-electron configuration will also have a strong influence on bonding. A σ-bonding system can be formulated using (d^2s)-hybrids on niobium and p-orbitals on the oxygen atom. These functions then form bonds to two sides so that a mesomeric system results (Fig. 14.15a). NbO has a metallic lustre and conducts electricity as well as niobium metal.[14.21] The (d^2s)-hybrid also provides bonds between the Nb atoms, since the orbitals of the heavier atoms are quite extended. Further, the d-electrons of the t_{2g} group can give rise to bonds between the metal atoms (Fig. 14.15b). For further bonding possibilities, refer to the theory of the bonding in $[Nb_6X_{12}]^{4+}$-complexes (chapter 27.2). Unfortunately, the (dsp^2)-hybrid functions which are discussed there cannot be calculated since the values for the $5p$-orbitals of Nb are unknown. Figure 14.15 shows, therefore, the values of the (d^2s)-hybrid.

All of the above mentioned substances are pronouncedly *antiferromagnetic*. By antiferromagnetism we understand an extensive antiparallel alignment of the spin moments of the d-electrons of neighbouring atoms. This antiparallel ordering persists up to high temperatures (the *Néel temperature*) if the d-shell participates appreciably in the mesomeric bonding system.

If even more electrons are packed into the oxide systems, compounds such as MnO, FeO, CoO, and NiO are obtained. All these oxides are dark-coloured. The spectra are more easily measured when these oxides are combined in mixed crystals with such oxides as MgO.[14.22] It is evident that the bonding concepts developed in chapters 9 and 10 for complex ions are also applicable to co-ordination structures. It is indeed possible to determine the valency and the symmetry of the immediate surroundings of a coloured metal atom in a co-ordination structure since the *d*-levels are split, in accordance with theory, particularly in oxides. This crystal field influence acts so that the inter-atomic distances do not vary monotonically

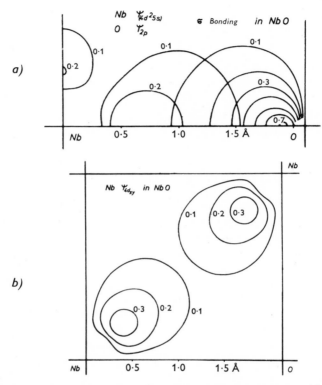

Fig. 14.15. Overlap of bonding functions in the NbO-structure.[4.7] (a) σ-bonding with $(d_\gamma^2 s)$-hybrid on Nb and p-orbital on oxygen. (b) σ-bonding via d_ε-orbitals on two neighbouring Nb atoms.

but instead, as Fig. 14.16 shows, they vary irregularly[14.2e] (compare also Fig. 14.1 and Table 14.1). VO and NiO show the smallest Me–O distances since the configurations d_ε^3 and $d_\varepsilon^6 d_\gamma^2$ fit in especially well with octahedral symmetry (see chapter 9.2). The inter-atomic distance is greatest in MnO, since the product functions of the half-filled *d*-shells have spherical symmetry in the lowest-lying state, ^6S.

The atomic ratios in the oxides MnO, FeO, CoO, and NiO are not always exactly 1:1, but are dependent on the partial pressure of oxygen at the time of preparation. When the oxides are stoichiometric, they are insulators. In non-stoichiometric $Ni_{1-x}\square_xO$ a proportion of the nickel atoms are tervalent. Current transport is then possible when a divalent nickel atom gives up one of its electrons to a tervalent one. In an electric field the tervalent nickel state wanders. This tervalent nickel appears as a positive charge so that non-stoichiometric NiO is a hole (*p*-type) conductor.

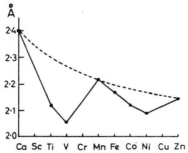

Fig. 14.16. *Inter-atomic distances in oxides of transition metals which crystallize in the rock-salt structure type.*[14.2e]

Electrical conductivity of the oxides as a function of doping was first investigated and explained by C. Wagner and his school.[14.23] NiO forms heterotypic mixed crystals with Li_2O, which have the rock-salt type structure in the range: $Ni_{1-x}Li_xO$ with $0 < x < 0.2$. The conductivity varies by five orders of magnitude from $10^{-5} \, \Omega^{-1} \, cm^{-1}$ for $x = 10^{-4}$, to $1 \, \Omega^{-1} \, cm^{-1}$ for $x = 0.1$. Despite the high degree of doping, the material remains a semiconductor, because of an activation energy of approximately 5 kcal/mole which the electrons must surmount if they are to wander from a bivalent to a tervalent nickel atom. This activation energy is principally the result of three factors:[14.24, 14.25]

(a) The *d*-electrons interact more strongly with themselves than with the ligands (Hund's rule). They thus belong more to the metal atom than to the bonding system.

(b) The surroundings of a tervalent nickel atom are somewhat different from those of a bivalent atom since the symmetry of the product functions and the bonding forces are different. The alteration in valence state thus requires a definite displacement of all other atoms in the immediate neighbourhood.

(c) In moving from one atom to another, the electron can be required to change its spin direction.

These oxides are also antiferromagnetic at low temperatures. The coupling is not, however, as strong as in NbO, TiN, TiO, etc. FeO becomes paramagnetic at 198°K. While the bonding in individual cases cannot yet be ascertained, the antiferromagnetism can be formally explained by the so-called *superexchange* mechanism of Kramers[14.26] and Anderson.[14.27]

14

From a p-electron pair on the O atom (Formula I), one electron can wander along a cube edge to the left Fe atom, while the other electron bonds the right Fe atom (Formula II).

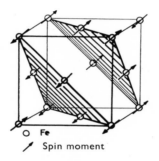

Formula III is equivalent to Formula II. Using neutron diffraction it has been determined that the spin moment of the d-electrons is directed perpendicularly to the (111)-plane of the lattice and that the spin directions are reversed on adjacent (111)-planes (Fig. 14.17).

O Fe

↗ Spin moment

Fig. 14.17. Orientation of the spin moments of the d-electrons on iron in FeO.

15

Rock-salt-like Structures

15.1 Germanium Telluride Structure, GeTe

If the atoms in rhombohedral arsenic are replaced alternately in all three directions by Ge and Te, the result is the GeTe structure.[15.1] In this lattice, for example, the upper positions of each double layer are occupied by Ge atoms and the lower by Te.

If GeTe is heated, the rhombohedral angle tends toward 90°, reaching this limit at 400°C. A high polymer, layer structure is thus transformed continuously and not suddenly into a co-ordination structure by heating.

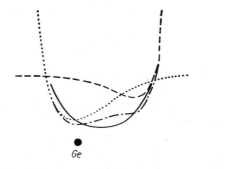

⊕   ●   ⊕
Te   *Ge*   *Te*

Fig. 15.1. *Schematic potential curve for the bonding of a* Ge *atom along a meso-meric chain in the crystal of* GeTe.[12.17a]

.... *Potential curve for the favoured bonding direction within a double layer.*

– – – – – *Potential curve for the unfavourable bonding direction between two double layers.*

–·–·–·– *Resultant of the two potential curves.*

————— *Resultant for the bonding via p-electrons in cubic* GeTe.

The rhombohedral distortion of the NaCl-type structure is brought about in GeTe, just as in As, by a weak hybridization of the *p*- and *s*-functions. Raising the temperature obviously reduces the extent of hybridization. In order to understand this, let us consider a Ge atom in the force field of the neighbouring Te atoms both in the same and in the neighbouring double layer. Schematic potential curves are reproduced in Fig. 15.1 using points and dashes. Their superposition gives the asymmetric curve (·——·——). The thermal vibrations must therefore also be asymmetric to the equilibrium position. With increasing temperature, the Ge atoms come closer and closer to the more distant Te atom, since here a weaker repulsive potential is effective. Since the hybridization adapts well to every particular position of the atoms, the two bonding directions become equivalent as the temperature increases. At last the layer structure is lost and an NaCl-type structure results as in PbS, with pure p-states as the bonding functions.

15.2 Melting Processes in Semi-metals

A three-dimensionally cross-linked high polymer can melt only when either individual bonds are broken (as, e.g., in the viscous glasses) or by a depolymerization. In this way, for example, the P_4-molecule of the vapour or melt results from highly polymeric, solid red phosphorus. Which processes now take place when semi-metals melt ?

In analogy to the processes which occur on heating rhombohedral GeTe, a short range rock-salt-like ordering is formed when highly polymeric, rhombohedral antimony is melted. Both the Na- and Cl-positions are occupied by Sb atoms.[15.2] The inter-atomic distance in the melt, 3·03 Å, corresponds to the weighted average of the two distances in the crystal $\frac{1}{2}(2\cdot908 + 3\cdot355) = 3\cdot132$.

Antimony atoms are very mobile in the melt, since each p-valence electron, which bonds in two directions, can without too great an expenditure of energy, go into a hybrid state (e.g., (sp)) which bonds in only one direction. In this way the bonds can follow the thermal motion of the atoms. Bonds are easily dissolved, where necessary, while other bonds are strengthened. Figure 15.2 illustrates how a bond is eliminated through a local transition of the valence shell from s^2p^3, with three mesomeric σ-bonding systems over p-electrons to $(sp)^3p^2$, since the solitary electron pairs oppose each other in (sp^1)-hybrids which do not bond. In contrast to this, with organic high polymers or glasses motion of the atoms is possible only by a cracking process. This requires a high energy of activation. Thus viscous melts result, and the viscosity is a close function of temperature.

InSb, which crystallizes in a highly polymeric zinc blende-type structure, also goes over into a rock-salt type short range ordering on melting. The higher co-ordination number, six instead of four, brings with it a denser packing of the atoms, so that InSb melts with a volume contraction despite the fact that the inter-atomic distance rises from 2·80 Å in the crystal to 3·17 Å in the melt.[15.3]

Molten germanium shows an NaCl-type structure only when heated to 300° above its melting point. The inter-atomic distance is 2·83 Å in place of 2·45 Å in the crystal. In the atomic distribution curve for germanium at 1270°[15.4] as well as in that for InSb, a little above the melting point,

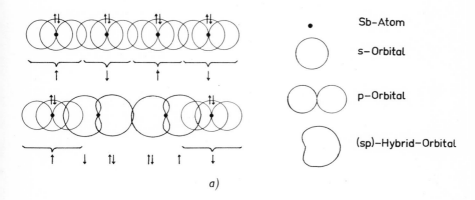

a)

Fig. 15.2. Schematic representation of the transition of a two-sided bond via p-electrons into a single-sided bond via electrons in (sp)-states.

only the nearest-neighbour maximum is well developed (Fig. 15.3). The distance between next-nearest neighbours fluctuates so strongly that the associated maximum in the atomic distribution curve is no longer visible. At 980°C (about 30° above the melting point), a strongly distorted NaCl-type structure is found for germanium. There are four nearest neighbours (distance 2·70 Å) and two further removed at 3·05 Å. The short range ordering of the atoms approximates to that in the crystal. In molten Ge and InSb, the same bonding systems are possible as in molten Sb; the only difference is that there is one electron less per atom than in Sb.

The vapour pressure of the melts is low, as long as molecules do not form in the vapour, e.g., Sb_4, or free atoms with a certain stability of the electron configuration, for example, Hg. Only the bonding system is movable because of the ease of alteration of the bonding functions (*p*- or hybrid functions). The alteration in the bonding state on melting, from tetrahedral ordering to octahedral, is apparent in the high entropy of melting, 6·74 cal/mole-deg. for germanium, whereas normally it would lie at 1·6–3·4 cal/mole-deg.

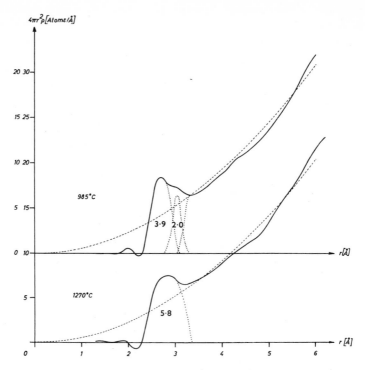

Fig. 15.3. Atomic distribution curve in liquid germanium at 960 and 1270°C.[15.4]

15.3 The Tin Sulphide Structure, SnS (B16-Type)

GeS, GeSe, SnS, SnSe, as well as SnTe at a pressure of 20 kbar,[15.5] crystallize in the orthorhombic class and belong to the same structure type; they are isotypic. The structure is characterized by double layers with the black phosphorus structure (Fig. 12.16a, b). The lattice points are occupied alternately by metal and non-metallic atoms. Small distortions are observed. Figure 15.4 shows the structure in a projection on the (001)-plane. The packing of double layers is different from that observed in black phosphorus. While in the latter case the double layers are so arranged that the phosphorus atoms lie on voids, in the structure of the above-named chalcogenides, the metal and non-metal atoms are ordered one over the other. Each atom then has three near and in the opposite direction three further-removed neighbours of the other type.

The cubic structures (e.g., PbS, SnTe), the rhombohedral (e.g., As and GeTe) and the orthorhombic (e.g., GeS) are thus closely related in their construction. They are differentiated essentially only by the degree of hybridization which is greater in the lighter atoms, and by the kind of hybridization which occurs more symmetrically in the rhombohedral but less symmetrically in the orthorhombic phases. The relationship of the bonding types can be shown by the extensive heterotypic mixed crystal formation which is possible, since the hybridization can adapt itself to the respective geometric conditions.

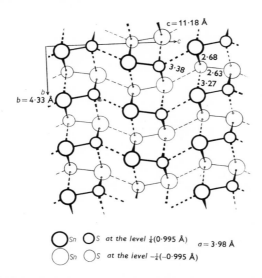

Sn ◯S at the level $\frac{1}{4}$(0·995 Å)

Sn ◯S at the level $-\frac{1}{4}$(−0·995 Å)

$a = 3·98$ Å

Fig. 15.4. SnS-structure in a projection parallel to the plane of the layer (parallel to the a-axis).

15.4 Thallium Iodide-Structure, TlI

In addition to the prototype TlI, the compounds InBr, InI, and NaOH (Fig. 15.5) also crystallize with this structure. TlI molecules are parallel to the c-axis of the tetragonal lattice and are so arranged that the ordering of the atoms is comparable to that in two adjacent (001)-planes of the rock-salt type structure. A double layer results. The adjacent double layers are displaced relative to one another by $a/2$ so that an atom in one layer is situated over a void in the other. Each atom has one nearest neighbour and four which are somewhat farther removed so that a co-ordination number of 5 results, giving an octahedron which lacks the sixth ligand.

The structure can be explained by remembering that the TlI-molecule is isoelectronic with the part of the I[—Hg—I] molecule in brackets. In place of the second iodine atom, a free electron pair is found in TlI, which is described by an (sp)-hybrid just as is the bonding pair. In the direction of the lattice line [110] empty p-quantum states on the Tl-atom alternate

with filled *p*-quantum states on I. The *p*-electron pairs on I fill the empty
p-states on Tl, so that a mesomeric bonding system in the direction [110]
is obtained similar to that along the [100]-line in a PbS crystal or along the
[110] and [1$\bar{1}$0]-lines in the structure of black phosphorus. The ratio of

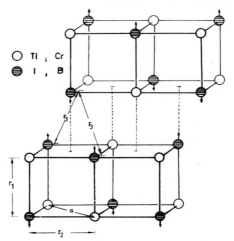

Fig. 15.5. Formation and superposition of double layers in the crystal of Tll.

next-nearest neighbour to nearest neighbour distances decreases here too
as the atoms become heavier. The following distances are found:

	r_1	r_2	r_2/r_1	r_3	r_3/r_1
InBr	2·80 Å	3·29 Å	1·17		
InI	3·23	3·46	1·02	3·95 Å	1·22
TlI	3·36	3·49	1·04	3·87	1·15

In red TlI, with the CsCl-type structure, the inter-atomic distance, r_1 is
3·64 Å and in the vapour state the Tl–I distance is 2·87 Å.

The crystal structure of CrB is geometrically closely related to the TlI
structure. The distance r_3 is shortened (to *ca.* 1·72 Å), since the boron
atoms come closer to each other, as shown by the arrows in Fig. 15.5.
Boron chains then result (valence angle B–B–B = 119°). The tetragonal
symmetry of the crystal is then reduced to orthorhombic. Many compounds with the general formula AB crystallize in the CrB structure,
when:[15.6]

    (a) A = Alkaline earth, rare earth, or transition elements such as Ca,
            Ce, Zr, V, Ni.
        B = B, Al, Ga, Si, Ge, Sn, Pb.

(b) A = Alkaline earth, rare earth or an element of the Ti group.
   B = An element of the Fe or Cu group, as Co, Ni, Rh, Pt, Ag.

15.5 Cinnabar Structure, HgS (B9-Type)

The black modification of HgS, as a mineral called metacinnabarite, has the zinc blende structure. Red HgS consists of spiral chains. Each mercury atom has in a linear arrangement two equally distant (2·36 Å) sulphur atoms as co-ordination partners (Fig. 15.6). The sulphur atoms in return couple two mercury atoms to each other. The corresponding valence angle

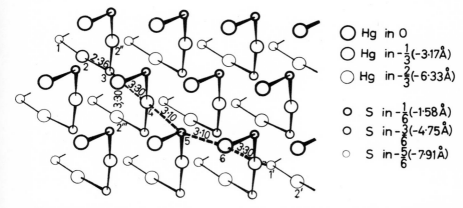

Hg in 0
Hg in $-\frac{1}{3}$(-3·17Å)
Hg in $-\frac{2}{3}$(-6·33Å)

S in $-\frac{1}{6}$(-1·58Å)
S in $-\frac{3}{6}$(-4·75Å)
S in $-\frac{5}{6}$(-7·91Å)

Fig. 15.6. Structure of cinnabar in a projection parallel to the chain direction (c-axis).

Hg–S–Hg is 105°. One can thus pick out of the structure spiral chains which wind along the c-axis through the crystal just as the selenium atoms do in a crystal of hexagonal selenium. Just as the packing of selenium chains in that structure results from a mesomeric bonding system, this is also the case for the cinnabar structure. Each atom of one kind is surrounded by six atoms of the second type in a distorted octahedral arrangement. This is very easy to see on a model. The valence angle is in general about 90°. Greater deviations occur only in the above-named valence angle Hg_2–2·36–S_3–2·36–Hg_2'' of 105° within a chain, and the angle Hg_2'''–3·30–S_3–3·30–Hg_4 of 69° (Fig. 15.6). The magnitude of the first angle corresponds to the normal valence angle on sulphur, with s-component added to the p-orbitals. The other valence angle belongs to two very weak bonds.

In the crystal, the atoms lie approximately along sets of lines which are parallel to the [211] (hexagonal indices) directions and to those lines generated from it by symmetry. They correspond to the [100]-directions in the PbS structure. Only relatively short inter-atomic distances occur along one such atom chain. One can therefore accept that there is bonding between the chains. In the arrangement Hg_4–3·10–S_5–3·10–Hg_6, a free electron pair on the sulphur atom with principally p-character can consecutively occupy the empty p-states on Hg_4 and on Hg_6. In the arrangement Hg_2–2·36–S_3–3·30–Hg_4 the sulphur atom must first break its bond with the Hg_2 atom in order to form a mesomeric bond with Hg_4. The distance S_3–3·30–Hg_4 is therefore relatively large.

HgSe[15.7, 15.8] and HgTe,[15.8, 15.9] which under atmospheric pressure have the zinc blende structure, assume the cinnabar type structure under pressures of 8 and 15 kbar respectively. The hexagonal form of HgO also crystallizes in the cinnabar structure.[15.10]

16

Further Structures of AB-Compounds

16.1 Boron Nitride Structure, BN

BN is isoelectronic with carbon. Under high pressure this compound can form a cubic diamond-type modification, just as does carbon itself.[16.1] Normally it occurs in a modification which consists of layers like graphite (Fig. 16.1a). Within these, the carbon atoms are alternately replaced by boron and nitrogen. The superposition of the layers is, however, different.

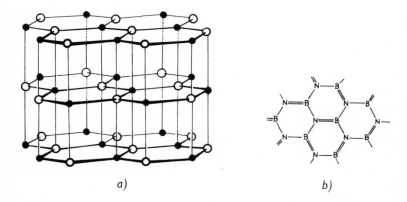

a)   *b)*

***Fig. 16.1.** **(a)** Structure of hexagonal BN. **(b)** A π-bonding system in one layer of the BN-structure.*

The atoms, B and N, lie alternately over one another in the line perpendicular to the layers. This probably results from very weak bonding between B and N. The building of the layer itself can be understood by a mesomeric bonding system like that in graphite (Fig. 16.1b). The relatively high nuclear charge on nitrogen results in a concentration and therefore localization of the π-electrons on the nitrogen. Therefore BN, in contrast to graphite, is an insulator and is white.

16.2 Lead Oxide Structure, PbO

Red lead oxide forms a layer structure with tetragonal symmetry (B10-type) (Fig. 16.2). The oxygen atoms in a layer form a square pattern, while the lead atoms lie alternately above and below the middle of the oxygen squares. As Fig. 16.2a shows, these three-layer sandwiches are simply laid one over another. Red PbO, SnO, and, anti-isotypically, LiOH crystallize in this structure.

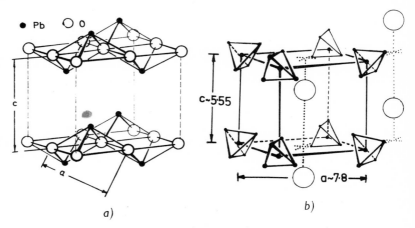

Fig. 16.2. (a) Structure of tetragonal (red) PbO. (b) $(PH_4)I$ structure.

In PbO and SnO, the oxygen, and in LiOH, the Li, have a somewhat distorted tetrahedral environment, so that one can assume (sp^3)-hybridization. Lead with four oxygen atoms forms a tetragonal pyramid. A fourfold symmetry about the Pb atom is given by p_x- and p_y-bonding functions providing the x- and y-axes are chosen parallel to the two a-axes of the structure while the z-axis is parallel to the c-axis of the crystal. A better overlap is obtained when a definite hybridization with the d-functions d_{zx} and d_{yz} occurs, since these hybrid functions point toward the corners of a four-sided pyramid (compare the structure of white tin, Fig. 12.26, and the (dp)-hybrid functions of Figs. 12.27a, b).

In the compounds described above, the axial ratio c/a is approximately 1·2. The compounds $[N(CH_3)_4]Cl$, $[N(CH_3)_4]Br$, $[N(CH_3)_4]I$, $[PH_4]I$, and $[NH_4]SH$ also form isotypic structures. Here, however, the ratio c/a is much smaller (0·7). In these cases one speaks of the '$[PH_4]I$-structure'. The formation of this structure depends on the packing possibility of tetrahedral ions $(PH_4^+, N(CH_3)_4^+, NH_4^+)$ with spherical ions (e.g., I^-), (Fig. 16.2b). These last ions are on the Pb-positions. The remaining CH_3 or H so order themselves that, seen from the oxygen positions of the

PbO-crystal, they jut out into the space above the vacant squares. Thus the N or P atoms are surrounded by a distorted cube consisting of four halogen atoms and four CH_3-groups or four H atoms.

Structures involving tetrahedral molecules are generally complicated. Solid SiF_4 in contrast shows a simple packing which is closely related to that of the $[PH_4]$I-structure. The silicon atoms considered alone have a body-centred arrangement. The SiF_4-tetrahedron in the cell middle is so arranged in the cell that its four F-atoms point to four corners of the unit cell. The SiF_4-molecules at the corners of the unit cell are then so

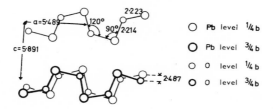

Fig. 16.3. Structure of the PbO-chains and their packing in the crystal of rhombic (yellow) PbO.

directed that their F atoms lie on the still free parts of the body diagonals of the unit cell.[16.2]

Yellow PbO forms a chain structure[16.3] (Fig. 16.3). The bond angle on Pb is 90°. Two p-orbitals on Pb take part in σ-bonding just as in PbS. Nevertheless the bonds are directed to only one side. In the opposite direction there is no atom. A degree of hybridization with the d-functions, d_{3z^2-1} and $d_{x^2-y^2}$ favours the one-sided bonding. The bond angle on oxygen, 120°, corresponds to an (sp^2)-hybridization. In the ac-plane these chains lie parallel to one another at the van der Waals' distance. Their superposition in the direction of the b-axis is much denser and of such a type that the chain directions alternate. In this way the Pb and O atoms in the b-direction do not lie directly over one another but are somewhat displaced. Their mutual distance is 2·487 Å ($r_3/r_1 = 2·487/2·214 = 1·12$) and the bond angle is 147·5°. In the b-axis direction there exists a certain relationship to red, tetragonal PbO. The p-orbital on the lead atom, which is parallel to the b-axis, is somewhat hybridized with a d-orbital.

16.3 Platinum Sulphide Structure, PtS (B17-type)

Another example in which the influence of the directions of the chemical bonding forces is particularly apparent is PtS. This compound crystallizes in the tetragonal class. Each S atom is tetrahedrally surrounded by four Pt atoms. Each Pt, in contrast, is in a planar arrangement with four S atoms

(Fig. 16.4). The tetrahedral configuration on sulphur comes about just as in the case of the zinc blende structure through an (sp^3)-hybrid. The complexes of bivalent Pt, for example, $K_2[PtCl_4]$, have a planar arrangement of ligands about the Pt atom. The electronic configuration on Pt is characterized as a (dsp^2)-hybrid. The four functions of this hybrid are directed to the corners of a square. Isotypic with PtS are PdS, PtO, and PdO. CuO and AgO form a distorted PtS structure (Jahn–Teller Effect).

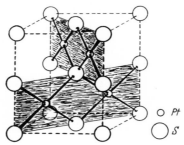

Fig. 16.4. PtS *structure.*

16.4 Nickel Arsenide Structure, NiAs (B8-type)[16.4]

In the nickel arsenide structure, the nickel atoms occupy the corners of a hexagonal cell. In each cell, one As atom (e.g., As atom 1 in Fig. 16.5) is so situated that it lies in the centre of a triangular prism formed by six Ni atoms (atoms No. 7–12). There are two possibilities for the incorporation

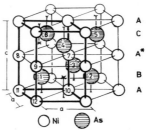

Fig. 16.5. NiAs *structure.*

of As in a prismatic environment of Ni atoms. These are realized alternately in the direction of the *c*-axis. There thus comes about a doubling of the primitive nickel sub-lattice along the *c*-axis. Each Ni atom (e.g., atom 7) is approximately octahedrally surrounded by six As atoms (Nos. 1–6). This structure type is characterized by completely occupied As places, while extensive vacancies can occur in the Ni sub-lattice, up to the composition $Me_{0.5}X_1$. The vacancies here generally occur only in every second metal layer (A*). These layers are completely empty at the composition $M_{0.5}X$. The structure corresponds then to the CdI_2-type.[16.5] On the other hand, up to two additional metal atoms can be accommodated in each unit cell in those places marked with a cross in Fig. 16.5. In such a position each metal atom is surrounded by five non-metallic atoms (e.g., 1, 2, 3', 4, and 4') in the form of a trigonal bipyramid. When all these positions are occupied, the composition Me_2X_1, as for example in Ni_2In, is obtained.

Apart from these disturbances in the regular build-up of the crystal structure, there are still others which result from a geometrical distortion of the lattice (e.g., MnP) or from an alteration in the layer sequence, as for example in TiP (Fig. 16.6). In the middle of the unit cell one finds a layer

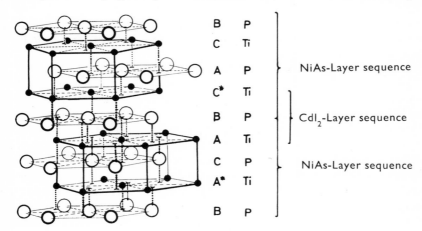

B	P	
C	Ti	NiAs-Layer sequence
A	P	
C*	Ti	
B	P	CdI_2-Layer sequence
A	Ti	
C	P	NiAs-Layer sequence
A*	Ti	
B	P	

Fig. 16.6. TiP structure.

of non-metallic atoms (P), which are surrounded not prismatically but octahedrally by six metal atoms (Ti). In those layers designated by a star, metal atoms can again be missing, as for example in Ti_3S_4.[16.6]

A great number of compounds with compositions from $Me_{0.5}X_1$ to Me_2X_1 crystallize in the NiAs structure or in one of the above-described variants of it. The metal atom, Me, can include those transition elements from the titanium to the nickel group. As the non-metal, the elements gallium, silicon, phosphorus, and sulphur are found as well as their higher homologues. Among the compounds which may be mentioned are: Ti_2Ga, TiS, $TiSe_{1.2}$ to $TiSe_2$, $Fe_{0.90}S$ to $Fe_{0.93}S$, Fe_1S_1 (distorted structure), Fe_7S_8, Fe_7Se_8, $Co_{0.55}Te$ to $Co_{0.8}Te$, $Co_{1.3}Sb$ to $Co_{1.03}Sb$, $Ni_{0.51}Te$ to Ni_1Te, Ni_2In to $Ni_{1.5}In$, Cu_2In to $Cu_{1.5}In$, $Ni_{0.95}As$ to Ni_1As, as well as a number of corresponding compounds with heavier atoms. There is also one gold compound with the NiAs structure, AuSn, and one with the MnP structure, AuGa.

The compositions with sulphur, selenium, and tellurium are distinguished by holes in the metal sub-lattice in the composition range from $Me_{0.5}X$ to Me_1X. Otherwise, filling of the metal positions is favoured, especially with the arsenides, antimonides, and bismuthides in the range from $Me_{1.5}X$ to Me_1X; and with silicides, stannides, germanides, and plumbides in the composition range from Me_2X to Me_1X. With gallium, indium, or thallium as the 'non-metallic' component the composition range is from Me_2X to $Me_{1.5}X$. NiSb appears to be the only compound whose range of homogeneity, $Ni_{1.18}Sb$ to $Ni_{0.85}Sb$ falls on both sides of the $1:1$ stoichiometric line, NiSb. In all other cases the homogeneity range ends at least at the composition $1:1$.

As the number of valence electrons in the non-metallic atom becomes greater, the number of vacancies in the metal sub-lattice increases. Similar relationships in typical valence structures will be observed, such as in the zinc blende and fluorspar structures.

At higher temperatures, wider homogeneity ranges are observed. With slow cooling, these frequently decompose into several narrow regions which differ not only in their composition but also in the nature of their vacancy ordering. Thus it comes about that the results reported in the literature on individual phases often are not in agreement.

The NiAs-phases are also distinguished by the fact that they can be either semiconductors or metallic conductors. Several representatives, for example PdTe and PtSb, become superconducting below $2°K$. In addition such magnetic properties as dia-, para-, ferro-, ferri-, and antiferro-magnetism are observed.

Unfortunately, not much can be said about the bonding in these substances. Certainly the d-functions on the metal atoms play an important role, as W. Klemm has pointed out.[16.5] Compounds with elements of the IV and V sub-groups with the approximate composition Me_1X_1 have a large axial ratio, $c/a = 1·64$ to $1·97$, while the corresponding compounds of nickel and the elements neighbouring it have a small axial ratio, $c/a \approx 1·3$. Nickel has sufficient d-electrons so that, in addition to bonding to the non-metallic atom, they can also take part in bonding with neighbouring metal atoms in the direction of the c-axis of the structure. In this way the c-axis is greatly shortened.[16.7]

17

Co-ordination Structures in AB₂-Compounds (C-Types)

Among the AB compounds we have mainly been considering co-ordination structures, along with a few layer structures (GeTe, SnS), and one chain structure (cinnabar). We have not discussed molecular structures such as ICl and similar compounds. In AB_2 compounds the appearance of co-ordination, layer, chain, and molecular structures is so characteristic that the discussion of the most important representatives will be divided accordingly.

17.1 Fluorspar Structure, CaF₂ (C1-type) and Derivatives

In CaF_2 the fluorine atoms, looked at alone, form a primitive cubic cell (i.e., only the cell corners are occupied). The centres of alternate cells are then occupied by calcium atoms so that the CaF_2 unit cell consists of eight cells of the fluorine sub-lattice, four of which are filled and four empty.

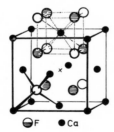

Fig. 17.1. CaF_2 *structure.*

The origin of the cell in Fig. 17.1 has been chosen not at a fluorine atom but rather at the centre of a calcium atom. The calcium fluoride structure is closely related to the zinc blende structure. One can combine the calcium atoms with either half of the fluorine atoms (○, or ◒) to obtain a zinc blende structure. Each F atom is tetrahedrally surrounded by four Ca atoms and each Ca atom by two tetrahedra of F atoms which together form a cube.

The fluorides and oxides of elements having large radii, in general, crystallize in the fluorspar structure, so that eight fluorine or oxygen atoms find a place around a metal ion. The ratio of the Goldschmidt ionic radii is either near to or greater than 0.73.

As representatives of this structure, one may mention: CaF_2, SrF_2, BaF_2, CdF_2, HgF_2, CeO_2, ThO_2 to AmO_2, UN_2, the superconducting $CoSi_2$, $NiSi_2$, and with statistical distribution of the metal atoms $KLaF_4$,[17.1] α-$K_2[UF_6]$,[17.1] $NaCaCdYF_8$, $NaTlF_4$,[17.2] $Me^{III}PaO_4$[17.3] (Me = RE or actinide), or of the non-metal atoms, AcOF. The distribution of the non-metal atoms is ordered in the compounds YOF, LaOF, PuOF.[17.4] If the metal and non-metal interchange their positions we have the '*anti-isotypic* structure'. Those substances crystallizing in the antifluorspar structure include: the alkali metal chalcogenides Li_2O to Rb_2O, Li_2S to Rb_2S, Li_2Se to K_2Se, Li_2Te to K_2Te and also Be_2C,[17.5] $BeAl(B)$,[17.6] Mg_2Si, Mg_2Ge, Mg_2Sn, Mg_2Pb, Ir_2P, Rh_2P, $PtAl_2$, $PtGa_2$, $PtIn_2$,[17.7] $AuAl_2$,[17.8] $AuGa_2$,[17.9] $AuIn_2$[17.10] Na_2Pt.

Among the antitypes, especially, there are many compounds derived from the CaF_2-structure by substitutions similar to those in the ZnS-structure (see chapter 13.6). In LiMg(N),[17.11] for example, the Li and Mg atoms are statistically distributed over the fluorine position while in LiZn(N),[17.11] AgMg(As), MgSb(Cu), MgBi(Cu),[17.12] CdSb(Cu)[17.13] those elements not enclosed in parentheses occupy the F-position in an ordered fashion—that is, they alternate—while the element in parentheses occupies the Ca-position. Further examples of a partly ordered, partly disordered arrangement of atoms over the F-position are $Li_3Al(N_2)$, $Li_3Ga(N_2)$,[17.14] $Li_5X(Y_3)$[17.15, 17.16] with X = Si, Ge, Ti and Y = N, P, As. The nitrides readily form mixed crystals with the corresponding oxides. Indeed the mixed crystal formation between Li_5SiN_3 or Li_5TiN_3 with Li_2O is without a miscibility gap.[17.16]

A series of hydrides crystallize in the fluorspar structure: LaH_2, CeH_2, PrH_2, NdH_2, and SmH_2.[17.17] These can take on further hydrogen up to almost a composition MeH_3[17.17, 17.18] (compare later, Li_3Bi structure). $Ti_{1.50}$ to $TiH_{1.99}$[17.19, 17.20] also have this structure, while TiH_2 and ThH_2[17.21] crystallize in a distorted fluorspar structure.

The above list contains an abundance of compounds for which the approximation given by the ionic model is no longer suitable. The question then arises, which orbitals on the metal and non-metallic atoms bring about the bonding. In CaF_2 itself the search for the bonding functions presents no difficulties. The $4s$- and $3d$-functions are the deepest lying energetically, and we can form the four $(d_\varepsilon^3 s)$ hybrid functions (Fig. 12.10). Each of these four functions is directed toward one of the four body diagonals of a cube and has large positive values in both the positive and the negative direction. The axes of these functions thus point to the eight fluorine atoms which cubically surround each calcium atom. The fluorine atoms form (sp^3)-hybrid functions which point toward the four calcium atoms which tetrahedrally surround them. Since each (d^3s)-hybrid function can bond either of two F atoms lying along a body diagonal, we can formulate a mesomerism. We associate one half of the fluorine atoms and the calcium atom into a zinc blende sub-lattice and can formulate the bonding as we did there. Only, instead of an (sp^3)-hybrid on the Ca atom, we find (d^3s)-hybrids. The other half of the fluorine atoms is then ionic. In the second mesomeric form the role of the ionic and bound fluorine atoms has reversed. This mesomerism can be expressed by a formula in which the zinc blende sub-lattice is designated by a bracket:

$$[F \ Ca]^+ F^- \longleftrightarrow F^- [Ca \ F]^+$$

or

$$[O \ Ce]^{2+} O^{2-} \longleftrightarrow O^{2-} [Ce \ O]^{2+}.$$

Charges exist only in the mesomeric, limiting formulas. Their super-position makes the charges disappear.

We must really search for an acceptable description of the bonding in compounds such as Be$_2$C and Mg$_2$Si, since here the ionic picture is a very poor approximation indeed. In the example of Be$_2$C, (sp^3)-hybrid functions are assigned to each atom. Here also one half of the Be atoms can be combined with the carbon atom to form a zinc blende-type sub-lattice having bonding like that in zinc blende, if the other half of the Be atoms is then ionic. If, however, an attempt is made to formulate a mesomerism,

$$[Be \ C]^{2-} Be^{2+} \longleftrightarrow Be^{2+} [C \ Be]^{2-}$$

the first (sp^3)-hybrid on C must be reflected through the centre in order to

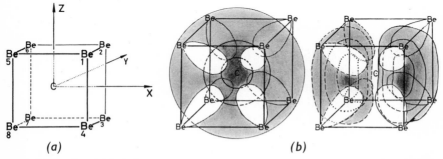

Fig. 17.2. Molecular functions in the Be$_2$C *structure. (a) Numbering of the atoms and the position of the co-ordinate system. (b) Schematic representation of the* Σ- *and one* Π-*molecular function.*

come to one which is acceptable for the second limiting formula. Using the term developed by Welker,[17.22] one speaks here of a directionally degenerate (sp^3)-hybrid. Quantum mechanically, we have the problem here that the functions reflected through the centre are linearly dependent on the four starting functions, and that the addition of a hybrid function and its reflected function leads to the disappearance of the p-functions. We can get around this difficulty by going back to molecular orbital theory. We form molecular functions from the s- and p-functions on the C atom and from those (sp^3)-hybrid functions of the eight neighbouring Be atoms which are directed towards the carbon atom, and which we designate ψ_1 to ψ_8 (Fig. 17.2).

$$\Psi_1 = \frac{1}{\sqrt{2}}\left[N'_C \psi_{C,s} \right.$$
$$\left. + N'_{Be} \frac{1}{\sqrt{8}}(+\psi_1 + \psi_2 + \psi_3 + \psi_4 + \psi_5 + \psi_6 + \psi_7 + \psi_8) \right]$$

$$\Psi_2 = \frac{1}{\sqrt{2}}\left[N_C \psi_{C,p_x} \right.$$
$$\left. + N_{Be} \frac{1}{\sqrt{8}}(+\psi_1 + \psi_2 + \psi_3 + \psi_4 - \psi_5 - \psi_6 - \psi_7 - \psi_8) \right]$$

$$\Psi_3 = \frac{1}{\sqrt{2}}\left[N_C \psi_{C,p_y} \right.$$
$$\left. + N_{Be} \frac{1}{\sqrt{8}}(-\psi_1 + \psi_2 + \psi_3 - \psi_4 - \psi_5 + \psi_6 + \psi_7 - \psi_8) \right]$$

$$\Psi_4 = \frac{1}{\sqrt{2}}\left[N_C \psi_{C,p_z} \right.$$
$$\left. + N_{Be} \frac{1}{\sqrt{8}}(+\psi_1 + \psi_2 - \psi_3 - \psi_4 + \psi_5 + \psi_6 - \psi_7 - \psi_8) \right]$$

These are then four functions, which can accept the eight valence electrons.

Which properties of the fluorspar structure can now be explained with the above formulations for the bonding?

(a) In the series Mg_2Si to Mg_2Pb we find semiconducting properties, which are very closely related to those of the elements Si to Sn.[17.22] The deeper basis for this lies in the relationships between the bonding in the compounds and these elements. In the diamond structure the electrons are localized in the space between each two atoms. In the fluorspar-type structure, the bonding electron pair is limited to the space of a centred cube octant independent of whether we choose (d^3s)-hybrids, directionally degenerate (sp^3)-hybrids or the molecular functions given above for the formulation of the bonding. As in the diamond structure the bonding functions are not continuously propagated since the axes of the (d^3s)- and (sp^3)-hybrid functions point into empty space behind the fluorine positions, just as do those of the p-orbitals. Historically, these semiconducting properties were indeed the reason for seeking a bonding type which is related to that in diamond.

(b) As in the diamond or zinc blende structure the atoms are bound together by appropriate bonding functions. A stable framework is formed. This framework nature can be recognized by the formation of heterotypic mixed crystals between CaF_2 and YF_3, SrF_2 and LaF_3,[17.23] or CeO_2 and $UO_{2.67}$.[17.24] Thereby Y, La, or U substitute for Ca, Sr, or Ce respectively. The excess fluorine atoms go into those cubes, not centred by a metal, which are marked by an × in Fig. 17.1. The framework remains intact, takes on a positive charge, and fits the excess fluorine atom into its holes. In the ionic model this is very hard to understand, since a fluoride ion is now in a lattice position where it is cubically surrounded by eight other fluoride ions.[17.25]

In the compound NaY_3F_{10}, Na and Y occupy the Ca-positions of a fluorspar structure. The two excess F atoms go, just as above, into the vacant centres of a fluorine cube (×). UO_2 can take on oxygen up to the composition $UO_{2.35}$. In the case of PaO_2 the interstices are larger and the oxygen uptake goes to the limit $PaO_{2.5}$.[17.3]

(c) Most oxides of the rare earths and actinides in the tervalent state, e.g., Y_2O_3, crystallize in a fluorspar-type structure in which some of the fluorine positions are unoccupied. With this arrangement of atoms all bonding functions, as in Ga_2S_3, can be occupied without difficulty by electrons (see chapter 13, section 6). However, those (d^3s)-hybrid functions which point toward a vacant position are occupied by electrons only in the one mesomeric form; those directed toward two vacant positions remain completely unoccupied. Were the oxygen lattice completely occupied, we should have to expect excess metal atoms in the vacant positions (×), which would strongly disturb the above formulated bonding system. Further A_2B_3 compounds are discussed in chapter 21, section 1.

(d) The complete symmetry of the fluorspar structure occurs only when the metal atom has the appropriate bonding functions available: three d- and one s-, or one s- and three p-functions or hybrid functions formed from these. In Bi_2OF_4,[17.26] which was formerly considered to be BiF_3, the excess F atoms are in the holes (×). The Bi atom does not remain in the middle of the cube but instead is displaced along the body diagonal since no suitable bonding function is available.[17.27] The 6s-state of Bi remains occupied by an electron pair so that a (sp^3)-hybrid cannot form. In PbF_2 also only the three 6p-functions are available for bonding. PbF_2

therefore has a fluorspar structure only at high temperature when the displacement of the Pb atom along one of the four body diagonals can take place statistically. $Cd_2Nb_2O_7$ crystallizes cubically in the fluorspar structure with vacancies in the O sub-lattice. The corresponding $Pb_2Nb_2O_7$ is rhombohedrally distorted.[17.28]

In Li_3Bi and β-Li_3Sb,[17.29] two Li atoms occupy the position of F atoms in a fluorspar structure while Sb or Bi occupies the Ca position. The additional Li atoms go into the vacant octants. The Li_2Bi sub-lattice is a negatively charged framework in the holes of which are found positively charged Li ions. Here, Bi and Sb remain in the cube centres since all s- and p-functions are available for bonding.

The alloy Fe_3Al (low temperature form), and the compounds Li_3Pb, Li_2MgPb, and β-Cu_3Sb also crystallize in the Li_3Bi type. While Li_3Bi and Li_2MgPb are semiconductors, since all bonding functions are filled with electron pairs, Li_3Pb is a metallic conductor since one electron per Pb atom is missing.[17.30] When there are electrons missing from the outermost valence shell, metallic conductivity frequently occurs, as Mooser and Pearson have shown.[17.31]

To the Li_3Bi group belong also the recently discovered grey compounds Li_2MeMe^{IV}, with Me = Zn, Cd, Hg, and Me^{IV} = Ge, Sn, and to the Li_3Pb group the intensely coloured compounds with Me = Cu, Ag, Au, and Me^{IV} as above as well as $LiCu_2Me^{IV}$ with Me^{IV} = Si, Ge, Sn.[17.32]

17.2 Rutile Structure, TiO_2 (C4-type)

In rutile, the titanium atoms, looked at alone, form a body-centred tetragonal structure. The arrangement of the oxygen atoms is such that each titanium is surrounded by them in a distorted octahedron. Each oxygen atom has three titanium atoms in a planar configuration as neighbours. These form an isosceles, almost equilateral triangle about the oxygen atom (Fig. 17.3).

In this structure type crystallize: difluorides and dioxides of a series of di- or tetravalent elements respectively, in so far as the Goldschmidt radius ratios are appropriate for co-ordination number 6 (0·41–0·73). Only MnO_2 and GeO_2 with the radius ratios 0·39 and 0·36 contradict this rule. As typical representatives one might mention: MgF_2, MnF_2, FeF_2, CoF_2, NiF_2, ZnF_2, TiO_2, OsO_2, IrO_2, GeO_2, SnO_2, PbO_2, the ferromagnetic CrO_2[17.33, 17.34, 17.35] and MgH_2.[17.36]

SiO_2 with the rutile structure (Stishovite) is formed under high pressure (160 kbar, 1300°C).[17.37, 17.38] The following compounds crystallize in the rutile type, probably with a statistical distribution of the metal atoms: $Me^{III}Me^{V}O_4$ with Me^{III} = Cr, Fe, Rh, and Me^{V} = Sb, Nb, and Ta, as well as $AlSbO_4$, $GaSbO_4$, and $RhVO_4$.

CaCl$_2$, CaBr$_2$, SnCl$_2$ as well as several dioxides with metal–metal bonds, which will be discussed in chapter 27.3 crystallize with a distorted rutile structure.

From the geometry of the structure, one can see that (sp^2)-bonding functions are being used on fluorine and oxygen. The bonding functions on the metals vary and are more difficult to specify. Most easily understood is the linear combination of (sp^2)-hybrid functions on the non-metallic atom with acceptable atomic orbitals on the metal atom to form molecular functions. Just as in the fluorspar structure these can be narrowed to the

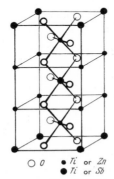

$\bigcirc$ 0 $\bullet$ Ti or Zn
$\bullet$ Ti or Sb

Fig. 17.3. Rutile and trirutile structures.

space from one non-metallic atom, over the metal atom to the next non-metallic atom. For the compounds MgF$_2$, ZnF$_2$, SnO$_2$, PbO$_2$ the s- and p-orbitals on the metal atom are available. For fluorides and oxides of transition metals there are molecular functions such as we considered in chapter 9. Since not all d-electrons or their product functions have complete octahedral symmetry, different metal–oxygen distances result. This effect is especially strong with those electronic configurations which show the Jahn–Teller effect such as Cr^{II} and Cu^{II} in an octahedral field. The fluorides CrF$_2$[17.39] and CuF$_2$[17.40] crystallize in strongly distorted rutile structures. Here one finds the distances:

$$\text{Cr–4F} = 2\cdot00 \text{ Å} \quad \text{and} \quad \text{Cr–2F} = 2\cdot43 \text{ Å}$$
$$\text{Cu–4F} = 1\cdot93 \text{ Å} \quad \text{and} \quad \text{Cu–2F} = 2\cdot27 \text{ Å}.$$

The difluorides of Mn^{II}, Fe^{II}, Co^{II}, and Ni^{II} are paramagnetic at room temperature. At lower temperatures anti-ferromagnetism is observed. Since in FeF$_2$ one t_{2g}-state is doubly occupied, we find two near neighbours, Fe–2F $= 1\cdot99$ Å and four further removed, Fe–4F $= 2\cdot12$ Å.[17.41]

TiO$_2$ itself crystallizes in two other forms: anatase and brookite. Each titanium atom here is surrounded by six oxygens in a distorted octahedron and the coupling of the octahedra is different.

In the so-called trirutile structure there crystallize the compounds $Me^{II}Me_2^{V}O_6$ (with Me^{II}: Mg, Fe, Co, and Ni, and Me^{V}: Sb and Ta), as well as WCr_2O_6 and $TeCr_2O_6$.[17.42] In this structure the Me^{II} and Me^{VI} atoms occupy the corners and body centre of an elementary cell which has been lengthened by a factor of three in the c-direction. The Me^{V} and Me^{III} atoms take up the remaining metal positions in the rutile structure (Fig. 17.3).

17.3 Modifications of SiO_2

There are at normal pressures three SiO_2-modifications which are thermodynamically stable and which lead to a tetrahedral configuration on Si extended into a space net of atoms: cristobalite, tridimite, and quartz.

17.3.1 *Cristobalite Structure, SiO_2 (C9-type)*

In this structure the silicon atoms alone form a diamond or zinc blende structure. The Si atoms here are not, as in the latter structure, coupled by joint electron pairs, but are rather coupled through the bivalent oxygen atoms (Fig. 17.4a). Besides SiO_2, there crystallize in this structure, BeF_2 and the so-called cristobalite ice which results from the condensation of water vapour at low temperatures.

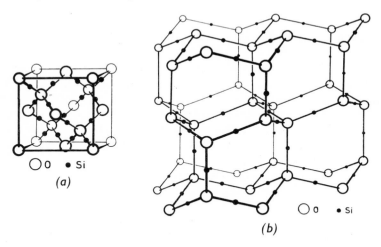

Fig. 17.4. (a) Cristobalite structure. (b) Tridymite structure.

In this ice modification, O atoms occupy the Si positions while the hydrogen atoms are approximately on the bonding line between two neighbouring oxygen atoms so that they stand nearer to one oxygen atom than to the other. In this way the distribution is such that each oxygen atom has two near (0·97 Å) and two farther removed (1·78 Å) hydrogen atoms as neighbours.[17.43] The hydrogen atoms in this situation can change their places very quickly. Hydrogen bonds hold the molecules together and bring about the tetrahedral arrangement with its limited space filling.

17.3.2 *Tridymite Structure, SiO$_2$ (C10-type)*
   In the tridymite structure (Fig. 17.4b) the Si-atoms take the places of Zn and S atoms in wurtzite. Coupling again takes place through the oxygen atoms. Common ice crystallizes in the tridymite structure. D$_2$O has been more exactly studied than water. The following distances at $-50°$C come from that study:[17.44]

O–O	2·76 Å
O–D	1·01 or 1·75 Å
D–O–D angle	109·5 + 0·5°

17.3.3 *Quartz Structure, SiO$_2$ (C8-type)*
   In quartz the Si atoms are also tetrahedrally surrounded by four O atoms and each O atom is at the same time the tip of two tetrahedra so that again two Si atoms are coupled to one another. The arrangement of tetrahedra is, however, complicated and can be pictured only with difficulty. The Si atoms by themselves form a spiral arrangement so that according to the direction of the spiral one can observe optically left- and right-handed quartz. BeF$_2$ can also crystallize in the quartz-type structure.

17.3.4 *Coesite Structure, SiO$_2$*
   There are two additional SiO$_2$-modifications in which [SiO$_4$] tetrahedra are cross-linked, namely keatite[17.45, 17.46] which can be prepared hydrothermally at 380–585°C under a pressure of 0·5–15 kbar, and coesite[17.47]

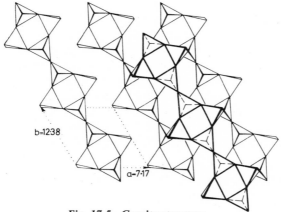

Fig. 17.5. Coesite structure.

which results at 500°C under 35 kbar pressure. In this latter,[17.48] each four $[SiO_4]$ tetrahedra (Fig. 17.5) first form rings which then form fibres parallel to the crystal plane (010). These are arranged in layers parallel to (001). The fibres become cross-linked only with other fibres on neighbouring layers. BeF_2 also assumes the coesite structure under pressure.[17.49]

17.3.5 General Properties of the SiO_2-Modifications

At normal pressure the stability limits of SiO_2-modifications are: quartz 870°, tridymite 1470°, cristobalite to the melting point 1710°. The transitions take place very slowly but can be catalytically accelerated by impurities, especially Li_2O. This catalytic activity is traceable to the ease of splitting an Si—O—Si bond by an ionic process

$$\equiv Si-O-Si\equiv + Li_2O \longrightarrow \equiv Si-O^- + {}^-O-Si\equiv + 2Li^+.$$

All SiO_2-modifications show small alterations in their optical properties at definite temperatures, which are due to reversible distortions in the structure:

α-β quartz at 573°
α-β tridymite at 120–160°
α-β cristobalite at 200–275°

The bonding angle on oxygen is not 180° but rather:

in α quartz 143°
in α cristobalite 150°
in β cristobalite 152°.

Oxygen is thus not found along the bonding line between two Si atoms but is laterally displaced from it.[17.50]

The bonding in all SiO_2-modifications is describable by an (sp^3)-hybrid function on the Si atom and hybrids on O whose mixing coefficients lie between those of an (sp)- and an (sp^2)-hybrid. The exact coefficients can be determined from the above-mentioned bonding angles.

The bonding between Si and O is frequently described as a mesomerism between homopolar and ionic bonding. Such an explanation, as we have already pointed out, is unfortunate. A more suitable explanation results from the assumption of covalent bonding in which, on account of the different effective nuclear charges, bonding functions on the silicon atom are more widely extended than are those on oxygen. Thus, the bonding electron pairs are shifted toward the oxygen nucleus.

17.4 Derivatives of the SiO_2-Modifications

In the modifications of SiO_2 (quartz, cristobalite, tridymite), silicon can be replaced by calcium, boron, aluminium, phosphorus, and arsenic

(Table 17.1). The symmetry of the crystal is often reduced by substitutions. In so far as unbalanced substitution of silicon by the elements mentioned leads to a decrease in the number of valence electrons, these are supplied by the addition of alkalies. The vacancies in the quartz structure are the smallest. Li atoms alone can be inserted there; in the tridymite structure the vacancies are the largest so that even K can be added. When all Si atoms are replaced by the large Al or Fe, the interstices are also large enough in the cristobalite structure to be filled by K.

Table 17.1. Derivatives of the SiO_2-modifications[17.60]

Quartz structures	Cristobalite structures	Tridymite structures
	increasing volume of voids $\longrightarrow$	
$AlPO_4$, $AlAsO_4$ $FePO_4$, $GaAsO_4$[17.52] BPO_4 at 46 kbar and 500°C[17.51] $BAsO_4$ at about 36 kbar and 450°C[17.52]	$AlPO_4$ BPO_4 $BAsO_4$[17.50] $MnPO_4$[17.52]	
$Li(AlSiO_4)$[17.53] Eukryptite Al replaceable by Ga, Si by Ge	$Na(AlSiO_4)$[17.54] Carnegieite $Na_2(CaSiO_4)$[17.54]	$K(AlSiO_4)$ Kalsilite $KNa_3(AlSiO_4)_4$ Nepheline
$BaZnO_2$[17.55]	$Me^I(Me^{III}O_2)$ with Me^I = K, Rb, Cs Me^{III} = Al, Ga[17.54, 13.14] $K(FeO_2)$[17.54] $Li(PN_2)$[17.56]	in rhombic distorted structures $\beta Na(Me^{III}O_2)$ Me^{III} = Al, Ga, Fe[13.14] $Li(Me^{III}S_2)$ Me^{III} = Al, Ga, In[13.14]
	$(NHg_2)NO_3.xH_2O$[17.57, 17.58] $(NHg_2)Br.xH_2O$[17.57, 17.58] $(NHg_2)F.H_3OF$[17.59] $(NHg_2)F.NH_4F$[17.59]	$(NHg_2)OH.I$ or $2H_2O$[17.57] $(NHg_2)I.xH_2O$[17.57] $(NHg_2)Br.xH_2O$[17.57] $(NHg_2)F.NH_4F$[17.59]

In Millon's Base $[NHg_2]OH$, and its salts the silicon atoms are replaced by N and the oxygen atoms by Hg. Since Hg has a strong tendency to form a valence angle of 180° ((sp)-hybrid), the Hg atoms here lie in the middle of the bonding line between each two N atoms. Since Hg atoms are large (radius 1·42 Å), they expand the structure so that large interstices result, producing larger sites for the anion. The nitrate $[NHg_2]NO_3$ has a cristobalite structure. By anionic exchange it is possible from this to form other compounds with the cristobalite structure. Most of the halides have the tridymite structure since the halogen atoms require larger interstices.

In Millon's Base, the radius ratio N : Hg is *ca.* 0·5. Also in the compound Me[FeO$_2$] the ratio is of this order. This fact shows unequivocally that the tetrahedral configuration in all these compounds is conditioned not by size ratios·but rather by the orientation of (sp^3)-hybrid functions on the Si atom or on the corresponding atoms.

17.5 Cuprite Structure, Cu$_2$O (C3-type)

The cuprite structure is very closely related to the cristobalite structure. One half of the O atoms here take the place of silicon and one half of the Cu atoms those of oxygen in cristobalite. In this sub-lattice oxygen has a tetrahedral configuration and the Cu atoms have two nearest neighbour ligands in a linear arrangement, as in the complex ions [Cl—Cu—Cl]$^-$ and [NH$_3$—Cu—NH$_3$]$^+$. Because of the Cu atoms the oxygen sub-lattice is widely expanded and large interstices result. Whereas in Millon's Base,

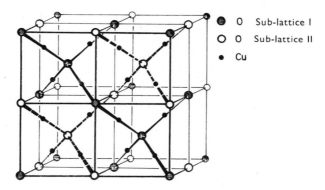

⊜ O   Sub-lattice I

◯ O   Sub-lattice II

● Cu

Fig. 17.6. Cuprite structure (Cu$_2$O).

because of the electrical charge on the framework, the interstices must be filled by anions and water, in Cu$_2$O a second sub-lattice can be inserted in the one described above. The two sub-lattices can be transformed into each other by a translation of 0 0 $\frac{1}{2}$. In Fig. 17.6, the O atoms of one sub-lattice are represented by filled circles, ⊜, and the other by empty circles, ◯. The bonding lines between oxygen atoms, in the middle of which are found the Cu atoms (●), are either dashed or solid. Ag$_2$O also crystallizes in this structure type.

17.6 Pyrite Structure, FeS$_2$ (C2-type)

S–S groups characterize the pyrite structure. The middle point of the S$_2$-group occupies the Cl-sites of a NaCl structure while the Fe atoms occupy the Na-positions (Fig. 17.7). Each S atom has one S atom and three Fe atoms as neighbours in a distorted tetrahedral arrangement. The surroundings of the Fe atoms consist of six S atoms from various S_2-groups in an octahedral arrangement.

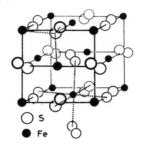

○ S

● Fe

Fig. 17.7. Pyrite structure (FeS₂).

The bonding functions on sulphur are (sp^3)-hybrids, those on iron (d^2sp^3)-hybrids. The iron atom, as in a low-spin complex, has the krypton configuration as in $K_4[Fe(CN)_6]$.

In the same structure type, with the same electronic configuration crystallize:

RuS₂, RuSe₂, RuTe₂, OsS₂, OsSe₂, OsTe₂
PdAs₂, PdSb₂, PtP₂, PtAs₂, PtSb₂, as well as
CoPS, CoAsS, and MeXY with Me = Rh and Ir
X = P, As, Sb, and Bi
Y = S, Se, and Te (Te, however, only in combination with As, Sb, and Bi).

The position of the bi- and tervalent non-metal atoms very frequently corresponds to a statistical distribution over the S-positions. In all the compounds named, the electronic configuration on the metal atom is that of the next following noble gas; the spin moment is then zero. In general one can say that the width of the forbidden zone becomes larger as: (a) the metal atom becomes heavier, (b) the non-metal atom becomes lighter, and (c) the valence of the non-metallic atom decreases, as Table 17.2 shows.[17.61]

PdSb₂, which is superconducting below 1·25°K, does not form mixed crystals with semiconducting PtSb₂ although it does with the superconducting AuSb₂.

In compounds such as CoS₂, NiAsS, NiSbS, NiAsSe, NiSbSe, and the corresponding Pd- and Pt-compounds there is one electron more than is necessary to form a noble-gas structure. The spin moment is found to be

$s = \frac{1}{2}$, when the compounds are made of light atoms. With heavy atoms diamagnetism can be observed. One always, however, finds metallic conductivity of the order of 10^4 ohm^{-1}-cm^{-1}, which apparently comes from the additional electron.[17.62]

Table 17.2. Width of the forbidden zone in Pyrites

Substance	E in kcal/mole
$RuSe_2$	14–23
$RuTe_2$	4·5
$PdAs_2$	0, metal
$PdSb_2$	0, metal
PtP_2	14
$PtAs_2$	11
$PtSb_2$	0·1
$PtBi_2$	0, metal

In NiS_2 and $NiSe_2$ there are two additional d-electrons available. NiS_2 is a semiconductor, $NiSe_2$, a metallic conductor. In MnS_2, $MnSe_2$, and $MnTe_2$, the krypton configuration lacks one electron.

The tendency to form noble gas shells is noticeable in Ir_3Te_8. Here, a quarter of all the metal positions is not occupied so that only an excess of $\frac{1}{3}$ electron per Ir atom is present instead of the one electron expected in the hypothetical $IrTe_2$.[17.63]

Many dichalcogenides of the heavy metals, such as $FeSe_2$ and $FeTe_2$, crystallize in the marcasite structure (C18-type). The metal atoms here form a body-centred orthorhombic cell. Each metal atom is again surrounded by six different disulphide groups in an octahedral orientation.

NaO_2 crystallizes below $-77°$ in the marcasite structure, and between -77 and $-50°C$ in the pyrite structure, in which also crystallize ZnO_2 and CdO_2.[17.64]

18

Layer Structures in AB$_2$-Compounds

18.1 Lead Iodide Structure, PbI$_2$ (C6-type)

In the PbI$_2$ structure, which is frequently also called the CdI$_2$ structure (Fig. 18.1), the iodine atoms alone form densely packed layers which are arranged as in a hexagonal packing of spheres. The Pb atoms are likewise arranged in layers, with the same structure as the I-layers; however, they only make use of the C-positions. The layer sequence ABAB... of the I-layer becomes ACBACB for the compound (compare cubic closest packing, Figs. 12.4a, b and 12.5a, b). Each Pb atom is surrounded by three I atoms of layer A and three of layer B, so that a distorted octahedron

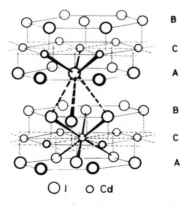

Fig. 18.1. PbI$_2$ structure.

results. Each I atom has to the one side three Pb atoms as neighbours and to the other side at a somewhat greater distance three I atoms in a strongly distorted octahedral environment. In the PbI$_2$-type crystallize:

(a) The di-iodides of the transition elements Ti, V, Mn, Fe, Co, Zn as well as of Mg, Ca, Cd, Ge, and Pb.
(b) The dibromides of Mg, Mn, Fe, and Co.
(c) A series of dichalcogenides of tetravalent elements such as TiS$_2$, TiSe$_2$, TiTe$_2$, ZrS$_2$, ZrSe$_2$, PtS$_2$, PtSe$_2$, PtTe$_2$, SnS$_2$.

(d) BiTeBr and BiTeI[18.1] and, probably with statistical distribution of the non-metallic atoms, AlSI.

(e) The metallic conducting Ag_2F.[18.2]

Closely related to the PbI_2-type is the brucite type, $Mg(OH)_2$. The positions of the O and Mg atoms are as in PbI_2. Hydrogen sits at the apex of the pyramid formed from one O and three neighbouring Mg atoms, so that the oxygens together obtain a distorted tetrahedral configuration. The H atoms thus point always toward the vacancies, which are formed by three OH-groups on the upper layer.

In the brucite-type structure crystallize: $Mg(OH)_2$, $Ca(OH)_2$, $Cd(OH)_2$, and a series of hydroxides of bivalent transition elements such as $Mn(OH)_2$, $Fe(OH)_2$, $Co(OH)_2$, $Ni(OH)_2$.

In the compounds $K_2[Me(OH)_6]$ with Me = Sn, Pb, Pt, the Mg-positions are so occupied by K and Me that a Me atom has only potassium nearest neighbours. The OH-groups then are nearer to the Me atoms than to the K atoms so that the layer structure of brucite is transformed into one with $[Me(OH)_6]^{2-}$ and K^+-ions as structural elements.

18.2 Cadmium Chloride Structure, $CdCl_2$ (C19-type)

In this structure, the geometrical construction of a metal layer and of the two neighbouring halogen layers is identical to that in the PbI_2 structure; however, the superposition of these packets of three layers is different. In

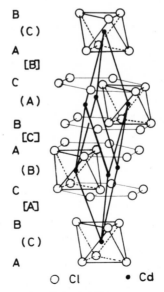

B
(C)
A
[B]
C
(A)
B
[C]
A
(B)
C
[A]
B
(C)
A

○ Cl   ● Cd

Fig. 18.2. $CdCl_2$ *structure.*

the cadmium chloride structure, the sequence of halogen layers is like that in cubic close-packing, A B C A B C, etc. (Fig. 18.2). The position of the metal layers is fixed by the two neighbouring halogen layers. It has a third possible packing arrangement (marked in parentheses in Fig. 18.2). This results in the next nearest neighbouring layer of halogen atoms having the same position as the metal layer. In this structure type crystallize the dichlorides of Mg, Mn, Fe, Co, Ni, Zn, Cd, and further NiI_2, $ZnBr_2$, β-$TaSe_2$,[18.3] as well as in the anti-structure Cs_2O.

In $NaCrS_2$ and $NaCrSe_2$, the Cr and S (or Se) atoms alone form a structure of the $CdCl_2$-type. Between those S- or Se-layers, which include no Cr atoms, are now embedded Na-layers. The location of the Na-layers is indicated in Fig. 18.2 by [ ]. One recognizes that the sequence of NaCr-layers taken separately from the chalcogenides is also A B C A B C .... The Na(CrS_2)-structure can thus be regarded as a distorted rock-salt-type structure with sulphur atoms in the Cl-positions and sodium and chromium alternating on the Na-places (see chapter 13, section 3).

Recently a series of compounds with the $NaCrS_2$-type structure has been found:

$$Me^IMe^{III}O_2 \quad \text{with } Me^I = \text{Na, K, Rb, and } Me^{III} = \text{Sc, In, Tl}$$
$$NaMe^{III}S_2 \quad \text{with } Me^{III} = \text{Sc, Y, In}$$
$$Na_2SnO_3 = Na\,(Na_{1/3}Sn_{2/3})O.$$

The Cr-positions are occupied by Sn and a proportion of the Na atoms.[13.12] We have already alluded to corresponding compounds formed with Li or Ag in place of the heavy alkali atoms in chapter 13, in connection with the discussion of derivatives of the rock-salt structure.

The recently discovered compounds such as $NaVS_2$, $NaVSe_2$, $Na_{0.8}TiS_2$, $Na_{0.95}TiSe_2$[18.4] deserve special mention. They are black and show high electrical conductivity. The titanium compounds in particular appear to have metallic character, which can be recognized in a sharply reduced paramagnetism (at 293°K $\mu_{eff} = 0.61$ instead of 1.73 Bohr magnetons). In tervalent Ti, the orbital of the one d-electron is so expanded that Ti—Ti bonding can occur (see chapter 27).

18.3 An Explanation of the PbI$_2$ and CdCl$_2$ Structures

At the time of the elucidation of the crystal structure of the above-named compounds, chemists were accustomed to think in terms of the ionic model, on account of its simplicity and serviceability, and since no other concepts of chemical bonding were available. It was therefore surprising to see that in these structures, layers of non-metals lie next to each other whereas, because of their negative charge, they should mutually repel one another. It was assumed then that the positively charged metal

16

layers polarized the anions and so attracted the negative charge on the non-metal atoms to them. Thus none of the charge appeared on the other side. Such a picture, however, cannot explain the occurrence and properties of the layer structures. Next, we notice that metal atoms, for which the co-ordination number 6 and octahedral co-ordination are characteristic, are preferred, such as tetravalent Pt and tervalent Cr. Further, in the CdI_2-type S, Se, Te, and I (as well as OH^-) are decidedly favoured as the non-metallic atom. It is known that these readily form complexes with the named metals. Chlorides favour the $CdCl_2$-structure. Fluorides and oxides never crystallize in these layer structures. In the compounds PtS_2 and $Na(CrS_2)$, the electronic configuration on the metal atom is surely comparable with that in $K_2 [PtCl_6]$ (noble gas configuration) or in $K_3 [Cr(SCN)_6]$. In VI_2, bivalent vanadium certainly has the same electronic configuration as tervalent Cr (d_ε^3).

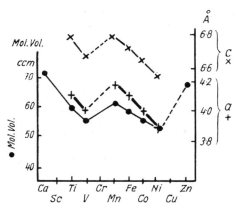

Fig. 18.3. Lattice constants and mole volumes in the di-iodides of the transition metals.[18.5]

All the named representatives are distinguished by a relatively short distance between the metal and non-metallic atom. One therefore cannot go wrong with the assumption that the same forces which are responsible for the formation of complex salts bring about here the formation of layers with octahedral co-ordination about the metal atom. This is also seen in the course of the lattice constants and the molar volumes[16.5, 18.5] of the iodides of the bivalent elements of the first long period (Fig. 18.3).

In Table 18.1, one recognizes that in a strong complex-former of high valence, Pt, the axial ratio, c/a, is appreciably smaller than with the weak complex-formers, such as Ti. In the latter, a value of $c/a = 1·63$ is found, which is expected if the structure is formed by close packing of spherical atoms, in the interstices of which are the metal atoms. In the first case there must be stronger forces operable between the triple layers, which are comparable to those which we have found between the double layers of rhombohedral As, Sb, and Bi. Also with the chalcogenides of Pt the compression becomes greater as the chalcogen atom becomes heavier. $PtSe_2$ is still a semi-conductor; $PdTe_2$ is actually a superconductor.[18.6]

Table 18.1

	c/a		c/a
PtS_2	1·419	TiS_2	1·675
$PtSe_2$	1·359	$TiSe_2$	1·697
$PtTe_2$	1·297	$TiTe_2$	1·734
PbI_2	1·52	SnS_2	1·623
BiTeBr	1·53	$SnSe_2$	1·63

As in the structure of rhombohedral As, one can trace in the PbI_2-type structures three sets of straight lines oblique to the layers, on which the atoms are arranged. In PbI_2 itself, the axes of the *p*-functions on both the metal and non-metallic atoms lie on these straight lines. Here also one can formulate mesomerism corresponding to that in PbS. This becomes clearer if one represents singly occupied *p*-functions by the symbol ⧓

	I	Pb	I	I	Pb	I
I	⧓	⧓	▮◀▶▮	⧓	⧓	▮◀▶▮
II	▮◀▶▮	⧓	⧓	▮◀▶▮	⧓	⧓
III	▮◀▶▮	⧓	⧓	⧓	⧓	▮◀▶▮

and doubly occupied ones by ▮◀▶▮. Formulas I and II are equivalent. In formula III we have four *p*-electrons in four neighbouring atomic orbitals. As in butadiene the outermost bonds (between Pb and I) can be dissolved in favour of the middle ones (between two I atoms). This results in weak bonding between the layers. The distance I–I (4·22 Å), is approximately 0·13 Å smaller than the I–I distance between the layers of elementary iodine (4·35 Å).

In the platinum chalcogenides we have on platinum a (d^2sp^3) hybrid. In the direction being considered there is not one but two quantum states

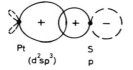 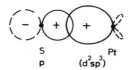

available. Here we have four electrons in four quantum states as in butadiene. In addition, the effective nuclear charge of tetravalent Pt is substantially greater than that of bivalent Pb. The extension of the (d^2sp^3)-hybrid functions of Pt is smaller than that of the p-orbital of Pb. In PbI_2, therefore, the bonding electrons are shifted more toward the I atom. In $PtTe_2$ they are divided more equally between the two atoms. Thus, the influence of mesomerism on inter-atomic distances is stronger.

The mesomerism depicted is not possible in the $CdCl_2$ structure, since the atoms do not lie along the above-mentioned sets of straight lines. The PbI_2 structure is therefore favoured. It is principally chlorides which crystallize in the $CdCl_2$ structure. The wide extension of the valence electron cloud on the metal makes possible interaction with those Cl

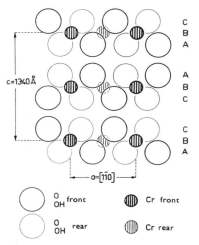

Fig. 18.4. Superposition of the layers in the crystal of CrOOH.

atoms on the next-nearest neighbouring layers, lying directly above and below the metal atoms. In the ionic picture one would speak of electrostatic forces, which pass through the halogen layer. The Cl attracts the valence electrons more strongly to itself and thus reduces the influence of directional forces on the mesomeric bonding system. Therefore weak metal–chlorine bonds result.

In the brucite structure, each oxygen atom is surrounded by three metal atoms and one hydrogen in a distorted tetrahedron. The bonding angle Me—O—Me is generally under $100°$. One can therefore assume that bonding functions to the metal have somewhat more p- and that to hydrogen somewhat more s-character than in a completely symmetrical (sp^3)-hybrid. The three first-mentioned hybrid functions can be combined with atomic orbitals on the metal into molecular functions as was done for complex salts. The fourth hybrid function is combined with the 1s-eigenfunction of hydrogen. Thus all the electrons on oxygen are provided for, and the proton finds no free electron pairs in the structure with which it can form an additional hydrogen bond.

In CrOOH,[18.7] the Cr atom has a pronounced tendency to form an octahedral configuration. The substance is therefore able to form a brucite layer in which half of all the hydrogen atoms are missing. Between the layers there are exactly as many hydrogen donors as acceptors available, so that all O atoms can take part in hydrogen bonding. It thus happens that the layer sequence is altered and the neighbouring oxygen layers lie exactly over one another, distance O–O = 2·55 Å (Fig. 18.4).

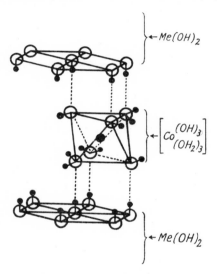

Fig. 18.5. Interposition of an octahedral complex $[\mathrm{Co(OH)_3(OH_2)_3}]$ **between the layers of the brucite structure.**[18.5]

If the hydroxides of divalent metals are precipitated from aqueous solution, water molecules are available with which the OH-groups can form hydrogen bonds. Since the layers are surrounded by water, a slimy precipitate results. Other substances with OH-groups, for example such aquo-hydroxo-complexes as $\mathrm{Co(OH)_3(OH_2)_3}$, can also be added. The oxygen on the added octahedral complexes has at least one free electron pair which can be so positioned that a hydroxyl group of the double layer can form a hydrogen bond with it (Fig. 18.5).[18.5] Since the added complexes cannot get close to one another, they do not densely cover the layer of hydroxyl groups. A ratio of about 4:1 between the number of metal atoms on the double layer and on the added complexes is found.

Also, the expansion of the interlayer distance from, e.g., 4·64 Å in $Co(OH)_2$ to 7·8 Å in $4Co(OH)_2.CoOOH.xH_2O$ fits in well with this concept. Feitknecht[18.8, 18.9] named structures of the above type, 'double-layer structures', and he symbolized them with the very clear formula:

$$4Co(OH)_2 \underset{\text{------}}{\overset{\text{------}}{\Big\langle}} (HO)_3Co(OH_2)_3$$

From this one can easily understand why hydroxides do not, at room temperature, crystallize in a fluorspar or rutile structure. The fact that amides do not occur in the brucite-type structure can be explained by the fact that the amide ion, NH_2^- has only two and not three free electron pairs.

18.4 Electron Configuration and Superconductivity

After having dealt with the most important types of structures, in which superconducting compounds occur, we shall try to throw some light on the connection between the possibility for superconducting behaviour and the electron configuration.[18.9a] Table 18.2 shows a list of compounds in which superconductivity is observed[18.9b−f, 18.6] ordered according to their crystal

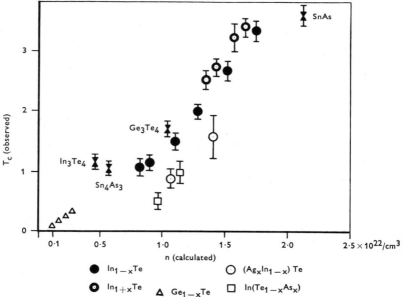

Fig. 18.6. *Carrier concentration and transition temperature in compounds with* PbS *or related structure.*[14.15]

structure. With the exception of two Pd-compounds, superconductivity only occurs if there are up to two electrons more than belong to the noble gas shell of the atoms involved or if one electron is missing. In the mixed crystal system ZrC–NbC, there is clearly seen an almost linear connection between the number of these additional electrons and the transition temperature.[18.9e] The same relation is also shown in Fig. 18.6 in which according to Geller[14.15] the transition temperature of compounds of the PbS or related structures is given as a function of the carrier concentration. This corresponds here, and also in the above mentioned mixed crystal system, to the number of singly occupied s-states. In section 14.7 we have discussed how these partly filled s-states form a special band. From these facts one may conclude that superconductivity can only occur when

Table 18.2. Transition temperature and number of electrons in superconducting compounds.

— superconductivity not yet found

0 ± 1... number of electrons in addition to or missing from noble gas shells.

NaCl-structure			CaF$_2$-structure		
ScN	—	0	CoSi$_2$	1·22	−1
TiC	—	0	PtGa$_{2·33}$	2·9	−1
ZrC	—	0	NiSi$_2$	—	0
Zr$_{0·74}$Nb$_{0·26}$C	3·6	+0·26	PtAl$_2$	—	−2
Zr$_{0·5}$Nb$_{0·5}$C	5·9	+0·5	AuAl$_2$	—	−1
Zr$_{0·23}$Nb$_{0·77}$C	9·3	+0·77			
NbC	12·0	+1	Pyrite-structure		
TiN	4·9–5·6	+1			
ZrN	8·9–9·1	+1	RhTe$_2$	1·51	+1
HfN	6·2	+1	PdSbSe	1·0	+1
NbC$_{0·3}$N$_{0·7}$	17·8	+1·7	PdSbTe	1·2	+1
TiO	—	+2	PdBiSe	1·0	+1
VN	7·5–8·2	+2	PdBiTe	1·2	+1
NbN$_{0·96}$	15·6 ≈	+2	PtBiSe	1·45	+1
NbN	14·7–16·0	+2	PtBiTe	1·15	+1
VO	—	+3	AuSb$_2$	0·58	+1
NbO	—	+3	PdSb$_2$	1·25	0
UC	—				
UN	—		CdI$_2$-structure		
			PdTe$_2$	1·53	0
			PtTe$_2$	—	0
			Spinel-structure		
			CuRhS$_4$	4·35	−1
			CuRhSe$_4$	3·5	−1

orbitals of a band overlap in such a way as to allow the electrons to move at least in one spatial direction without having to cross atomic nodal surfaces.

An incomplete occupation of s-states in compounds is comparatively rare. It can, as shown in Table 18.2 and Fig. 18.6, occur if other extremely stable bonding systems dominate in the formation of the compound. Such bonding systems were discussed in connection with refractory materials having the rock salt-structure, in the lead sulphide group, in the fluorite- and in the pyrite-structures with Pd^{IV} and Pt^{IV} atoms which are able to form especially stable co-ordination compounds.

Superconductivity is more frequently found in compounds and alloys containing elements as Nb, Mo, and W since in these heavy atoms the energetic competition between the s- and d-states is more pronounced. With the light elements as Ti, V, and Cr the s-state is energetically favoured and is, therefore, only seldom not completely filled by the bonding system. In the Pd-atom, the d-orbital is more stable than the s-orbital, as the free atom has the electron configuration $4d^{10}5s^0$ instead of $3d^8 4s^2$ with Ni and $5d^9 6s^1$ with Pt. Therefore, the Pd-atom can also form superconducting compounds such as $PdSb_2$ and $PdTe_2$,[18.9g] although the number of the electrons is exactly right to completely fill the noble gas shells of all atoms in the two compounds. The reason for this may be that for the energetically unfavoured 5s-state a spread out 5s-orbital is characteristic. Therefore, the orbital must be compressed in the lattice. This is made easier by transferring a part of the 5s-electrons into an excited s-band, discussed in section 14.7 for TiN.

Hilsch and Buckel[18.9h] discovered some years ago that amorphous films built up by metallic atoms can be superconducting if prepared by condensation of gaseous metals at liquid helium temperatures. The first such case discovered was Bi, followed by Be, Ga, and films of Sn with the addition of 10 per cent Cu. The s-functions are spherically symmetric. Therefore, an ordering of the atoms is not necessary for the formation of an s-band.

Matthias[18.9b, c, d, i] has shown that for alloys, superconductivity is very often found in the neighbourhood of a certain ratio between the number of all valence electrons and the number of all atoms. For each lattice type there exists a characteristic ratio. For the compounds of NaCl-structure of Table 18.2 and Fig. 18.6 this is 4,5, e.g., TiN((4 + 5)/2); SnAs((4 + 5)/2).

Since little is known about their bonding systems usually one cannot test this hypothesis about superconductivity for alloys. In the case of white tin which is superconducting up to $3\cdot7°K$ we have discussed (section 12.5) three mesomeric bonds which require about three electrons per atom leaving the s-state only partly filled.

18.5 Molybdenite Structure, MoS₂ (C7-type)

The molybdenite structure is closely related to the CdI_2-type. The molybdenum layer is sandwiched between two sulphur layers. The six S atoms which surround a Mo atom, however, do not form an octahedron but rather a trigonal prism. The layer sequence is ABA BAB ... (Fig. 18.7). In the MoS_2-type crystallize MoS_2, $MoSe_2$, $MoTe_2$ below 900°C, WS_2, WSe_2, α-NbSe₂, α-TaSe₂.[18.3] $NbTe_2$, $TaTe_2$, WTe_2 and the high-temperature form of $MoTe_2$[18.10] crystallize in distorted PbI_2 structure types with bonds between the metal atoms.

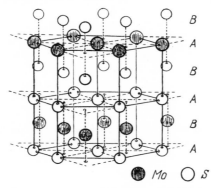

Fig. 18.7. Molybdenite structure (MoS₂).

A prismatic arrangement cannot be explained electrostatically, since the anions mutually repel one another and an octahedral arrangement would be preferred. The functions

$$\varphi_1 = \frac{1}{\sqrt{6}}\left(\psi_s + \sqrt{2}\,\psi_{d_{x^2-y^2}} + 0\psi_{d_{xy}} + \psi_{p_z} + \sqrt{2}\,\psi_{d_{zx}} + 0\psi_{d_{yz}}\right)$$

$$\varphi_2 = \frac{1}{\sqrt{6}}\left(\psi_s + \sqrt{2}\,\psi_{d_{x^2-y^2}} + 0\psi_{d_{xy}} - \psi_{p_z} - \sqrt{2}\,\psi_{d_{zx}} + 0\psi_{d_{yz}}\right)$$

$$\varphi_3 = \frac{1}{\sqrt{6}}\left(\psi_s - \frac{1}{\sqrt{2}}\psi_{d_{x^2-y^2}} - \sqrt{\frac{3}{2}}\,\psi_{d_{xy}} + \psi_{p_z} - \frac{1}{\sqrt{2}}\psi_{d_{zx}} + \sqrt{\frac{3}{2}}\,\psi_{d_{yz}}\right)$$

$$\varphi_4 = \frac{1}{\sqrt{6}}\left(\psi_s - \frac{1}{\sqrt{2}}\psi_{d_{x^2-y^2}} - \sqrt{\frac{3}{2}}\,\psi_{d_{xy}} - \psi_{p_z} + \frac{1}{\sqrt{2}}\psi_{d_{zx}} - \sqrt{\frac{3}{2}}\,\psi_{d_{yz}}\right)$$

$$\varphi_5 = \frac{1}{\sqrt{6}}\left(\psi_s - \frac{1}{\sqrt{2}}\psi_{d_{x^2-y^2}} + \sqrt{\frac{3}{2}}\,\psi_{d_{xy}} + \psi_{p_z} - \frac{1}{\sqrt{2}}\psi_{d_{zx}} - \sqrt{\frac{3}{2}}\,\psi_{d_{yz}}\right)$$

$$\varphi_6 = \frac{1}{\sqrt{6}}\left(\psi_s - \frac{1}{\sqrt{2}}\psi_{d_{x^2-y^2}} + \sqrt{\frac{3}{2}}\,\psi_{d_{xy}} - \psi_{p_z} + \frac{1}{\sqrt{2}}\psi_{d_{zx}} + \sqrt{\frac{3}{2}}\,\psi_{d_{yz}}\right)$$

of a (d^4-sp)-hybrid are directed toward the six corners (1–6 in Fig. 18.8) of a trigonal prism and are available for bonding with the chalcogenides.

WSe_2 is diamagnetic and a semiconductor with $\Delta E = 1·4$ eV. The free electron pair can be provided for only in the $5d_{3z^2-1}$ states not used for bonding. α-$TaSe_2$ is paramagnetic and has a high electrical conductivity, like a metal. It is thus related in its properties to those substances crystallizing in the pyrite structure which have one electron more than would correspond to a noble gas, as for example CoS_2 (see 17.6). See also the metallic properties of VO_2 and IrO_2 (chapter 27.3).

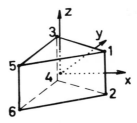

Fig. 18.8. Numbering of the atoms and positions of the co-ordinate axes for the construction of a (d^4sp)-hybrid.

Just as in layer structures such as PbI_2 and $CdCl_2$, alkali metal can be imbedded between the layer sandwiches. Compounds such as $Me^I_{0.5}Me'X_2$, where Me^I = Na, K, Rb, Cs, Me' = Mo, W, and X = S, Se, but not Te, are known. In addition, $K_{0.5}ReS_2$ and $Rb_{0.8}ReS_2$ have also been prepared. These compounds are black to bluish-black and strongly diamagnetic since presumably there are direct Me–Me bonds (see chapter 27).[18.4, 18.11]

18.6 Mercuric Iodide Structure, HgI_2 (C13-type)

In red HgI_2 both the metal atoms and the iodine atoms form layers with square arrangements. Each mercury atom is tetrahedrally surrounded by iodine atoms, two on an upper, and two on a lower layer. Each iodine atom belongs to two mercury atoms. The layer sequence of the iodine atoms, looked at alone, is A B A B ..., since a low-lying iodine atom in the upper double layer lies in the hole formed by four of the higher-lying iodine atoms of a lower double layer (Fig. 18.9).

An electrostatic calculation of the structure is not possible since from the Goldschmidt radius ratios, Hg must have a co-ordination number 6. Bivalent Hg has a predilection to assume a noble-gas configuration with co-ordination number 4 and tetrahedral arrangement of the ligands (cf. $K_2[HgI_4]$). The (sp^3)-hybrid functions here thus lead to the tetragonal layer structure described above. γ-ZnCl$_2$ and ZnBr$_2$ crystallize in the same structural type.[18.12]

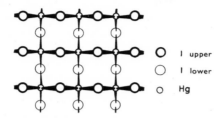

I upper

I lower

Hg

Fig. 18.9. HgI$_2$ *structure in a projection perpendicular to a layer.*

18.7 Derivatives of the PbO Structure

A frequently encountered derivative of the PbO structure is the BiOCl-type structure. It can be derived geometrically from the PbO-type, by adding Cl atoms both above and below the squares of oxygen atoms as long as there are no Bi atoms there. These latter take up the Pb-position (Fig. 18.10). Each Bi atom is then pyramidally co-ordinated on one side to four O atoms and on the other side, also pyramidally, to four Cl atoms. The superposition of these sandwiches made up of five atom-layers, ClBiOBiCl is such that the Cl atoms lie on vacancies. In this structure-type crystallize:

> BiOX with X = F, Cl, Br, I[18.13, 18.14]
> PbFX with X = Cl, Br
> MeOX with Me = Rare Earth, Actinide;
>   X = Cl, Br, I[18.15, 18.16, 18.17]
> MeOX with Me = Th, U; X = S, Se, Te[17.1, 18.18]
> UNX with X = Cl, Br, I as well as ThNCl[18.19]
> MeHX with Me = Ca, Sr, Ba; X = Cl, Br, I[18.20]
> MeSF with Me = La, Ce, Eu[18.21]

Compounds of the rare earths and actinides here show the same structure as compounds of tervalent Bi. This similarity in structure types between compounds of the rare earths and actinides, with those of the tervalent elements As, Sb, Bi is often observed (e.g., Sb$_2$S$_3$ structure, chapter 21.4). In these compounds with the rare earths,[18.17] for example, LaOCl, one finds a short distance between a halogen atom of one layer and the nearest metal atom of the next packet of layers, if the halogen atom is small (Br and especially Cl) and the metal atom relatively large. In this case, the empty d- and f-states of the metal (e.g., d_{3z^2-1}) can be co-occupied by the electron pairs in p_z-states of the halogen atoms.

If we replace a proportion of the Bi atoms in BiOCl with elements of lower valence such as Cd, Ba, or Li, we obtain compositions such as $Me^{II}BiO_2Cl$, $LiBi_3O_4Cl_2$ or generally Me_2O_2Cl. The metal atoms are generally statistically distributed. They form strongly coherent layers with oxygen, just as in the PbO structure. However, only one Cl atom per metal atom is added to the layer. These Cl atoms fit in the same position as in BiOCl. Each Cl, however, belongs simultaneously to two BiO-layers (see Fig. 18.10).

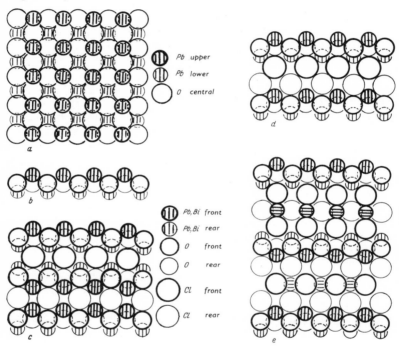

Fig. 18.10. *Derivatives of the tetragonal* PbO *structure.* (*a*) PbO-*layer in projection parallel to* c (*perpendicular to the plane of the layer*). (*b*), (*c*), (*d*), *and* (*e*) *Side view of the structure of the layer packets (projection parallel to* a).

> (*b*) *in* PbO
> (*c*) *in* Me_2O_2Cl X_1
> (*d*) *in* BiOCl X_2
> (*e*) *in* $Me_2O_2Cl_2ClMe_{1-x}$ X_3

Additional derivatives of the BiOCl structure are obtained by melting together BiOCl with the halides of Li, Na, Ca, Sr, Ba, Cd, and Pb.[18.22] Between the sandwich layers of BiOCl additional metal halide layers are then added, as Fig. 18.10 demonstrates. Sandwiches made up of two halogen layers and one metal-halogen layer are formed. In the latter the atomic arrangement is like that in the (100)-planes of the sodium chloride structure. The metal positions, however, are occupied only so far as the stoichiometry permits. Examples are $(Cd_{0.5}Bi_{1.5})O_2Cl_2ClCd_{0.75}$, or in general $Cd_{1-2x}Bi_{1+2x}O_2Cl_2ClCd_{1-x}$. If we represent a sandwich of three layers on the PbO structure with Bi, and the halogen layers, irrespective of their metal content, with H, we obtain the following sequences for the three structure types, which were designated X_1, X_2, and X_3 by Sillén.

Type	Sillén Designation	Sequence
Me_2O_2Cl	X_1	H Bi H Bi
$Me_2^{III}O_2Cl_2$	X_2	H H Bi H H Bi
$Me_2O_2Cl_2ClMe'_{1-x}$	X_3	H H H Bi H H H Bi

The layer sequence can now be widely varied so that a very great number of such oxyhalides with varying compositions is possible. Simple layer sequences are, for example,

X_1X_2 $\quad$ $SrBi_3O_4Cl_3 = Me_2O_2Cl + Me_2O_2Cl_2$

$X_1X_1X_2$ $SrBi_2O_3Br_2 = 2Me_2O_2Br + Me_2O_2Br_2$

X_2X_3 $\quad$ $Ca_{2-3x}Bi_{3+2x}O_4Cl_5 = Me_2^{III}O_2Cl_2$
$$+ Me_{1-2x}^{II}Me_{1+2x}^{III}O_2Cl_2ClMe_{1-x}^{II}.$$

Oxyhalides of tervalent Sb are mostly built very differently; the above-mentioned three structure types are only rarely found in Sb-compounds. For example, $PbSbO_2Cl$ has the layer sequence X_1.

19

Chain and Band Structures in AB$_2$-Compounds

19.1 Silicon Disulphide Structure, SiS$_2$ (C42-type)

The silicon disulphide structure is formed from parallel chains in the manner of Fig. 19.1. Each silicon atom is tetrahedrally surrounded by four sulphur atoms, which in turn bond two silicon atoms with each other. SiSe$_2$, BeCl$_2$, and a very unstable modification of SiO$_2$[19.1] crystallize in the same structure type, as does Be(CH$_3$)$_2$, if one only considers the substructure formed by Be and C.[19.2]

○ S ○ Si

Fig. 19.1. SiS$_2$-*chain in the* SiS$_2$ *structure.*

The structure of the SiS$_2$-crystal follows immediately from the tendency of the Si atom to form tetrahedral bonds and from the bivalence of sulphur with its bent valencies.

In K(FeS$_2$), the iron and sulphur atoms separately also form chains like SiS$_2$. This results from the tendency of tervalent iron to assume a tetrahedral configuration, such as can be seen in the compound Fe$_2$Cl$_6$.

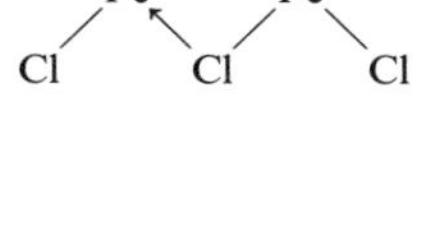

The potassium ions are in the space between the chains. In TlS, TlSe, and InTe, the building blocks are tetrahedral chains like those in SiS_2; here, however, with the composition $(Me^{III}X_2)^-$. The monovalent Me-atoms are found between these chains.

19.2 Palladium Dichloride Structure, PdCl₂ (C50-type)

The compounds of bivalent Ni, Pd, and Pt, as well as in part Cu^{II}, strive after planar ordering, as was explained in the discussion of the PtS-type. This leads in $PdCl_2$, $CuBr_2$, and $CuCl_2$ to a band-like arrangement of the atoms as shown in Fig. 19.2a.[19.3] Figures 19.2b, c show the

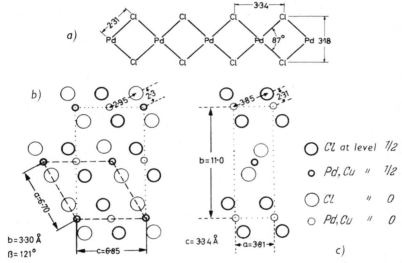

Fig. 19.2. (a) Construction of a PdCl₂-*band. (b) and (c) Arrangement of the bands in the crystal (projection parallel to the band direction),*
(b) in CuCl₂, *(c) in* PdCl₂.

structure of $CuCl_2$ and $PdCl_2$ in a projection parallel to the chain direction. In $CuCl_2$ the arrangement of chains is such that two further chlorine atoms on neighbouring chains belong to the co-ordination sphere of copper. Thus, the distorted octahedral configuration, brought about by the Jahn–Teller effect, results. If the Cu–Cl distances become equal one obtains layers like those which characterize the PbI_2 structure. In $PdCl_2$ the Cl atoms on neighbouring chains separate from the Pd atoms. They lie much more in the holes formed by the Cl atoms of one chain.

20

Molecular Structures

The packing arrangement of the simple molecules AB_2, as for example CO_2, is generally of less interest. One does attempt, however, to obtain by crystal structure analysis, a clarification of the form of the molecule itself. Therefore, only one case will be considered here in which the packing arrangement gives information on special bonding forces between the molecules, which otherwise would be unobservable.

20.1 Mercuric Bromide Structure, $HgBr_2$ (C24-type)

In rhombic $HgBr_2$, the linear molecules are ordered into layers parallel to (001) (Fig. 20.1). Aside from the different inter-atomic distances, the

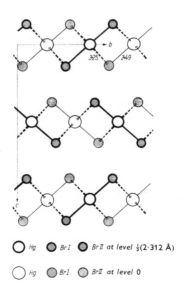

| ○ Hg | ◉ BrⅠ | ◒ BrⅡ at level $\frac{1}{2}$(2·312 Å) |
| ○ Hg | ◉ BrⅠ | ◒ BrⅡ at level 0 |

Fig. 20.1. Structure of $HgBr_2$ ***in projection on the*** (100)-***plane.***[20.1]

layers of this structure are similar to those in PbI_2 or in $CdCl_2$. In the Hg atom, if we ignore the $p\pi$-bonding, there are two unoccupied p-quantum states, while in the bromine atom, two p-states are filled with free-electron pairs. These have the tendency to occupy the free p-quantum states on Hg in the manner of a semi-polar bond. Correspondingly, each Hg atom is neighboured not only by two bromine atoms at a distance of 2·49 Å, but in addition by four more bromine atoms in a square arrangement at a distance of 3·25 Å, so that a compressed octahedron results. The radius ratio is $r_2/r_1 = 1·30$. The bonding angle on the Hg atom is in the range of 89–91° and those on the Br are 90·6 and 90·9°. Mesomerism then results such that the one electron pair on the bromine atom which is above and to the left in Fig. 20.1 forms a bond by occupying a free p-state on Hg; in the second mesomeric form this bond is with the opposite bromine atom which is more below and to the right.

If we now pass on to $HgCl_2$, with the lighter chlorine, we again find a structure having linear Cl—Hg—Cl molecules as building elements. The packing here is different from that in the bromide, and is no longer so dense. The shortest intermolecular distance between Hg and Cl, $r_2 = 3·37$, is even larger than in mercuric bromide with $r_2 = 3·25$ Å. The bond angles deviate, in some cases sharply, from 90°. As we have frequently emphasized, the light element, chlorine, has less tendency to develop mesomeric bonding via p-quantum states.

17

21

Structures of A_2B_3-Compounds

21.1 A_2B_3 Structures as Derivatives of other Structure Types

In our discussion of the fluorspar structure we have already indicated that vacancies in the non-metal sub-lattice lead one to the structure type of Y_2O_3, the so-called C-rare earth oxide type. α-Mn_2O_3, In_2O_3, and U_2N_3 also crystallize in this type. We might mention here that by varying the number of vacancies in the O sub-lattice, a series of different rare earth oxides can be produced, all of which are derived from the fluorite structure, An example is:[21.1, 21.2]

$$\begin{aligned}
PrO_{1.5} &= Pr_2O_3 & PrO_{1.82} &= Pr_{11}O_{20} \\
PrO_{1.714} &= Pr_7O_{12} & PrO_{1.83} &= Pr_{12}O_{22} \\
PrO_{1.778} &= Pr_9O_{16} & PrO_2 &= PrO_2 \\
PrO_{1.80} &= Pr_{10}O_{18}
\end{aligned}$$

The A-type which occurs along with the C-type in lighter rare earths, is more complicated and will not be discussed here.[21.3] With the roles of the metal and non-metal elements interchanged, the compounds α-Be_3N_2, Be_3P_2, Mg_3N_2, Mg_3P_2, Mg_3As_2, Ca_3N_2, Zn_3N_2, and Cd_3N_2 also crystallize in the C-rare earth type.

The Ga_2S_3-structure is derived from the zinc blende structure by vacancy formations in the metal sub-lattice (compare chapter 13, section 6). In_2S_3, which crystallizes in a structure derived from spinel by vacancy formation, will be considered later.

21.2 Corundum Structure, α-Al_2O_3 (D5$_1$-type)

Corundum, Al_2O_3 will be looked at as an example of the formula type A_2B_3, because it is easy here to see how those factors which influence the build up of structure: the stoichiometric ratio, the size of atoms and their tendency to have definite bonding directions with one another, can be harmonized.

Aluminium frequently shows a co-ordination number of 6 relative to oxygen, e.g., $Al(OH)_3$ structure (chapter 22, section 1). A common co-ordination number for oxygen is 4, with tetrahedral arrangement of the ligands. The co-ordination numbers 4 and 6 match the stoichiometric ratio 2 : 3. Since it is impossible to continuously connect regular tetrahedra and octahedra in three dimensions without having gaps, distortions of the co-ordination polyhedra must occur.

The oxygen atoms in the corundum structure, taken alone, lie approximately in sheets which are arranged in the same sequence as in hexagonal close-packing, A B A B A ... (Fig. 21.1). Between each two oxygen layers lies an aluminium layer, C. If all lattice points on the C-layers were occupied

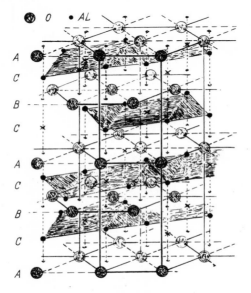

Fig. 21.1. Corundum structure (Al_2O_3).

by atoms, an atomic ratio of 1 : 1 would result. However, every third lattice point on C is unoccupied. The Al atoms on a layer form hexagonal rings, the centres of which are empty. In successive aluminium layers, all three possibilities for vacancies (×) are successively used.

Such a structure with planar aluminium layers would give a prismatic environment to the oxygen atoms, in which two positions in the co-ordination polyhedron are not occupied. In order at least to approach a tetrahedral configuration, the Al-atom must be displaced in the direction of the c-axis, two upward and two downward (Fig. 21.2). The aluminium hexagonal rings are thereby slightly puckered. Two aluminium atoms are then somewhat nearer to a given oxygen atom than the other two Al atoms. Each aluminium atom is somewhat nearer to the three neighbouring atoms on one oxygen layer than to the three neighbours on the other layer. The ratio of inter-atomic distances is: $r_2/r_1 = 1.06$.

The co-ordination polyhedron about the aluminium is geometrically equivalent to that about an arsenic atom in the rhombohedral modification of that element. A weak hybridization of p-orbitals with s-states permits the Al atom to adjust itself to the lattice distortion brought about by stoichiometry.

In this structure type crystallize: α-Al_2O_3, γ-Al_2S_3, Ti_2O_3, V_2O_3, Cr_2O_3,[21.4] α-Fe_2O_3, Rh_2O_3, α-Ga_2O_3, Co_2As_3.[21.5]

The ilmenite ($FeTiO_3$) structure can be derived from that of corundum by replacing alternate Al-layers by Fe- and Ti-layers, respectively. The Fe atom in ilmenite can be replaced by Mg, Mn, Co, Ni, and Cd. Further representatives of this type are: $FeVO_3$, $LiNbO_3$, $CrRhO_3$, $FeRhO_3$, the ferrimagnetic $NiMnO_3$ and $CoMnO_3$,[21.6, 21.7] and under high pressure $MgGeO_3$.[21.8]

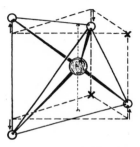

Fig. 21.2. Development of distorted $[OAl_4]$-*tetrahedra in the corundum structure.*

The difficulty we have mentioned in forming a structure can also be eliminated by giving equivalent atoms different co-ordination numbers, for example 6 and 4 to the metal and 4 and 3 to oxygen. This situation is realized in β-Ga_2O_3.[21.9] Its structure is, however, so complex that it cannot be well described pictorially.

21.3 Bismuth Telluride Structure, Bi_2Te_3 (C33-type)

In the series Bi_2Te_3, Sb_2S_3, As_2S_3, and As_2O_3 we shall show how the build-up of the structure is determined by hybridization, which becomes more and more important as the atoms become lighter.

Bi_2Te_2S[21.10] has, in principle, the same crystal structure as Bi_2Te_3.[21.11] This structure is shown in Fig. 21.3. The atoms are arranged in layers as in a face-centred cubic structure. With regard to position, the layer sequence is A B C A B C ..., with regard to occupation, the layers are ordered: Te, Bi, S, Bi, Te. The distances within this five-layer sandwich are short:

3·05 and 3·12 Å (in Bi_2Te_3 3·22 and 3·12 Å). Between adjacent sandwiches the distance is 3·69 Å (in Bi_2Te_3 3·57 Å). The bond angles within a sandwich are 90·0 and 89·7° (Bi_2Te_3 85·5 and 89·3°). Between neighbouring tellurium layers, however, it is 72° (75·7°) and thus substantially smaller.

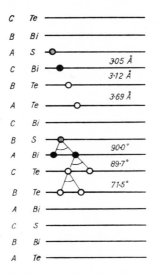

Fig. 21.3. Representation of the layer sequence in the structure of Bi_2Te_2S. *Bond distances and angles are noted.*[20.1]

As in the PbI_2-structure three lines, nearly mutually perpendicular, and oblique to the planes of the layers on which all atoms lie can be drawn through every atom. Thus p-orbitals of each atom can take part in σ-bonding. Within a layer, in the direction of one such straight line, to every five atoms there are five p-orbitals, one per atom. However, there are six valence electrons, as one can see. To a first approximation one can say that each of the five p-states is singly occupied and that the sixth electron forms an electron pair with a single electron already available on an atom with higher effective nuclear charge (S or Te). There is a series of bonding possibilities, three types of which are illustrated in Fig. 21.4. Bonds between the tellurium layers either do not occur or are energetically unfavourable. In the last formula of Fig. 21.3 the bonding system is equivalent to that in butadiene or in PbI_2. The distance between tellurium layers must therefore be increased relative to the distance Bi-Te. It must, however, remain smaller than that which would be calculated from the van der Waals' forces.

Crystal symmetry permits yet a further mesomeric bonding system through the structure using d-states; namely, σ-bonds using d_γ (e_g)-groups, and π-bonds as in the Cl_2-molecule through d_ε (t_{2g}) electrons.

After five atoms the mesomeric bonding system comes to a non-favoured position where the next atom lies at a greater distance. Electron exchange along a bonding chain within the five-layer sandwich can easily take place as in an aromatic compound. The passage of an electron from one packet to the next (in aromatic compounds from one molecule to the next) is hindered. It is thus understandable that these compounds are semiconductors with a finite energy gap. They show a high Peltier effect, and on this account they have been considerably studied recently.

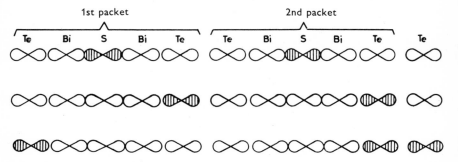

Fig. 21.4. *Three possibilities for the distribution of valence electrons in a mesomeric σ-bonding chain of the* Bi_2Te_2S *structure.*

In Sb_2Te_3, 45 per cent of all Sb atoms and in Bi_2Te_3, 25 per cent of all Bi atoms can be replaced by indium. The electrical properties are only slightly altered. One can therefore assume that the 5s-orbitals of indium are not occupied by electrons and remain empty when indium is added into this layer structure.[21.12]

21.4 Antimonite (Stibnite) Structure, Sb_2S_3 ($D5_8$-type)

In Sb_2S_3, the atoms form thread-like molecules, consisting of ortho-condensed hexagonal rings. At first glance, these appear to be explainable by normal valence coupling of shared electrons between each pair of atoms (Fig. 21.5). If, however, one looks more closely, one observes that the distances between atoms which are not directly bound to one another are appreciably shorter than the corresponding van der Waals' distances, and that the valence angle varies around 90°. One can associate these phenomena completely with bonding functions having predominantly p-character. Subsequently, we shall describe the structure so that it will become evident how with the assumption of a mesomeric bonding system between several structural formulas—preferred bonds within the fibre molecules and unfavoured ones both within and between fibres—one can come to an understanding of this quite complex structure.

In Fig. 21.5, one can see clearly that the S(I) atom, which forms only one, normal bond with Sb(II), has also four mesomeric $p\sigma$-bonds, which are transversely arranged, approximately perpendicular to the first-mentioned bond. Two of these couple two, neighbouring, thread molecules to form a band, $(Sb_2S_3)_2$. The two other bonds are saturated within the molecule, in such a way that an S(I) atom is a near neighbour to an Sb(I) atom. The last bonds bring about folding within the molecule which is closely related to that in black phosphorus.

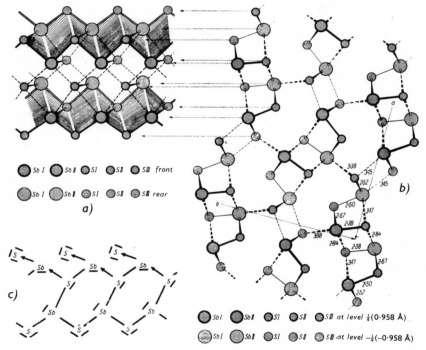

Fig. 21.5. *Structure of stibnite* (Sb_2S_3).[20.1]
  (a) Perspective representation of a double band.
  (b) Projection of the structure on the (100)-*plane.*
  (c) Bonding scheme within a band according to the octet theory.

The bands themselves are again joined by mesomeric bonds via the Sb(I) and S(II) atoms. Since in this case, the sulphur and antimony atoms already form two or three more favoured bonds, respectively, that portion of the mesomeric bonding in the backward direction is not so pronounced. The shortest inter-atomic distance between bands is 3·15 Å. By these means, the bands are combined into layers which are parallel to the (010)-planes.

In the direction of the b-axis, these layers are laid over one another in such a way that an additional weak mesomeric bonding comes about between the S(II) and Sb(II) atoms. The associated inter-atomic distance 3·38 Å, is relatively large. Since, in addition, the number of mesomeric bonds between layers is small, the crystals show perfect cleavage parallel to the (010)-planes.

If one considers the mesomeric bonds which come from the sulphur atoms, one can determine that the S(I) atom forms the strongest ones, because it has only one preferred bonding direction to an antimony atom. The S(II) atom takes part in two favoured bonds and three less favoured ones, one of which leads to the S–Sb distance of 3·15 Å and the two others to the distance 3·38 Å. The S(III) atom, which enters into three favourable bonds to neighbouring antimony atoms, is apparently no longer able to form further mesomeric bonds.

The resonance bonds of antimonite differ markedly from those of black phosphorus in that they extend over only a fixed region of the structure, namely along the limited atomic series: S(II)–3·15–Sb(I)–2·50–S(III) and S(III)–2·67–Sb(II)–2·84–S(I)–3·17–Sb(I)–2·52–S(II)–3·38–Sb(II)–2·38–S(I). In this sentence, the numbers between the named atoms are inter-atomic distances.

If individual bonds are now considered, the following can be determined: in the Sb(I) atom, the valence angle varies about 90°. This is essential if the bonding is via electrons with p-character.

The S(I) atom has five antimony atoms as co-ordination partners. The lines connecting the atoms point toward five corners of an only slightly distorted octahedron. This, too, is easy to explain from the character of p-electrons. The same consideration serves also for the S(II) atom. The S(III) atom has only three co-ordination partners which form valence angles of 92 and 101° with one another. It is interesting to observe the properties of the Sb(II) atom. If one ignores those S(II) neighbours which belong to other layers, the Sb(II) atom has a distorted octahedral configuration with five of the six places occupied by S(I) and S(III) atoms. The sixth co-ordination position is split. This branch of the p-function can enter into two mesomeric bonds with neighbouring S(II) atoms. The p-orbital on the Sb(II) atom forms an angle of 45° with p-orbitals on two neighbouring S(II) atoms. Thereby the extent of the overlap is reduced. Mesomerism can still occur; however, in this case the bond is not especially strong as we have already noted above for other reasons.

Table 21.1 shows that the chalcogenides of bismuth and antimony crystallize in the same structure type as Bi_2Te_2S, for which pronounced mesomerism between p-electrons appears to be characteristic as long as heavy elements are involved in the compound. The low symmetry of stibnite is reserved for compounds with lighter elements. This is found also in tervalent rare earth and actinide compounds with S, Se, and Te. Table 21.1 gives a summary of these.

Table 21.1. Representatives of the Bi_2Te_2S and Sb_2S_3 structures types.

Bi_2Te_2S-type	Sb_2S_3-type	
Bi_2Te_3		Gd_2Se_3[13.31]
Bi_2Se_3	Bi_2S_3	Gd_2Te_3[13.31]
Sb_2Te_3	Sb_2Se_3	Th_2S_3[18.18]
Bi_2Te_2S	Sb_2S_3	Th_2Se_3[21.13]
$Bi_2(S, Se)_3$	$Bi_2(S, Se)_3$	U_2Se_3[18.18]
		Np_2Se_3[18.18]

21.5 Orpiment Structure, As_2S_3

As_2S_3, which is present in nature, is called orpiment (aurum + pigmentum) because of its intense gold colour. It crystallizes in a monoclinic cell formed from nets which are arranged perpendicular to the *b*-axis.[21.14]

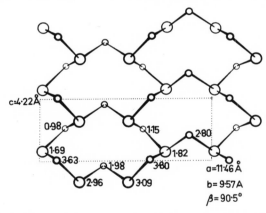

Fig. 21.6. Projection of the orpiment structure (As_2S_3) perpendicular to the (010)-plane.

Figure 21.6 shows one such net. The As atoms looked at alone form a puckered layer of hexagons in the boat form. Each As atom is surrounded by three S atoms in the form of a triangular pyramid. The three S atoms form bonds to the three next-nearest neighbour As atoms. The bond angles on As just as on the S atom are 99° while the As–S inter-atomic distance varies from 2·21 to 2·28 Å. The distances between neighbouring atoms on various As_2S_3-nets are large. Mesomeric chains are not formed since the atoms are relatively light.

As_2O_3 can occur in two modifications: monoclinic claudetite which is made up of nets similar to those in orpiment,[21.15] and cubic arsenolite which consist of As_4O_6-molecules.[21.16] This latter has the same adamantine-like structure as P_4O_6. The arsenic atoms looked at alone form a tetrahedron. The O atoms are above the edges of the tetrahedron and bond the As atoms together. In all these substances van der Waals' distances are observed between neighbouring molecules.

22

AB₃-Compounds

22.1 Layer Structures of CrBr₃ (DO₅-type) and Al(OH)₃

The compounds AsI_3, SbI_3, BiI_3, $ScCl_3$, α-$TiCl_3$,[22.1] VCl_3, $FeCl_3$, and the low-temperature forms of $CrCl_3$ and $CrBr_3$,[22.2] crystallize in a form similar to that of lead iodide. The difference here is that every third position on the metal layers is unoccupied. One layer is illustrated in Fig. 22.1. As in the corundum structure, all three possible arrangements of the vacancy positions are used in successive layers. It must, of course, be pointed out that the halogen layers are somewhat distorted by vacancy formation.

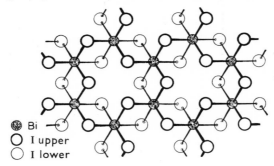

Bi
I upper
I lower

Fig. 22.1. BiI₃ *structure.*

Since the structure determinations have frequently been made on powders rather than single crystals, it is possible that the metal atoms do not really have exactly these atom positions.

$AlCl_3$,[22.3] α-$IrCl_3$,[22.4] and $RhCl_3$[22.5] are also built up of three-layer sandwiches (Fig. 22.1). In these cases, however, only two of the possible vacancy positions in adjacent layers of the metal sub-lattice are used. Thereby hexagonal symmetry is lost and the crystal becomes monoclinic. Further, the layer sequence of the Cl-atoms corresponds to that of a face centered cubic structure (ABC ABC···).

If the vacancies in the $FeCl_3$ structure are filled by tungsten atoms, and the iron atoms are removed, one arrives at the structure of WCl_6.[22.6] The atoms in the halogen layers are displaced toward the W atoms. The building elements of the triple layers are now octahedral WCl_6 molecules.

The structure of $Al(OH)_3$ (hydrargillite) is interesting. The Al and O atoms form layers which with the exception of a slight distortion agree with Fig. 22.1.[22.7] Here each oxygen atom has only three co-ordination partners, two aluminium atoms and one hydrogen atom. The latter has now the choice between two positions on a co-ordination tetrahedron: (a) that of the H atoms in brucite or (b) in the neighbourhood of the vacancies in the Al sub-lattice. In order that hydrogen bonds between layers can develop, both positions are equally occupied. If the formula for aluminium hydroxide is written $Al_{2/3}HOOH$, one can recognize the analogy to CrOOH. Just as in this, the O atoms on neighbouring triple layers are directly over one another, and the layer sequence for the O atoms A C C A A C ... arises. Those H atoms within the layer are apparently shifted somewhat toward the neighbouring O atoms in the O-layer, to which they belong. They are then able to take part in weak hydrogen bonding.[22.7] The exact position of the hydrogen atoms is not known.

22.2 Lithium Nitride Structure, Li_3N

In lithium nitride,[22.8] two-thirds of the lithium atoms form a planar net like the carbon atoms on a graphite layer (Fig. 22.2). In the centre of the hexagonal rings are the nitrogen atoms. Such layers are stacked in such a

O N at level 0   • Li at level $\frac{1}{2}$
o Li at level 0

a)   b)

Fig. 22.2. Li_3N structure. (a) in projection perpendicular to the layer (parallel c), (b) in projection parallel to the layer (parallel a).

way that like atoms lie perpendicularly over one another. In the centre between each two nitrogen atoms on neighbouring nets are the remaining lithium atoms.

Since this structure has large vacancies, which according to the ionic model should not exist, one can conclude that directed valencies are present.

The Heitler–London approximation of atomic functions must be somewhat stretched in order to reproduce the bonding. Much better suited to this task is the molecular orbital method, which we have already considered in a geometrically similar case, the π-bonds of benzene (Fig. 22.3). Each of the lithium atoms in the graphite-like layers is surrounded by three nitrogen atoms. Since their nuclear forces are weak, easy (sp^2)-hybridization is possible. Each of these hybrid functions is directed toward a nitrogen atom. Just as in the LiF structure the bonding functions of Li are widely extended. Within the domain of the highly charged N nucleus these hybrid functions are naturally completely distorted. However, the compression of these functions, which takes place in the crystal, ensures that the magnitude of the (sp^2)-hybrid function is increased in the vicinity of the Li nucleus. The geometry of these functions thus plays some role in making the layer structure of the compound possible.

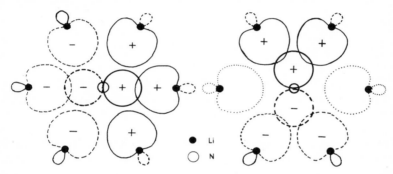

Fig. 22.3. Molecular bonding functions in one layer [Li₂N]⁻ *of the* Li₃N-*structure.*

The nitrogen atom is tervalent. Both p-orbitals on this atom lying in the plane of the layer have the symmetry of the π-molecular functions of benzene. They overlap with (sp^2)-hybrid functions as shown in Fig. 22.3. The third p-orbital on each N atom has its axis perpendicular to the layer and can thus overlap well with (sp)-hybrid functions on the Li atoms between the layers.

22.3 Tysonite Structure, (La, Ce)F₃ (DO₆-type)

Tysonite is a naturally occurring mixed crystal of LaF₃ and CeF₃. In lanthanum trifluoride itself, one lanthanum and one fluorine together form a hexagonal layer like that formed by boron and nitrogen in hexagonal boron nitride (Figs. 22.4 and 22.5). The two other F atoms stand one above and one below a La atom.[22.9, 22.10] Each La atom is thus surrounded by five F atoms at the apices of a trigonal bipyramid. The five La–F distances are almost equal, 2·36 Å. The packet taken from three layers, two having only fluorine atoms and one both fluorine and lanthanum, is so arranged that the purely fluorine layers lie in holes above and below the hexagonal rings of the middle layers of the two adjacent packets. In this way, each La atom obtains six more prismatically arranged co-ordination partners at a somewhat greater distance (2·70 Å, $r_2/r_1 = 1·15$). The fluorine atoms on the purely fluorine layers have as co-ordination partners four La atoms in the form of a distorted tetrahedron (La–F distances: three 2·70 Å, one 2·36 Å).

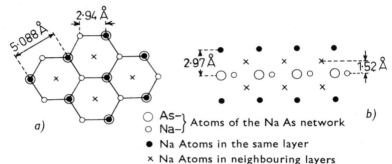

Fig. 22.4. *Tysonite structure (a) in projection perpendicular to the layer (parallel c), (b) in projection parallel to the layer (parallel a).*

In the tysonite-type structure crystallize trifluorides of rare earths and actinides such as: CeF_3, PrF_3, NdF_3, SmF_3, EuF_3, HoF_3, TmF_3, AcF_3, $ThOF_2$, UF_3, NpF_3, PuF_3, and AmF_3.[17.1] Several of these trifluorides are dimorphic and crystallize also in the YF_3 structure which is frequently found among the rare earths, but which will not be discussed here.

The mixed fluorides, $BaThF_6$ and $BaUF_6$ also form a tysonite structure with statistical occupation of the metal positions.[17.1] Further, SmH_3 and

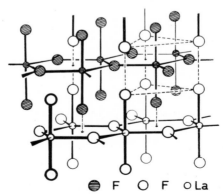

Fig. 22.5. *Two triple layers of the tysonite structure.*

trihydrides of the rare earths with the exception of Eu and Yb crystallize in a distorted tysonite structure.[17.17]

Anti-isotypic to tysonite are those alkali metal compounds with phosphorus and its homologues having the general formula Me_3X, which are marked by a cross in Table 22.1. This antistructure is referred to as the Na_3As-type.

Table 22.1. *Structure of compounds* Me_3X *where* Me = *alkali metal and* X = P *and homologues*[22.11]

	Li	Na	K	Rb	Cs
P	+	+	+	−	−
As	+	+	+	+	?
Sb	+ ⊡	+	+	+	⊡
Bi	⊡	+	+	⊡	⊡

+ = Na_3As structure
⊡ = Li_3Bi structure
− = compound not known
? = structure not known

Distortions are observed in the above-mentioned fluorides; the atoms do not assume ideal lattice positions. These distortions are not found in the alkali compounds. Li_3Sb is dimorphous and crystallizes also in the Li_3Bi structure type (derivative of the CaF_2 structure, chapter 17, section 1). Rb_3Bi, Cs_3Sb, and Cs_3Bi crystallize in a Li_3Bi-type structure in which the atoms have partially exchanged places. The exact positions of the atoms are not yet known.[22.11]

In attempting to ascertain the bonding functions, it is best to proceed from the BN-like net. Just as in BN itself, the (sp^2)-hybrid functions on the alkali atoms and especially on the As atoms fit in with the crystal geometry (As–Na distance, 2·94 Å). The p_z-function on arsenic is still free when p_x and p_y lie in the plane of the net. These facilitate mesomeric bonding with the two Na atoms below and above the net (As–Na distance 2·97 Å).

In the trifluorides, in place of (sp^2)-hybrids a (d^2s)-hybrid is formed and in place of p_z, a d_{3z^2-1}-orbital is used. The (d^2s)-hybrid is given by the following linear combinations:

$$\varphi_1 = \frac{1}{\sqrt{3}}\left(\psi_s + \sqrt{2}\,\psi d_{x^2-y^2}\right)$$

$$\varphi_2 = \frac{1}{\sqrt{3}}\left(\psi_s - \frac{1}{\sqrt{2}}\,\psi\,d_{x^2-y^2} - \sqrt{\frac{3}{2}}\,\psi_{d_{xy}}\right)$$

$$\varphi_3 = \frac{1}{\sqrt{3}}\left(\psi_s - \frac{1}{\sqrt{2}}\,\psi\,d_{x^2-y^2} + \sqrt{\frac{3}{2}}\,\psi_{d_{xy}}\right)$$

As the polar diagram (Fig. 22.6) shows, the essential difference between a (sp^2)- and a (d^2s)-hybrid is that in the latter the three functions are gerade and have equal values in both positive and negative directions. The basis for this is the gerade nature of both d- and s-functions. The axes of the (d^2s)-hybrid functions form an angle of $120°$ with each other just as do the axes of (sp^2)-hybrid functions. From these (d^2s)-hybrids by appropriate combination with p_z-, d_{zx}-, and d_{yz}-functions, there is obtained the previously mentioned (d^4sp)-hybrid which is directed to the corners of a trigonal prism (Fig. 18.7, chapter 18).

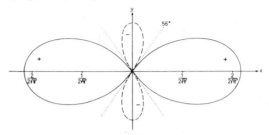

Fig. 22.6. Polar diagram of a (d^2s)-hybrid with $d_{x^2-y^2}$ and d_{xy}.

If one forms the hybrid functions:

$$\varphi_1 = \frac{1}{\sqrt{3}}\left(\psi_{p_z} - \sqrt{2}\,\psi_{d_{zx}}\right)$$

$$\varphi_2 = \frac{1}{\sqrt{3}}\left(\psi_{p_z} + \frac{1}{\sqrt{2}}\psi_{d_{zx}} - \sqrt{\frac{3}{2}}\psi_{d_{yz}}\right)$$

$$\varphi_3 = \frac{1}{\sqrt{3}}\left(\psi_{p_z} + \frac{1}{\sqrt{2}}\psi_{d_{zx}} + \sqrt{\frac{3}{2}}\psi_{d_{yz}}\right)$$

Each of these functions has large values in the direction of two corners of a prism (1,2 or 3,4 or 5,6 in Fig. 18.7, chapter 18, after rotating this prism by $180°$ around the threefold axis). Thus F atoms prismatically arranged about a La atom can be bound.

22.4 Rhenium Trioxide Structure, ReO₃ (DO₉-type)

The unit cell of ReO_3 is cubic with metal atoms in the corners. Between each two metal atoms, in the centre of the edges are the oxygen atoms which bond two metal atoms together. Therefore each Re atom is octahedrally surrounded by six O atoms (Fig. 22.7). ReO_3, $TiOF_2$,[22.12] $TiOOHF$,[22.12, 22.13] $MoOF_2$,[22.14] and NbO_2F to $NbO_{1.25}F_{1.75}$,[22.14] crystallize in this same structure type, and also $CaPbF_6$,[22.15] but with an alternating ordered cation distribution.

The hydroxides $Sc(OH)_3$ and $In(OH)_3$ crystallize in a similar structure type. Here the valence angle on O is no longer 180° but rather 143°.[22.16]

In the trifluorides VF_3, FeF_3, CoF_3, and RuF_3, as well as RhF_3, PdF_3, and IrF_3 we again find coupling of MeF_6-octahedra via the common fluorine atom just as in the ReO_3 structure. Here, however, the valence angle on the fluorine atom is approximately 140° in the first group and 132° in the second. In addition, the position of the metal atoms no longer corresponds to a primitive cubic structure.[22.17]

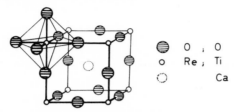

O ¦ O

o Re ¦ Ti

○ Ca

Fig. 22.7. ReO_3 *and* $CaTiO_3$ *(perovskite) structures.*

If we now look back at the Goldschmidt ionic radii, we find that the radius ratios in the above-mentioned metal fluorides range from 0·43 to 0·51. These ratios agree very well with octahedral co-ordination. The Goldschmidt radii for the lanthanide and actinide elements in the tervalent state are approximately 50–80 per cent larger so that these trifluorides can assume higher co-ordination numbers such as $5 + 6 = 11$ in tysonite.

The structure of $Fe(CN)_3$ is derived from that of rhenium trioxide. The cyanide groups here bond the iron atoms together. The surroundings of the iron atoms are like those in $K_3[Fe(CN)_6]$. The carbon atoms of the cyanide group are coupled with one half of the iron atoms, and the nitrogen atoms are associated with the other half.

The cyanide groups force the iron atoms rather far apart, so that in the middle of the cells large interstices result. These holes can be filled with water. In Berlin Blue, $K[FeFe(CN)_6]$ these holes are alternately filled by potassium and water while in the compound $K_2[FeFe(CN)_6]$ all the holes are occupied by potassium. The structure of Berlin Blue is also assumed by the following compounds: $K[MnFe(CN)_6]$, $K[CoFe(CN)_6]$, $K[NiFe(CN)_6]$, $K[CuFe(CN)_6]$, and $K[RuFe(CN)_6]$.[22.18, 22.19]

The deep colour of Berlin Blue is due to the fact that the bivalent Fe atoms, which are essentially surrounded by the carbon atoms of the CN-groups, can by the expenditure of light energy give up an electron to the tervalent iron which is surrounded by nitrogen.[22.20] If the nitrogen and carbon atoms were statistically distributed about the bi- and tervalent metal atoms, electron transfer would require no energy since both positions would be energetically equivalent. The substance would then have to be metallic in appearance and a metallic conductor (cf. the tungsten bronzes, discussed in section 1 of chapter 23).

18

23

Ternary Compounds

23.1 Perovskite Structure, $CaTiO_3$ ($E2_1$-type)

The structure of perovskite, $CaTiO_3$ (ABO_3) is closely related to that of ReO_3. The Ti(B)-atom takes the place of rhenium while the Ca(A) fits in the centre of the cubic unit cell (Fig. 22.7). Titanium is then octahedrally surrounded by six oxygen atoms, while calcium is surrounded by twelve oxygens. Ca and O together form a face-centred cubic structure like that in metallic copper. From this fact alone one can determine that this structure is stable only when atoms of similar size are on the A- and O-positions.

The distance B–O is $a/2$; the A–O distance corresponds to half the face diagonal $\sqrt{2}\,(a/2)$. Strictly speaking, the equation for the radii of the atoms must be:

$$R_A + R_O = t\sqrt{2}(R_B + R_O), \quad \text{with } t = 1.$$

If one holds to the ionic picture and uses ionic radii, this condition can be fulfilled only approximately. Going back to the Goldschmidt ionic radii, the *tolerance factor*, t is found to be between 0·8 and 1. For low values of the tolerance factor, $t = 0.8-0.9$, the perovskites are not strictly cubic but are distorted. When the tolerance factor is lower than 0·8 other structures occur, e.g., the ilmenite structure in $FeTiO_3$. When the factor is between 0·9 and 1, undistorted cubic perovskites can result.

The following combinations crystallize in either ideal or distorted perovskite structures:

(a) *Oxides*

A = Ca, Sr, Ba, and B = Ti, Zr, Hf, Sn, Ce, Tc,[23.1] as $CaTiO_3$, $BaCeO_3$, etc.; in addition $SrTiO_{2.5}$ and $SrVO_{2.5-2.7}$,[23.2] $BaFeO_{2.5}$[23.3] with holes in the O sub-lattice

A = Rare earth, B = Al, Sc, V, Cr, Mn, Fe, Co, Ga, as $LaMnO_3$, $La_{2/3}TiO_3$ (with vacancies in the La sub-lattice).

Further compounds such as:

$$Pb(Sc_{0.5}Nb_{0.5})O_3, \quad Pb(Fe_{0.5}Nb_{0.5})O_3.$$

La $(Me^{II}_{0.5}Ru_{0.5})O_3$ with Me^{II} = Mg, Ni, Zn.[23.4]
$Me^{II}(Ni_{0.5}Me^{VI}_{0.5})O_3$ and $Me^{II}(Ni_{1/3}Me^{V}_{2/3})O_3$ with Me^{II} = Sr,
Ba; Me^{V} = Nb, Ta, Sb; Me^{VI} = W, U, Te.[17.42]
Ba $Me^{IV}O_3$ with Me^{IV} = Th to Am.[23.5]

(b) *Fluorides*
KBF_3 with B = Mg, Cr, Mn, Fe, Co, Ni, Cu, Zn.[23.6]

(c) *Oxifluorides*
$Me^{I}NbO_2F$ with Me^{I} = Li, Na, K.[23.7]

(d) *Chlorides and Bromides*
$CsBCl_3$ and $CsBBr_3$ with B = Cd and Hg,[23.8, 23.9] $CsAuCl_3$.[23.10]
$CsCaCl_3$,[23.10a] $KMnCl_3$.[23.10b]

(e) *Sulphides*
$ATiS_3$ with A = Sr, Ba.[23.11]
$AZrS_3$ with A = Ca, Sr, Ba.[23.12]

(f) An antitype is found in $ISAg_3$.[23.13]

Examples of compounds having the ideal cubic structure are:

$SrTiO_3$		$EuTiO_3$	$KMnF_3$
$SrZrO_3$	$BaZrO_3$	$LaMnO_3$	$KFeF_3$
$SrHfO_3$	$BaHfO_3$		$KCoF_3$
$SrSnO_3$	$BaSnO_3$		$KNiF_3$
	$BaCeO_3$		$KZnF_3$[23.6]

Examples of compounds having a distorted Perovskite structure include:[23.14]

$CaTiO_3$
$BaTiO_3$ (4 forms and 1 hexagonal high-temperature form with differently coupled TiO_6-octahedra; no longer a perovskite since at least part of the octahedral faces are joined.)
$PbTiO_3$ (3 forms)
$PbZrO_3$
$PbHfO_3$ $KMgF_3$
$NaNbO_3$ (4 forms) $KCuF_3$
$KNbO_3$ (4 forms) $RbCuF_3$[23.6, 23.15, 23.16]
                        $KCrF_3$

The type of distortion is often unknown although the compounds are of great technical interest for their electrical and magnetic properties. The three low-temperature forms of $BaTiO_3$, for example, are ferroelectric; $NaNbO_3$, $PbZrO_3$, and $PbHfO_3$ are anti-ferroelectric. Mixed crystals containing manganese partially in the tetravalent state, such as $LaCa_{0.2}Mn_{0.8}O_3$ or $La_xSr_{1-x}MnO_3$ are ferromagnetic, while $GdFeO_3$ and $LaFeO_3$ are anti-ferromagnetic.

A substance is called *ferroelectric* when it is spontaneously and reversibly polarized in an electric field (high dielectric constant), because parallel dipoles are produced in the crystal. Ferroelectrics show hysteresis curves in a variable electric field similar to those obtained for ferromagnetic substances in a magnetic field. *Antiferroelectric* substances also contain electric dipoles; however, these are antiparallel so that the resultant moment is zero.[23.14]

The perovskite structure can be considered as an ReO_3-framework with large metal atoms filling the holes in the centre of the cells. The bonding of oxygen to the atoms in the Ti-positions is strong. Even π-bonding between these atom positions can be observed in coloured perovskites by the

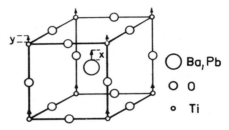

Fig. 23.1. *Distortion of the perovskite structure in* $BaTiO_3$ *and* $PbTiO_3$.

magnitude of the crystal field splitting [17.42, 23.17] and in $K[MnF_3]$ by nuclear magnetic resonance measurements.[23.18] The frame-like nature coupled with easy alteration of the bond angles on the O atom permits the structure to be easily distorted and should allow it to form glasses (cf. chapter 29). It is further evident in the easy formation of holes in the metal, as well as in the oxygen sub-lattice.

It is the distorted perovskite structures which are ferroelectric. The cause of the electrical polarizability—often very strong—is still debated. It is probably due to bonding systems which can be easily altered in an electric field and which can follow the movements of the atoms in the cage. The continuous transition of tetragonal $BaTiO_3$ into the cubic form with increasing temperature[23.19] (cf. Fig. 23.1), is analogous to the continuous transition of GeTe from rhombohedral to cubic. The strong distortion which is found in lead-containing perovskites also shows the influence of the directed orbitals on lead.

Reports on the type of distortions in tetragonal forms of $BaTiO_3$[23.20] and $PbTiO_3$[23.21] can be found in the literature. The results, however, do not appear to be too reliable.[23.22] The metal atoms are displaced in the direction of the *c*-axis as is clear from Fig. 23.1. From the degree of displacement one obtains the co-ordination numbers and distances of Table 23.1.

Table 23.1. Co-ordination numbers and distances on the tetragonal forms of $BaTiO_3$ *and* $PbTiO_3$

BaTiO₃		PbTiO₃	
Ti–O	Ba–O	Ti–O	Pb–O
$1 \times r_1 = 1.86$ Å	$4 \times r_1 = 2.79$ Å	$1 \times r_1 = 1.78$ Å	$4 \times r_1 = 2.53$ Å
$4 \times r_2 = 2.00$ Å	$4 \times r_2 = 2.82$ Å	$4 \times r_2 = 1.98$ Å	$4 \times r_2 = 2.80$ Å
$1 \times r_3 = 2.17$ Å	$4 \times r_3 = 2.88$ Å	$1 \times r_3 = 2.38$ Å	$4 \times r_3 = 3.20$ Å
$r_2/r_1 = 1.08$	$r_2/r_1 = 1.01$	$r_2/r_1 = 1.11$	$r_2/r_1 = 1.10$
$r_3/r_1 = 1.13$	$r_3/r_1 = 1.03$	$r_3/r_1 = 1.32$	$r_3/r_1 = 1.23$

The lead compound is thus significantly more distorted than the barium compound. Lead has four near neighbours in analogy to tetragonal PbO. The bond angle O—Pb—O is 159°.

In $KCuF_3$, the Jahn–Teller effect leads to distortion of the $[CuF_6]$-octahedra so that four F-neighbours stand nearer to Cu (2×1.89 Å and 2×1.96 Å), than do the two others (2.25 Å). A similar phenomenon is observed in $KCrF_3$.[23.6, 23.15, 23.16]

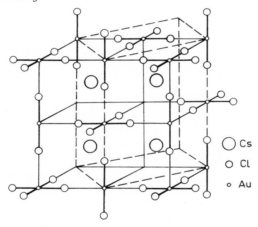

Cs
Cl
Au

Fig. 23.2. $CsAuCl_3$ *structure. The unit cell is indicated by broken lines.*

Distortions in $CsAuCl_3$ are also known.[23.10] The structure (Fig. 23.2) contains mono- and tervalent gold as one can deduce from the type of distortions. These are such that one half of the gold atoms have two near-neighbour chlorine atoms in a linear arrangement just as does mercury in $HgBr_2$. The other half have four chlorine atoms as neighbours in a square arrangement (cf. PtS structure). The influence of the bonding functions on the metal atom (*sp*)- and (*dsp²*)-hybrids is again noticeable. Monovalent gold can be replaced by silver without changing the crystal structure.

An interesting distortion, with retention of the cubic symmetry, occurs when the B-positions of the perovskite lattice are alternately occupied by atoms of considerably different valencies, for example, in $Ba_2[BaMe^{VI}O_6]$ with $Me^{VI} = U$,[23.22a] Np, or Pu.[23.22b] The O atoms are no longer centred between a Ba and a Me^{VI} atom, but are closer to the Me^{VI} atoms. If one considers the $[Me^{VI}O_6]$ groups as ionic islands in the structure the result is the frequently encountered structure type of $(NH_4^+)_3[FeF_6]^{3-}$ which is typical for many complex salts of corresponding composition. If one removes the Ba^{2+}- or $(NH_4)^+$-ions from the B-sites the $K_2[PtCl_6]$ structure results. A large number of octahedrally co-ordinated complex salts of analogous composition crystallize in this structure, in which the Pt and K atoms, considered separately, form a CaF_2 structure.

The so-called tungsten bronzes also crystallize in the perovskite structure, when they have the compositions Na_xWO_3 with $x = 0.32$–0.93,[23.23] and the bronzes which can be prepared under high pressure Na_xMoO_3 ($x = 0.90$ to 0.97; 65 kbar) and K_xMoO_3 ($x = 0.89$ to 0.97).[23.24] In these phases not all the A-positions are occupied by sodium, and vacancies are found. These substances have metallic lustre, in the case of the tungsten bronzes colours from gold ($x \approx 1$) and red ($x \approx 0.6$) to deep violet ($x \approx 0.3$), and they are good electrical conductors.

These properties result from the fact that penta- and hexavalent tungsten occupy equivalent lattice points, if one ignores the fact that because of the different valencies on W, local distortion can occur and the number of vacancies around a W atom can vary. The transfer of an electron from a pentavalent to a hexavalent tungsten atom thus requires little or no energy (cf. chapter 26, section 23).

The corresponding lithium compound is cubic from $x \approx 0.3$ to 0.6. The K-, Rb-, and Cs-compounds are known only for lower values of x ($x \approx 0.3$–0.6). These phases and also the Na- and Li-compounds with $x \approx 0.3$ are no longer cubic but rather crystallize in a tetragonally distorted structure or in structures in which the WO_6-octahedra are coupled differently so that the relationship to the perovskite structure is lost (see chapter 26, section 2).

23.2 Derivatives of the Perovskite Structure

The strong bonding between atoms on the Ti- and O-positions of the perovskite structure, i.e., those atoms occupying the ReO_3 sub-lattice, leads to the retention of this atom grouping in two dimensions even though stoichiometry no longer permits a three-dimensional perovskite network.

Thus in SnF_4 there is a strong tendency for tetravalent Sn to form an octahedral environment to the planar structure of Fig. 23.3.[23.25] Such a net represents a segment of the perovskite, or ReO_3 structure. The super-

position of the nets occurs in such a way that the free peaks of the octahedra
of one layer lie in the holes formed by the peaks of the octahedra on the
neighbouring layers. Since the distance between neighbouring peaks on one
layer is relatively large, the points of the octahedra are sunk so deeply into
these holes that the F atoms on neighbouring layers are at approximately
the same level. SnF_4,[23.25] PbF_4,[23.25] and NbF_4[23.26, 23.27] crystallize
with this structure.

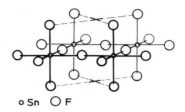

o Sn   O F

**Fig. 23.3. Layer of the SnF_4 structure. × symbolizes the position of the corners of
octahedra in neighbouring layers.**

If the nets are stacked so that the peaks of the octahedra lie over one
another and form tetragonally-distorted cubes, larger atoms can fit into
these holes. Such structures are found in the compounds $MeAlF_4$ (Me =
K, Rb, NH_4, Tl).[23.28]

While $KNiF_3$ crystallizes in the perovskite structure, K_2NiF_4 crystallizes
in a derivative of the perovskite structure (Fig. 23.4).[23.29] If three adjacent

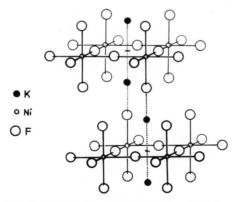

● K

o Ni

O F

Fig. 23.4. Two layers of the K_2NiF_4 structure.

(100) planes in perovskite are combined into a layer, this has exactly the
stoichiometry required for K_2NiF_4. Two neighbouring K–F layers are
positioned over one another as in the KF structure (rock-salt type).

The following compounds crystallize in the K_2NiF_4 type:

$$Me_2^I NiF_4 \text{ with } Me^I = K, Rb, NH_4, Tl^{23.30}$$

$$Me_2^I CoF_4 \text{ with } Me^I = K, Rb, Tl^{23.31}$$

$Me_2^I CuF_4$ with Me^I = Na, Rb, Tl.[23.31] These compounds show Jahn–Teller distortion of the $[CuF_6]$-octahedra.

Also: K_2MgF_4,[23.32] Sr_2TiO_4,[23.33] Ca_2MnO_4,[23.33] $SrLaAlO_4$,[23.33] Ba_2SnO_4,[23.34] Ba_2PbO_4,[23.34] Ba_2TcO_4,[23.1] Sr_2IrO_4,[23.35] Nd_2CuO_4,[23.36] La_2NiO_4,[23.37] rhombic distorted La_2CoO_4,[23.37] Cs_2CrCl_4[23.38] Rb_2MnCl_4.[23.10b]

If the perovskite-like layers have the thickness not of one perovskite unit cell (= 3 atom layers), but of n unit cells, there result compounds having the general formula $A_{n+1}B_nO_{3n+1}$. Such structures with $n = 2$ and 3 have been found in $Sr_3Ti_2O_7$[23.39] and $Sr_4Ti_3O_{10}$.[23.39] Corresponding compounds of Zr^{IV},[23.39a] Fe^{IV}, and Mn^{IV},[23.39b] as well as $K_3Mn_2Cl_7$[23.10b] crystallize in the same structure type.

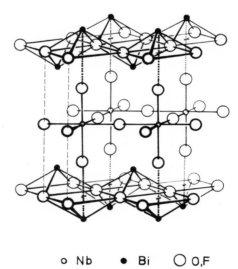

o Nb   • Bi   ○ O,F

Fig. 23.5. Structure of Bi_2NbO_5F.

A further possible variation in the perovskite structure results from a combination of the above-described structures with those of the tetragonal PbO structure. Figure 23.5 shows the structure of Bi_2NbO_5F. If one uses the ionic formulation, $(NbO_3F)^{2-}(BiO)_2^+$, the structural relationships become clearer. In so far as F is substituted for O in the BiO-layers, the formulas can be altered. The bismuth atoms combine with the oxygen atoms to form a highly polymeric network. At the same time, they are related to the perovskite-like layers, even though they are more weakly bound, since they are found in the vicinity of the B-position (Ti) of the perovskite lattice. Further examples of this type of packing are: $(TaO_3F)^{2-}(BiO)_2^+$, $(TiO_2F_2)^{2-}(BiO)_2^+$,[23.40] $Ba_2MeF_6 = (MeF_4)^{2-}$ $(BaF)_2^+$ with Me = Co, Ni, Zn, Cu.[23.41] The Cu salt is again distorted by the Jahn–Teller effect.

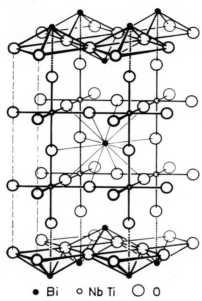

● Bi   ○ Nb Ti   ◯ O

Fig. 23.6. Structure of Bi_3NbTiO_9.

Figure 23.6 shows the structure of $Bi_3NbTiO_9 = (BiNbTiO_7)^{2-}$ $(BiO)_2^+$.[23.40] Just as in $Sr_3Ti_2O_7$ perovskite layers with a thickness of $2a$ (a = lattice constant) are combined with $(BiO)^+$-layers. Two Bi atoms belong to the latter layer and one occupies the A (Ca)-positions of the perovskite structure. Compounds having perovskite layer thicknesses of $3a$: $(Bi_2Ti_3O_{10})^{2-}(BiO)_2^+$ [23.40] and $4a$: $(BaBiTi_4O_{13})^{2-}(BiO)_2^+$ are also known.

23.3 Spinel Structure, $MgAl_2O_4$ (H1₁-type)[23.42, 23.43]

In this structure, the oxygen atoms have an approximately face-centred cubic order like that which is characteristic for the chlorine sub-lattice in NaCl or the sulphur sub-lattice in zinc blende. The aluminium atoms now regularly occupy half of the octahedral interstices occupied by Na atoms in NaCl while the magnesium atoms fill a quarter of the tetrahedral

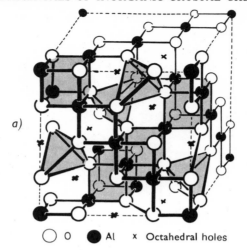

○ O   ● Al   × Octahedral holes

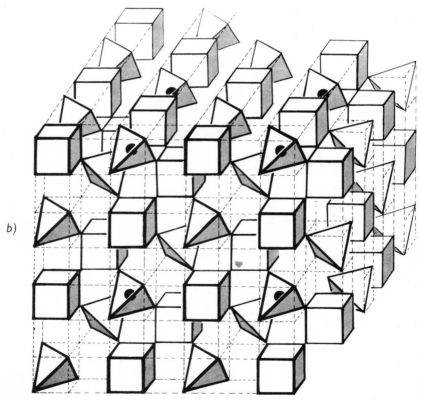

Fig. 23.7. Spinel structure ($MgAl_2O_4$). *(a) The figure shows in the foreground the octahedral holes* (×), *which are unoccupied, as well as the* $[MgO_4]$-*tetrahedra and their cross-linking with the cubes of four* Al *and four* O *atoms. (b) The figure shows the spatial coupling of* $[MgO_4]$-*tetrahedra and the* $[Al_4–O_4]$-*cubes. The corners of the unit cells are given by the* Mg-*positions* (●).

interstices, which are occupied by zinc in zinc blende. The distribution of metal atoms in the structure is such that each oxygen atom is surrounded by four metal atoms (3 aluminium and 1 magnesium) in the form of a slightly distorted tetrahedron (cf. Fig. 23.7a, b).

A graphic representation of the structure giving the geometrical relationships is very difficult to make. A clear picture can be obtained only from a model. Despite this problem we must discuss the structure here since it is widespread and substances crystallizing in this structure have important technical significance.

It must be pointed out that the O atoms do not form a perfect face-centred cubic sub-lattice. Depending on the size of the included metal atoms the oxygen atoms are displaced either toward the tetrahedral sites or in the reverse direction, i.e., in the direction of a body diagonal.

Definite size relationships among the constituent atoms are also required here. These relationships are satisfied especially by the transition metals in the first long period. The most important representatives of this structure-type are:

$A^{II}B_2^{III}O_4$ with A = Mg, Mn, Co, Ni, Cu, and Zn
  B = Al, Cr, Fe, and less frequently Mn, Co

examples: $NiAl_2O_4$, $MgCr_2O_4$, $FeCr_2O_4$, Mn_3O_4, Fe_3O_4, Co_3O_4.

$A^{IV}B_2^{II}O_4$ with A = Ti, Sn
  B = Zn, Co

examples: $TiZn_2O_4$, $SnCo_2O_4$.

On considering such spinels as $NiFe_2O_4$ and $TiZn_2O_4$, it is surprising to find that in the first case bivalent Ni is occupying tetrahedral interstices, whereas it is tervalent Fe that prefers tetrahedral environments. In the second place it is just as surprising that Zn should be found in octahedral and Ti in tetrahedral positions. A more exact study has shown that these total formulas cannot be used to derive the actual positions of atoms in the crystal structure. Atoms try to fit into those places most suitable for them. Thus, in $NiFe_2O_4$ one Fe^{III} goes into the tetrahedral position while the Ni and the other Fe atom occupy the two octahedral positions. If we wish to show the positions of the atoms by means of a chemical formula, we write, e.g., $Fe^{III}(Ni^{II}Fe^{III})O_4$.

The most important of the so-called *inverse* spinels are:[23.44, 23.45]

$$Fe^{III}(Mg^{II}Fe^{III})O_4 \qquad In^{III}(Mg^{II}In^{III})O_4$$
$$Fe^{III}(Fe^{II}\ Fe^{III})O_4 \qquad Zn^{II}(Zn^{II}\ Ti^{IV})O_4$$
$$Fe^{III}(Ni^{II}\ Fe^{III})O_4 \qquad Zn^{II}(Zn^{II}\ Sn^{IV})O_4$$
$$Fe^{III}(Cu^{II}\ Fe^{III})O_4 \qquad Co^{II}(Co^{II}\ Sn^{IV})O_4$$

If the differences in co-ordination tendencies of individual metals are not as great as in the examples above, the various types of atoms can fit into octahedral and tetrahedral positions more or less statistically. Statistical distribution becomes more and more pronounced as the preparation temperature and the cooling rate are increased. Typical examples include:

$$(Fe_{0.9}Mg_{0.1})(Mg_{0.9}Fe_{1.1})O_4, \qquad (Fe_{0.2}Mn_{0.8})(Mn_{0.2}Fe_{1.8})O_4.$$

At high temperatures, the bi- and tervalent iron atoms in $Fe^{III}(Fe^{II}Fe^{III})O_4$ are statistically distributed in the octahedral positions. This substance thus shows high electrical conductivity. Below 120°K long-range ordering occurs and the electrical resistance suddenly increases.[23.46] An ordered arrangement of the atoms on octahedral positions is also found in $Fe(Li_{0.5}Fe_{1.5})O_4$.[23.47] The distribution here is such that the lithium atoms have only iron atoms as neighbours. Only above 1020°K are Li and Fe statistically distributed over octahedral places. It is also possible to have an ordered arrangement of atoms in tetrahedral positions with $Li_{1/2}Fe^{III}_{1/2}(Cr^{III}Cr^{III})O_4$[23.48] and β-$In_2S_3 = \square_{1/3}In_{2/3}(InIn)S_4$.[23.49, 23.50]

The following substances which crystallize in the spinel structure should also be mentioned: $Al(Li_{0.5}Al_{1.5})O_4$, γ-Al_2O_3,[23.49, 23.51] $Fe(Li_{0.5}Fe_{1.5})O_4$, γ-Fe_2O_3, and α- and β-In_2S_3.

In $\gamma Fe_2O_3 = Fe_{2.67}O_4$, there are vacancies in the octahedral positions. The distribution of the atoms over the tetrahedral and octahedral positions can be represented by the formula, $Fe(\square_{1/3}Fe_{5/3})O_4$. This substance, however, frequently contains water so that a mixed crystal system with $H_{1/2}Fe_{1/2}(FeFe)O_4$ may be found. In the same way, common spinel easily takes up Al_2O_3 so that a mixed crystal region exists in the system $MgAl_2O_4/\gamma$-Al_2O_3.

In non-stoichiometric $Fe_{1-x}O$, with the NaCl-structure, the number of tervalent Fe atoms is given by $2x$. It can be shown that these form clusters in the crystal within which the structure of γ-Fe_2O_3 is realized, that is with Fe^{III} on tetrahedral positions.[23.52]

We shall now mention several substances crystallizing in the spinel structure and give their cation distribution:

$Li_2NiF_4 = Li(LiNi)F_4$[23.53]
$K_2Me(CN)_4 = Me(KK)(CN)_4$, with $Me = Zn$, Cd, and Hg,[23.54]
Ni_3S_4, Co_3S_4, Al_5O_6N to $Al_6O_6N_2$[23.55]
$Me^I_{1/2}Me^{III}_{5/2}S_4 = Me^I_{1/2}Me^{III}_{1/2}(Me^{III}Me^{III})S_4$, with $Me^I = Cu$, Ag;
$Me^{III} = Al$, In[23.56]
$Me^{II}Cr_2S_4 = Me^{II}(CrCr)S_4$ with $Me = Zn$, Cd, Hg[23.57]
$CuCr_2X_4 = Cu(CrCr)X_4$ with $X = S$, Se, Te[23.57]
$Me^{II}_{7/3}Sb_{2/3}O_4 = Me^{II}(Me^{II}_{4/3}Sb_{2/3})O_4$ with $Me = Co$, Zn[23.58]

$LiZnNbO_4 = Zn(LiNb)O_4$ with bonds between the Nb atoms (see chapter 27, section 2).[23.43]

Under high pressure:

$Mg_2GeO_4 = Ge(MgMg)O_4$ and $Ge(LiAl)O_4$[23.59]
$Me_2^{II}SiO_4 = Si(Me^{II}Me^{II})O_4$ with Me = Fe, Co, Ni.[23.60]

Further, the spinels form an extensive series of mixed crystals among themselves so that the structure type is widespread. In such a series the existence region for the normal and inverse spinels can be separated from each other by a two-phase region, for example:

$$Ge(Zn_xNi_{2-x})O_4 \quad \text{for} \quad 0 \leqslant x \leqslant 0 \cdot 3$$
$$Zn(Zn_{x-1}Ni_{2-x}Ge)O_4 \quad \text{for} \quad 1 \cdot 1 \leqslant x \leqslant 1 \cdot 35.[17.42, 23.60a]$$

The unusual stability of the spinels, which can be seen for example in their high melting points and their frequent occurrence, arises apparently from the ability of the metal atoms to find appropriate co-ordination positions in this structure and from the fact that oxygen atoms can have tetrahedral co-ordination while at the same time nearly all the atoms have a relatively dense packing.

Simple bonding relationships are observed in $ZnCo_2O_4$. The bonding functions on Zn and O are (sp^3)-hybrids while the octahedral (d^2sp^3)-hybrid is characteristic for tervalent cobalt. The spinel is, therefore, expected to be diamagnetic. One finds experimentally a weak paramagnetism which results probably from structural disorders (high preparation temperature).[23.61]

In chapter 9 we discussed bonding in the so-called ionic complexes. The electrostatic considerations treated there can easily be carried over into the crystal lattice. The symmetry of the product functions brings about in the crystal, too, a definite gain in energy and a preference for a given co-ordination polyhedron. The details cannot be examined here but they may be found in the original literature.[23.62, 23.63] Only one, long known, experimental observation will be mentioned, namely, that spinels containing bivalent copper and tervalent manganese are generally not cubic but show a tetragonal distortion. This comes about from the Jahn–Teller effect which is characteristic for these ions.

L. Néel[23.64] pointed out that there is a strong interaction between the metal atoms on tetrahedral and octahedral positions, which seeks to orient the spin moments of the paramagnetic atoms antiparallel to each other. The corresponding tetrahedral–tetrahedral and octahedral–octahedral interactions on the other hand are very weak and can lead to either parallel or antiparallel ordering. The strong tetrahedral–octahedral interaction causes the spin moments on all atoms of a given position to be mutually parallel and antiparallel to those on the other position:

$$Fe^{III} \qquad (Fe^{II} \qquad Fe^{III})O_4$$

$$\uparrow\uparrow\uparrow\uparrow\uparrow \quad \downarrow\downarrow\downarrow\downarrow\Uparrow \quad \downarrow\downarrow\downarrow\downarrow\downarrow$$

The tervalent iron moments are thus compensated while the bivalent moments remain uncompensated and parallel.

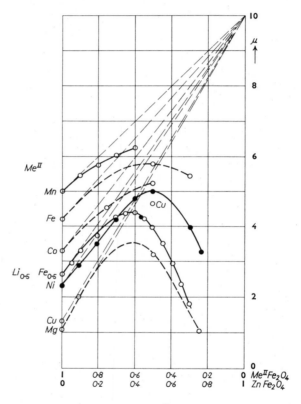

Fig. 23.8. Saturation magnetization of $Me^{II}Fe_2O_4/ZnFe_2O_4$ *mixed crystals.*[23.45]

The mixed crystal system $Me^{II}Fe_2O_4/ZnFe_2O_4$[23.45] has been extensively studied. The saturation magnetization is given in Fig. 23.8. As long as the zinc content (tetrahedral position) is not too great, the iron atoms on the tetrahedral position can continue to exert their influence and bring about the above-mentioned antiparallel ordering. The saturation magnetization then approaches the value $\mu = 10$. When the zinc content becomes too high, the formerly weak octahedral–octahedral interaction becomes stronger than the octahedral–tetrahedral. Then an antiparallel spin arrangement on the octahedral site atoms takes over and the saturation magnetization tends toward $\mu = 0$.

The bonding functions on oxygen can be described either by (sp^3)-hybrids or by molecular orbitals such as were considered for the CH_4-molecule. Then, according to the Kramers mechanism of superexchange, a p-electron pair can give up one electron to the metal atom on the tetrahedral position and form a bond with the atom in the octahedral position or vice versa. This brings about the above-described strong antiparallel coupling between metal atoms on the tetrahedral and octahedral positions. The bond angle Me_{tetr}—O—M_{oct} is not the optimal $180°$, but smaller; the strength of this coupling is also a function of the size of the angle.

24

Structures having Polyanions from Identical Atoms

24.1 Island Structures

24.1.1 *Calcium Carbide Structure, CaC₂*

Calcium carbide is an example of a simple structure with a polyanion (Fig. 24.1). It crystallizes in an NaCl-type structure which is extended along the c-axis. The Cl atoms, however, are replaced by linear C_2-groups. In this structure crystallize: CaC_2, SrC_2, BaC_2, UC_2, the corresponding carbides of the lanthanides and actinides as well as KO_2, RbO_2, and CsO_2.

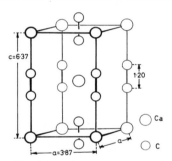

Fig. 24.1. CaC_2 *structure.*

Recently the C–C distances have been determined by neutron diffraction. They vary considerably for different compounds.

C–C distance		C–C distance	
CaC_2[24.1]	1·20 Å	HC≡CH	1·20 Å
LaC_2[24.2]	1·28 Å	H_2C=CH_2	1·32 Å
UC_2[24.3]	1·34 Å	H_3C—CH_3	1·54 Å

The C–C distance in CaC_2 corresponds to that in acetylene while in the lanthanum and especially the uranium compound the distance is greater.

One can therefore assume that the valence electrons on carbon, especially in UC_2, enter into stronger bonds with the valence electrons of uranium so that the bonding within the C_2-group is weakened.

A number of s-, p-, d-, and f-orbitals on the metal can take part in σ- and π-bonding with the C–C groups. If the nuclear charge on the metal is low the behaviour of the valence electrons will be principally determined by the orbitals we have discussed under acetylene. Here one can use the ionic model and talk of C_2^{2-}-ions, at least to a first approximation. When the nuclear charge of the metal (La, U) becomes larger, the σ-bonding is strengthened by the s-, p_z-, and d_{3z^2-1}-orbitals of the metal. Further the $p\pi$-orbitals of the acetylene core form a pronounced mesomeric π-bonding system, mainly with the d_{yz}- and d_{zx}-electron states of the metal. This mesomeric bonding system runs along the direction $[001]$ and must produce metallic properties. The electrical conductivity of LaC_2 is indeed of the same order of magnitude as that in metallic lanthanum.

The O–O distance in KO_2 (1·28 Å) lies between that in the oxygen molecule (1·21 Å) and that in hydrogen peroxide (1·49 Å).[24.4] This is further evidence for a bond order of 1·5 in this compound (cf. Table 7.1).

Dumb-bell shaped X_2 groups are found also in the structures of ThC_2,[24.5] U_2C_3,[24.3] Pu_2C_3,[24.6] Na_2C_2, Li_2O_2, Na_2O_2, Na_2S_2, Na_2Se_2, K_2S_2, and K_2Se_2.[24.7]

24.1.2 Structures with X_4-groups

Recently a series of structures has been found in which the non-metals form tetrahedral groups as in the P_4-molecule. Examples are compounds of the type:

$$MX \text{ with } M = Na, K, Rb, Cs^{24.8, \, 24.9, \, 24.10}$$
$$X = Si, Ge, Sn, Pb \text{ as well as } BaSi_2.^{24.11}$$

By the ionic model, X_4^{4-} ions are isoelectronic with the P_4-molecule. It is thus surprising that the X_4^{4-} ion can form so easily in the crystal. The bonding angle is only 60° and the metastable P_4-molecule comes about only by a thermal cracking of the high-polymer networks of red or black phosphorus. The packing of the alkali and X_4^{4-} ions in the crystal is complicated; it depends on the relative sizes of the structural elements, and will not be discussed in detail.

In a crystal of cubic $CoAs_3$[24.12] are square groups of four As atoms. These are so arranged that each Co atom is octahedrally surrounded by six As atoms from various As_4 groups, while each As atom has as neighbours in a tetrahedral arrangement, two As atoms and two Co atoms. In this way each atom, in analogy to the situation with the pyrite structure, attains a noble-gas configuration. Compounds having the same structure include $CoSb_3$,[24.13] IrP_3, PdP_3,[24.14] RhP_3, $RhAs_3$, $RhSb_3$.[24.13]

24.1.3 *Structures of Polyiodides*[24.15]

In sections 11.3 and 11.4 we extensively discussed the structures of elementary iodine, bromine, and chlorine. The somewhat shorter distances between the molecules comes about because of ionic bonding components in the mesomeric system, the influence of which is small since the ionic components in the mesomeric system are not energetically favourable here. In a polyiodide, e.g., the I_3^--ion, this negative charge is already available so that ionic structures are now favoured. This effect is shown clearly in the structures of several polyiodides which have only recently been explained.

The following structure was found for the linear anion in NH_4I_3:[24.16]

$$I^- \qquad I\text{————}I \qquad r_2/r_1 = 1{\cdot}10$$
$$3{\cdot}10 \qquad 2{\cdot}82$$

Just as in elementary iodine, it is the *p*-orbitals which form the σ-bonds to the two sides. If one considers the tri-iodide ion by itself, there must be a second mesomeric form I————I   I – which is equivalent to the one shown above, in so far as the same inter-atomic distances are energetically favoured. This, however, is not necessarily the case in a crystal, especially when the cationic constituents prefer to group themselves around one anionic iodine atom. If we use the ionic model, the displacement of one valence electron then requires energy. Large cations, such as K^+, Cs^+, NH_4^+, $N(CH_3)_4^+$ ease the electronic displacement. Therefore the polyiodides are known only in compounds having large cations with a low charge and are not observed with lithium or magnesium. In

$$\left[As(-\!\!\big\langle\!\bigcirc\!\big\rangle\!-)_4\right]^+ I_3^-,$$

with an especially large cation, the distance between the iodine atoms is equal. Instead of $3{\cdot}10$ Å and $2{\cdot}82$ Å, it is $2{\cdot}90$ Å.[24.17]

This concept of the bonding in the polyiodides was originally developed by R. E. Rundle[24.18] in connection with his explanation of the structure of the polyiodide, $[N(CH_3)_4]I_5$ (Fig. 24.2). The polyiodide ion is V-shaped.

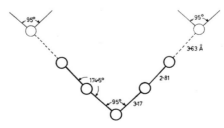

Fig. 24.2. Form of the I_5^- ions in the crystal of $[N(CH_3)_4]I_5$.

The two legs stand almost normal (95°) to one another, as one would expect from p-electron bonds. Each leg is approximately straight (174·5°) and the p-orbitals, whose axes lie along one such leg, are incorporated into the mesomeric bonding system. The distance to the tip of the next polyiodide ion, which incidentally does not lie in the same plane, is $r_3 = 3·63$ Å. This short distance $r_3/r_1 = 1·29$ suggests bonds between neighbouring I_5^- ions. The $[N(CH_3)_4]^+$-ions lie in the vacant spaces of the structure.

24.1.4 Structures of the Polysulphides

We have already discussed the structure of pyrite with the S_2-group. In sections 11.3.3 and 11.4 we have indicated that longer S- and Se-chains occur in both *cis*- and *trans*-configurations. The *cis*-configuration leads to rings like S_6, S_8, and Se_8, while the *trans*-arrangement is characteristic of the chains of hexagonal Se and Te.

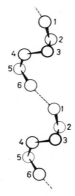

Fig. 24.3. S-chain in the structure of Cs_2S_6.

The same structural principles are obeyed by polysulphides having the general form $Me_2^I S_x$ or $(R_3NH)_2S_x$, of which representatives having x as high as nine have been isolated. Only a few polysulphides have so far been structurally explained while the crystal structures of a series of sulphanes are known.[24.19] As a typical example we shall consider the structure of Cs_2S_6 (Fig. 24.3).[24.20]

The S atoms form long, screw-shaped, parallel chains just as in the structure of hexagonal selenium. Every six sulphur atoms form one chain element within which short inter-atomic distances are found. These distances are, however, not equal but are alternately 2·02 Å and 2·11 Å ($r_2/r_1 = 1·04$). The distance between two end atoms on neighbouring S_6-groups of one chain is 3·39 Å ($r_3/r_1 = 1·58$ Å), while the shortest van der Waals' distance in rhombic sulphur is 3·692 Å ($r/r_1 = 1·81$). One can then conclude that a formulation of these units according to the customary valence scheme $^-$S—S—S—S—S—S$^-$ cannot be completely correct, since the negative ends would have a tendency to repel one another and in addition they would tend to be surrounded by cations. The caesium atoms, however, do not lie between the ends of the chains but rather fill the space along the sides of the chains, without showing any preference for the chain ends.

In Table 24.1 the inter-atomic distances, valence angles and dihedral angles are summarized. In rhombic sulphur we find an inter-atomic distance of 2·05 Å, bond angle 108°, and dihedral angle 99·3°. On the average, the bond lengths and angles in the S_6-chains are also somewhat expanded.

Table 24.1. Inter-atomic distances, valence angles, and dihedral angles in the crystal of Cs_2S_6

Inter-atomic distance		Valence angle		Dihedral angle	
S_1–S_2	1·99 Å	$S_1S_2S_3$	110·5°	$S_1S_2S_3/S_2S_3S_4$	101·2°
S_2–S_3	2·10 Å	$S_2S_3S_4$	106·4°	$S_2S_3S_4/S_3S_4S_5$	98·1°
S_3–S_4	2·03 Å	$S_3S_4S_5$	109·7°	$S_3S_4S_5/S_4S_5S_6$	118·6°
S_4–S_5	2·12 Å	$S_4S_5S_6$	109·7°		
S_5–S_6	2·03 Å				
S_6–S_1	3·39 Å				

24.2 Chain Structures

24.2.1 *LiAs Structure*

In LiAs[24.21] and the isotypic compounds NaSb[24.21] and KSb,[24.22] the As or Sb atoms form chains in the form of fourfold screws arranged parallel to the *b*-axis of a monoclinic cell and between which are found the alkali atoms (Fig. 24.4). The direction of rotation on neighbouring chains is reversed.

If one formulates the compounds ionically, Na^+Sb^-, the chain-forming atoms are isoelectronic to the other chain-formers, Se and Te. The form of the chain, however, is completely different, since the intermediate alkali atoms permit no bonding in the backward direction. Hybridization is thus favoured. The valence angles lie in the neighbourhood of the tetrahedral angle, namely 105·2° and 108·3° in the case of LiAs, and both angles 108° in the case of NaSb.

In analogy to Cs_2S_6, one observes here besides the fluctuation in bonding angles, an alternation in the inter-atomic distances within a chain. These distances are given in Table 24.2. The distances between antimony atoms here are shorter than in metallic antimony itself, $r_1 = 2·908$ Å. The backward bonding is missing, and because of hybridization the valence

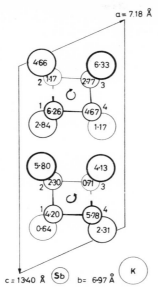

Fig. 24.4. Structure of KSb *projected on* (010). *The height of the atoms is given in Ångstroms.*

electrons are concentrated in the space between each two atoms. The bonding is thus strengthened.

Table 24.2 *Shortest atomic distances in the structure of* LiAs, NaSb, *and* KSb.

LiAs:	$As_1-As_2 = As_3-As_4 = 2\cdot454$ Å	$\dfrac{r_2}{r_1} = 1\cdot008$	
	$As_2-As_3 = As_4-As_{1'} = 2\cdot472$ Å		
NaSb:	$Sb_1-Sb_2 = Sb_3-Sb_4 = 2\cdot857$ Å	$\dfrac{r_2}{r_1} = 1\cdot004$	
	$Sb_2-Sb_3 = Sb_4-Sb_{1'} = 2\cdot845$ Å		
KSb:	$Sb_1-Sb_2 = Sb_3-Sb_4 = 2\cdot81$ Å	$\dfrac{r_2}{r_1} = 1\cdot025$	
	$Sb_2-Sb_3 = Sb_4-Sb_{1'} = 2\cdot88$ Å		

24.2.2 $HgPbP_{14}$ *Structure*

Polyphosphides, MeP_x, whose P-content is not too high, ($x \leqslant 4$), have been known for a long time. Those with a high phosphorus content have only recently been discovered. Up to now the structure of only one of these latter has been determined, that of the compounds $MePbP_{14}$ with Me = Zn, Cd, Hg,[24.23, 24.23a] Fig. 24.5a, b.

The phosphorus atoms form parallel zig-zag chains. These chains are combined in pairs, as in the structure of Hittorf phosphorus (Fig. 12.15), into a ⌣-shaped groove. The Pb atoms and additional P atoms saturate the remaining free valencies of the P atoms on the edge of the groove and thereby close the groove, forming a tube having a pentagonal cross section.

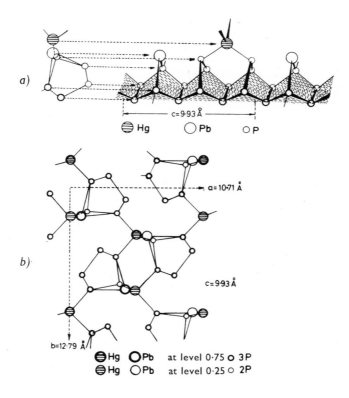

Fig. 24.5. *Structure of* HgPbP$_{14}$. *(a) Structure of a tube-shaped molecule. (b) Projection of the structure in direction of the molecular axis (c-axis).*

The free valencies on the two bridging P atoms are saturated by Me atoms. The environment of the Me atom is a distorted tetrahedron since these additionally co-ordinate to two P atoms on neighbouring chains.

The difficulty in preparing well-crystallized polyphosphides having high phosphorus content apparently results from the structure. The atoms must arrange themselves in a complicated way. Improperly coupled atoms make it very difficult for a well-ordered structure to develop, as is well known for hexagonal Se and organic linear polymers.[24.24]

24.3 Net Structures

24.3.1 $CaSi_2$ Structure (C12-type)

In the $CaSi_2$ structure,[24.25] the Si atoms, considered alone, form puckered layers having hexagonal symmetry, such as are characteristic for the structure of rhombohedral, metallic arsenic. The bonding angle of 103° also supports the idea of partial hybridization between s- and p-orbitals. The distance between the Si atoms (2·48 Å) is greater than that in the structure of elementary Si (2·347 Å; $r_2/r_1 = 2·48/2·347 = 1·06$). The Ca atoms are between the layers and are so arranged that they are approximately octahedrally surrounded by six Si atoms (cf. Fig. 24.6).

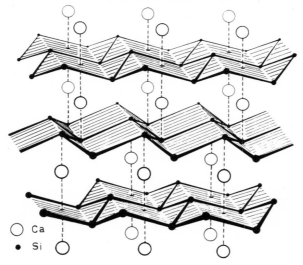

○ Ca
● Si

Fig. 24.6. Sequence of Si and Ca layers in $CaSi_2$ crystals.

If one formulates the compound ionically as $Ca^{2+}Si_2^-$, one sees that the negatively charged Si atoms can mutually repel one another. The valence electrons on calcium occupy, essentially, that crescent-shaped hybrid function which stands perpendicular to the plane of the layer and points outward. If the valence electrons on calcium were to locate themselves in the space between each pair of Si atoms, these electrons would diminish the mutual repulsion of the atomic nuclei and the inter-atomic distance would become smaller.

The extent of hybridization cannot be too great since the bonding angle is 103°. Therefore the functions which enter into the Si—Si bonds must have a larger p-component. The bonding is weakened relative to an (sp^3)-hybrid, so that for this reason, too, the Si atoms move away from one another.

24.3.2 *AlB$_2$ Structure (C32-type)*

The boron atoms taken alone form hexagonal layers like the carbon atoms in graphite[24.26] (Fig. 24.7). Above and below the centre of each boron hexagon is found an aluminium atom. Thus, the atoms of the boron layers stand vertically one over the other, as do also those of the aluminium layers. The co-ordination polyhedron of aluminium is similar to that in sandwich-compounds of the type of dibenzenechromium.

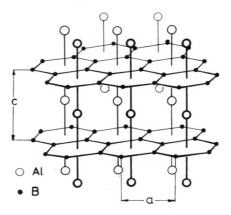

Fig. 24.7. AlB$_2$ structure.

The bonding between boron atoms, like that in graphite, occurs by means of (sp^2)-hybrid functions. Each two neighbouring p_z-orbitals can jointly overlap with p-orbitals on aluminium, which fit into the symmetry of the crystal, provided their x-, y-, and z-axes are inclined to the plane of the layer.

In AlB$_2$, the aluminium can be replaced by magnesium[24.27] as well as by the transition metals: Sc, Ti, Zr, Hf, V, Nb, Ta, Cr, Mo,[24.28] Os, Ru, Ag, Au[24.29] and the rare earths.[13.2] The s- and d-orbitals can overlap with the p_z-orbitals on boron just as in the sandwich compounds.

We have previously seen that the rare earths and actinides frequently behave crystal-chemically like those elements for which p-electron configurations are characteristic. Here again we can see this analogy, for in addition to the rare-earth compounds mentioned above, UB$_2$, USi$_2$, and PuSi$_2$[24.30] crystallize in the AlB$_2$-type structure. ZrBe$_2$, HfBe$_2$,[24.31] MeGa$_2$ with Me = Ca, La[24.30] or rare earth,[13.2] and LaCu$_2$[13.2] also crystallize in this type.

24.3.3 *Graphite Compounds*[24.32]

(a) *Carbon Monofluoride.* Fluorine can be easily added to the double bonds on the carbon atoms of a graphite structure. Puckered double layers of carbon atoms are formed. A representation of these layers can be obtained by peeling them off a diamond structure perpendicular to the body diagonals [111] (see Fig. 12.25b). The free valencies on the C-atoms in the direction of the body diagonal are saturated by F atoms. Figure 24.8 shows the formation of one CF-layer. The superimposition of these layers is irregular.[24.33]

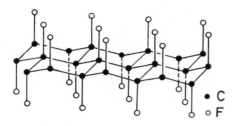

Fig. 24.8. Structure of a layer in carbon monofluoride.

(b) *Graphite Compounds with an Electron Excess in the Carbon Layers.* Just as the larger aromatic ring systems are able to form cations and anions, the pronounced mesomeric, metal-like bonding system of a graphite layer is able to take on and give up electrons. It can be reduced by a series of metals and oxidized by such reagents as bromine. Among the graphite–metal compounds, those with potassium have been especially well studied.

Figure 24.9 shows the structure of C_8K.[24.34] Between each two carbon layers there is a potassium layer. There are four possible ways of setting this layer on the carbons and all four are used in consecutive layers. The position of the graphite layers remains the same since in this way each K atom can be surrounded both above and below by carbon hexagons just as is Cr in dibenzenechromium. Figure 24.10a shows the geometric arrangement of a potassium layer; it corresponds to a dense packing of spheres.

The amount of inserted K can be reversibly changed at high temperatures by varying the potassium vapour pressure over the graphite compound. In this way the compounds $C_{24}K$, $C_{36}K$, $C_{48}K$, and $C_{60}K$[24.34] can be isolated. The K-layers in these compounds are not so densely occupied (Fig. 24.10a). Just as in the transition from the PbI_2 to the $CrBr_3$ structure every third metal position remains unoccupied. In addition, potassium layers are now found only in every second, third, fourth, or fifth interlayer position as Fig. 24.11 shows. These are referred to as the second to fifth degrees. Those carbon layers which neighbour a potassium layer lie directly above one another while the others retain the layer sequence of hexagonal graphite.

C_8K is a metallic conductor which shows a negative temperature coefficient. In the direction of the layers the conductivity is about ten times as large as in pure graphite while perpendicular to the layers it is small although still a hundred times greater than in the corresponding

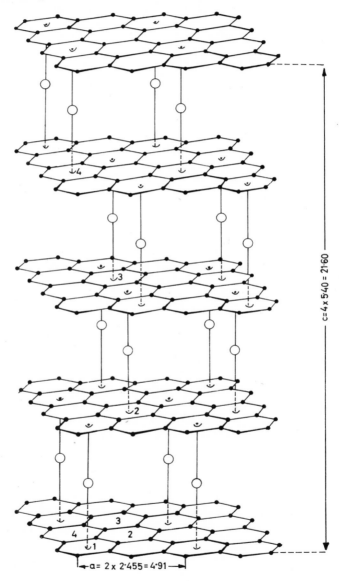

Fig. 24.9. Structure of C_8K.

direction in graphite itself.[24.35] By the addition of K-atoms the number of $p\pi$-electrons in the conduction band is appreciably increased.

Rb and Cs form insertion compounds analogous to those with potassium while the addition of sodium is more difficult and leads only to a sixth-degree compound $(C_{64}Na)$.[24.36] Recently it has been possible[24.37] to add Li to graphite leading to compounds of the first, second, and third degrees. The compositions are LiC_6, LiC_{12}, and LiC_{18}, since the lithium layers are different in construction from the potassium ones (Fig. 24.10b).

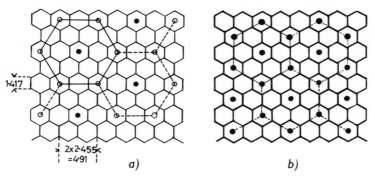

a)   b)

*Fig. 24.10. (a) Packing of a K-layer in C_8K. **In the potassium poorer compounds the centres of the hexagons ($\bullet$) are vacant**[24.34]. (b) Packing of lithium atoms in C_6Li.*

In the presence of liquid ammonia all the alkali metals and alkaline earths as well as Al and Eu can be introduced. In this case the layers have a deficiency of metal and contain NH_3. Several examples with a layer sequence of the first degree are $C_{10.6}Li(NH_3)_{1.6}$, $C_{12.5}K(NH_3)_{2.1}$, $C_{10.9}Ba(NH_3)_{2.5}$; and of the second degree $C_{28}Li(NH_3)_{1.7}$, $C_{28.3}Ba(NH_3)_{3.9}$. In their properties these compounds resemble the alkali–graphite compounds.[24.36]

(c) *Graphite Compounds with Electron Deficiencies in the Carbon Layers.* In the presence of oxidizing agents, graphite reacts with concentrated acids. With sulphuric acid, for example, the blue compound of the first degree, $C_{24}^+HSO_4^- H_2SO_4$ is formed.

By the reaction of graphite with elemental bromine, the compound C_8Br is very easily formed. It has a structure of the second degree. The superposition of the layers is severely disturbed so the structure cannot be unambiguously explained.[24.38, 24.39] Linear polybromide chains are probably the structural elements of the halogen layers. The distance between two Br atoms, 2.455 Å, fixed by the carbon layer, agrees with the shortest distances in a Br_2-crystal, $r_1 = 2.27$ Å and $r_2 = 3.31$ Å. Chlorine also forms a compound, C_8Cl, at low temperature, which, however, is unstable and decomposes even in a chlorine atmosphere at 0°C. The bromine compound under the same conditions is not decomposed until a higher temperature.[24.40] The tendency of Cl to form bonds to both sides is only very weak. The inter-atomic distances in a crystal of pure chlorine are $r_1 = 1.98$ and $r_2 = 3.32$ Å. Elementary iodine cannot be inserted between the carbon layers since the distance between the I-atoms of a polyiodide chain is probably too large (in I_2 itself $r_1 = 2.67$, $r_2 = 3.57$).

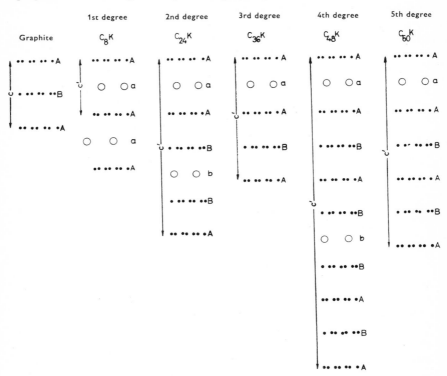

Fig. 24.11. Sequence of layers in graphite–potassium compounds.

In the presence of elementary chlorine, metal chlorides such as $BeCl_2$, $AlCl_3$, $FeCl_3$, $HgCl_2$, $PtCl_4$, and WCl_6 can be deposited between the carbon layers. These compounds can be formulated on the ionic model, as for example, $C_n{}^+Cl^-.3AlCl_3$. Little is known so far about their structure.[24.41, 24.42]

Graphite compounds with an electron deficiency in the carbon layers conduct electricity better than graphite itself.[24.43]

24.4 Space Net Structures

24.4.1 *NaTl Structure (B32-type)*

In this structure, the Na as well as the Tl atoms each considered separately form diamond-like sub-structures which are mutually displaced by $a/2$ in the direction of a cube edge (Fig. 24.12).

Zintl, who first described these compounds, gave a plausible explanation of this structure.[24.44] If we write this compound as Na^+Tl^-, according to the ionic model, the Tl^- ions have four valence electrons just like carbon. They can therefore form a diamond-like sub-lattice, whose negative charge is neutralized by the sodium ions found in the holes.

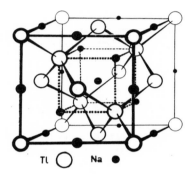

Tl ◯   Na ●

Fig. 24.12. Structure of NaTl.

In this structure crystallize: NaTl, NaIn, LiIn, LiGa, LiAl, LiCd, and LiZn. LiCd and LiZn are electron-deficient structures, since there are not enough valence electrons to fully occupy all (sp^3)-hybrid functions. They are therefore closely related to alloys. A definite phase breadth is found in NaTl and LiCd, ($Na_{0.46}Tl_{0.54}$ to $Na_{0.58}Tl_{0.42}$,[24.45] $Li_{0.39}Cd_{0.61}$ to $Li_{0.75}Cd_{0.25}$),[24.45] which results from the ability of one atom type to substitute for the other in the structure. This appears to be possible because this structure can only occur when the shortest Na–Na and Tl–Tl distances are equal and the spatial extension of the atoms is similar.

Zintl-phases of the NaTl-type are either diamagnetic (NaTl itself) or, more generally, weakly paramagnetic.[24.46] This, however, in no way invalidates the theoretical valence concept of Zintl, for incompletely filled bonding functions in a crystal normally lead to paramagnetism only when the electrons are found more deeply within an atom (*d*- and *f*-electrons) and when these do not appreciably take part in a bonding system which extends throughout the crystal.

24.4.2 *ThSi$_2$ Structure*

In the structure of ThSi$_2$, each Si atom is surrounded by three others in the form of an equilateral triangle just as in the structure of USi$_2$(AlB$_2$-type). The inter-atomic distance (2·39 Å) is about 1 per cent larger than in elementary silicon. The coupling of the triangles is, however, not two- but three-dimensional (Fig. 24.13). In the holes of this three-dimensional open

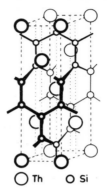

○ Th   ○ Si

Fig. 24.13. Structure of ThSi$_2$.[24.48a]

network are lanthanide or actinide metal atoms.[24.47, 24.48] The germanides of these metals also crystallize in the ThSi$_2$ structure.[13.2] Bonding between the silicon atoms is certainly characterized by (sp^2)-hybrid functions. How the still free *p*-functions on the silicon atoms combine with the orbitals on the metal atoms has not yet been examined.

24.4.3 *CaB$_6$ Structure* (*D2$_1$-type*)

The CaB$_6$ structure, explained by M. von Stackelberg and F. Neu-mann,[24.49] is formally derived from the CsCl structure, in which the Cs

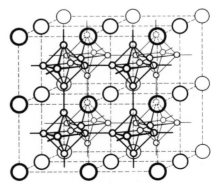

Fig. 24.14. Structure of CaB$_6$.[24.49a]

atoms are replaced by calcium and the Cl atoms by octahedrally arranged B_6-groups (Fig. 24.14). These B_6-octahedra are bonded together via their corners. The B–B distance is 1·7 Å and corresponds to that in the structure of AlB_2. The Ca atoms are found in the holes which are formed from the framework of coupled B_6-octahedra. The elements strontium, barium, the rare earths, and the actinides[13.2] can take the place of calcium.

A similar structure is that of UB_4,[24.50, 13.2] in which the B_6-octahedra are bound together via additional B atoms in a somewhat more complex fashion. The holes are then larger and can accept more metal atoms.

In UB_{12},[24.51, 13.2] B_{12}-groups occupy the Cl-positions of a NaCl-structure. Their coupling is such that holes are formed, the centres of which lie at the Na-positions of a NaCl-structure. These holes are filled with U-atoms.[24.52]

25

Structures having Polyanions containing Various Types of Atoms; Silicates

Structures with polyanions containing various atoms are very common. Here we can consider only a few characteristic and easily described examples. Among these, the most important are the silicates, the construction principles of which are simple and which will therefore be examined first.[25.1]

25.1 Island Structures

Island silicates can be divided into three groups: (a) orthosilicates, island silicates in a narrow sense, (b) group silicates such as the derivatives of bisilicic acid, and (c) ring silicates, derivatives of cyclic metasilicic acid.

25.1.1 *Olivine Structure Mg_2SiO_4 ($H1_2$-type)*

In an idealized olivine structure [25.2] the O atoms form a close-packed layer sequence ABAB... like the O atoms of the brucite structure (compare Fig. 18.1). Between each pair of O layers is an Mg layer, C, in which, however, only half of the available sites is occupied. One can write the layer sequence symbolically as $A_{\frac{C}{2}}B_{\frac{C}{2}}A_{\frac{C}{2}}B$... rather than ACBACB... in the brucite structure. Three O atoms of one layer plus a neighbouring O atom from the next O-layer form a tetrahedrally shaped structure (Fig. 25.1, compare Fig. 12.3). A part of these tetrahedra is now regularly centred by Si atoms, so that $[SiO_4]$-groups are formed. With the incorporation of Si atoms the positions of the O atoms are altered somewhat. The symmetry of the structure is no longer hexagonal but orthorhombic. In addition, the $[MgO_6]$-octahedra and the $[SiO_4]$-tetrahedra are distorted.[25.3, 25.4]

In this structure, Mg can be readily replaced by other divalent atoms of similar size, especially Fe and Mn; however, even the larger Ca atoms can be incorporated, e.g., in the mineral glaukochroite ($CaMnSiO_4$) and in

γCa_2SiO_4 which is formed during the hardening of Portland cement.[25.5] Naturally occurring olivine contains iron. Chrysoberyll, Al_2BeO_4, Mg_2GeO_4, $LiFePO_4$, and Na_2BeF_4 also crystallize in this structure-type.

If some of the O atoms in a Mg_2SiO_4-layer are replaced by hydroxyl, an equivalent number of Si atoms must disappear. One then comes to a group of minerals having the general formula $(Mg_2SiO_4)_m(Mg(OH)_2)_n$, the chondrodites.[25.6]

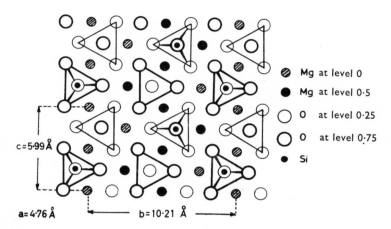

Fig. 25.1. *Idealized structure of olivine* (Mg_2SiO_4). *Only those silicon atoms are depicted which lie between the two oxygen layers.*

25.1.2 *Thortveitite Structure,* $Sc_2Si_2O_7$ *($S2_1$-type)*

The $[Si_2O_7]$-group has six O atoms on the periphery, which can belong simultaneously to the co-ordination polyhedra of neighbouring metal atoms. If one writes the formula $(ScO_3)_2Si_2O$, one recognizes that Sc can form a layer package with O, like that formed by Cr with Br on $CrBr_3$. Above and below the empty spots in the Sc sub-lattice are positioned the $[Si_2O_7]$-double tetrahedra, the size of which fits in with the distance of the O atoms in the $[ScO_3]$-layers (Fig. 25.2). One can thereby see that $[Si_2O_7]$-groups are formed so that the oxygen atoms bound to silicon may fit into the co-ordination polyhedra of the metals. In order that the crystal structure can grow perpendicular to the layer by adding new $[ScO_3]$-layers, the two $[SiO_4]$-tetrahedra of one disilicate residue must stand staggered to each other like the tetrahedra in the zinc blende structure. The $[Si_2O_7]$-group then takes on the appearance of an octahedron, stretched along a threefold axis. The bonding angle Si—O—Si is $180°$.[25.7, 25.8] Magnesium pyrophosphate, $Mg_2P_2O_7$, has the same structure.

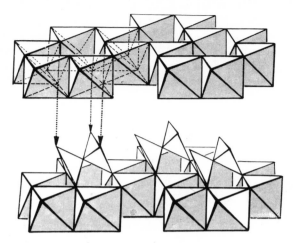

Fig. 25.2. Thortveitite structure ($Sc_2Si_2O_7$). *Two* $[ScO_3]$-*layers and their coupling with* $[Si_2O_7]$-*groups are represented. In order to give a better view the upper* $[ScO_3]$-*layer is somewhat displaced.*

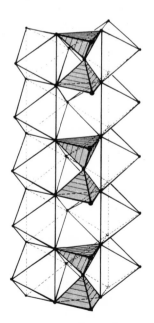

Fig. 25.3. Lateral view of the coupling of $[CaO_6]$-*octahedral chains and* $[Si_2O_7]$-*groups in tricalcium silicate hydrate.*

25.1.3 *Tricalcium Silicate Hydrate, $Ca_6Si_2O_7(OH)_6$*

Tricalcium silicate hydrate, which is an essential component of hardened cement, is according to Belov[25.9] formed of $[CaO_6]$-octahedra which are stacked vertically by sharing edges. These chains are then laterally juxtaposed via the corners or also the edges so that tubes result, the cross sections of which are parallelograms or triangles. In the first type of holes oxygen is bound not only with Ca, but also partially with H. In the triangular holes fit now the $[Si_2O_7]$-groups, if the SiO_4-tetrahedra take on the eclipsed configuration, i.e., a prismatic appearance (as in wurtzite). Figure 25.3 shows the coupling of $[CaO_6]$-octahedra and $[Si_2O_7]$-prisms in a lateral and Fig. 25.4 in a basal projection.

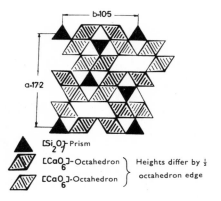

Fig. 25.4. Projection of the tricalcium silicate hydrate structure in the chain direction.

25.1.4 *Benitoite Structure, $BaTi(Si_3O_9)$ ($S3_2$-type)*

Among the cyclic silicates are frequently found rings of three Si and three O atoms, $[SiO_3]_3^{6-}$ as well as rings of six Si and six O atoms, $[SiO_3]_6^{12-}$ (Fig. 25.5). The mineral benitoite $BaTi[Si_3O_9]$ belongs to the first group. The structure of this mineral is shown in a projection parallel to the c-axis of a hexagonal system (Fig. 25.6).[25.10] The rings lie over one another in the direction of the c-axis. They are, however, slightly rotated relative to one another. The Ti and Ba atoms bind the rings together. Each titanium atom is octahedrally surrounded by six oxygen atoms which belong to various ring systems. The oxygen atoms around the barium atom form a very strongly distorted octahedron.

BaTi(Ge_3O_9) also crystallizes in the benitoite structure. The mineral Wadeite, $K_2ZrSi_3O_9$, also contains $[Si_3O_9]^{6-}$-rings.[25.11]

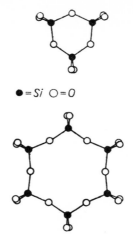

$\bullet = Si$ $\bigcirc = O$

Fig. 25.5. Structure of $\left[Si_3O_9\right]^{6-}$ **and** $\left[Si_6O_{18}\right]^{12-}$**-rings.**

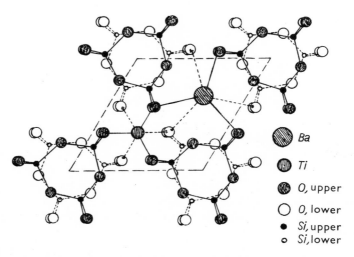

Ba

Ti

O, upper

O, lower

Si, upper

Si, lower

Fig. 25.6. Structure of benitoite, $BaTi(Si_3O_9)$**, in a projection parallel to the** c**-axis.**
Shown also are two superposed rings and their coupling with $\left[TiO_6\right]$**-octahedra and**
large $\left[BaO_6\right]$**-polyhedra. Superposed O atoms are shown somewhat displaced.** [25.39]

25.1.5 Beryl Structure, $Al_2Be_3(Si_6O_{18})$ ($S3_1$-type)

An example of a mineral in which rings of six $\left[SiO_4\right]$-tetrahedra are
present as structural elements is the hexagonal beryl, $Al_2Be_3(Si_6O_{18})$.[25.12]
As with benitoite, the rings are twisted relative to one another. Between
the rings are the Be and Al atoms. The beryllium atom is tetrahedrally

surrounded by four oxygen atoms (from four different rings). The aluminium atom is octahedrally co-ordinated, coupling six rings together (Fig. 25.7). Since the ring centres lie over one another, channels result which can accept free atoms, as for example gaseous He or the ions F^-, OH^-, alkali$^+$. In the latter cases, Al, Be, or Si are replaced by elements of other valence.

The same ring systems are found in (a) dioptase: $Cu_6(Si_6O_{18}).6H_2O$,[25.13] (b) tourmaline: $(Na,Ca)(Li,Al)_3Al_6(OH)_4(BO_3)_3(Si_6O_{18})$.[25.14] The mixture of metals on the (Na,Ca) and (Li,Al) positions must contain a total of seven equivalents. (c) Cordierite: $Mg_2Al_3(AlSi_5O_{18})$[25.15] where one Si atom per ring is replaced by Al.

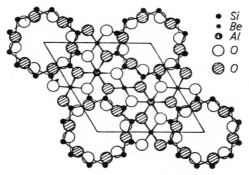

• Si
• Be
◑ Al
○ O
◒ O

Fig. 25.7. Structure of beryl, $Al_2Be_3(Si_6O_{18})$. The framework of two superposed $[Si_6O_{18}]$-rings are represented as well as their coupling via $[BeO_4]$-tetrahedra and $[AlO_6]$-octahedra.[25.39]

25.2 Chain Structures

The $[SiO_4]$-tetrahedra in the chain structures are coupled to form infinite chains having the formula $(SiO_3)_n{}^{2n-}$, which lie parallel in the crystal. A simple, frequently occurring form of chain is shown in Fig. 25.8a, b in both horizontal and vertical views. Every three atoms of the base of such a tetrahedron lie in a planar band over which lie the silicon atoms over which in turn lie the oxygen atoms at the peaks of the tetrahedra. Minerals having this structural element are called pyroxenes. The most important representative of this group is diopside, $CaMg(SiO_3)_2$.[25.16]

As Fig. 25.8c shows, the chains lie in the crystal in such a way that the base planes as well as the apical planes face each other. Nevertheless they are not nearest neighbours, since a metal atom lies in between.

Since the cross section of the pyroxene chains is fixed and the size of the incorporated metal atom can vary only insignificantly, the planes, which are parallel to the chain direction when the crystal is cleaved, have an approximately constant angle to one another of $93°$ or $87°$, which can be used to identify a pyroxene. In addition to the silicates, pyroxene chains are also found in the compounds: $MgGeO_3$, $RbPO_3$, $LiAsO_3$, NH_4VO_3, and $LiNa(BeF_3)_2$.

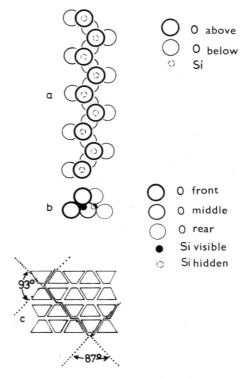

Fig. 25.8. *Pyroxene structure. (a) Basal view of a* $[SiO_3]^{2-}$*-chain. (b) Lateral view of a* $[SiO_3]^{2-}$*-chain. (c) Packing of the* $[SiO_3]^{2-}$*-chains in crystals and the position of the cleavage planes.*[25.16a]

To date, six different coupling modes have been found by which $[SiO_4]$-tetrahedra are combined into chain-like structures. These are reproduced in Fig. 25.9.[25.17, 25.18, 25.19]

The structural elements of the triple chains appear again in the fivefold and sevenfold chains. The fourfold chain has a pronounced spiral character. The $[Si_2O_7]$-group occurs in combination with $[MeO_6]$-octahedra of large metal atoms such as Na, K, Ca, and the rare earths. The edge of a $[CaO_6]$-octahedron is 3.8 Å long, that of a $[SiO_4]$-tetrahedron, 2.6 Å, and that of a $[Si_2O_7]$-prism, $4–4.2$ Å. As Figs. 25.9 and 25.10 show, a good adjustment to the geometrical conditions required by

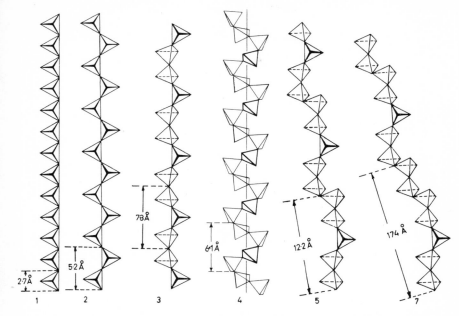

Fig. 25.9. *Various forms of chain-like coupling of* $[SiO_4]$*-tetrahedra.*[25.17]

Single chains	*Double chains*	*Triple chains*
$CuGeO_3$	Pyroxene	$CaSiO_3$
K_2CuCl_3	$CaMg(SiO_3)_2$	(wollastonite)
Ba_2ZnS_3[25.20]	(diopside)	$NaPO_3$
		(Madrell's salt)
	$MgGeO_3$	$NaAsO_3$
	$RbPO_3$	$Ca_2NaH(SiO_3)_3$
	$LiAsO_3$	$CaGeO_3$
	NH_4VO_3	$NaBeF_3$
	$LiNa(BeF_3)_2$	

Quadruple chains	*Quintuple chains*	*Septuple chains*
$AgPO_3$	$(Mn,Ca)SiO_3$	$(Mn,Fe,Ca,Mg)SiO_3$
(Kuroll's salt)	(rhodonite)	(pyroxmangite)

the metal–oxygen octahedra can be obtained by rotation, by altering the valence angle, Si—O—Si, and by combination with $[SiO_4]$-tetrahedra. Because of the complicated appearance of the $[Si_2O_7]$-group, and the generally low symmetry of the crystals, the crystal structures of the silicates containing large cations have only recently been elucidated, especially by Belov and his school.

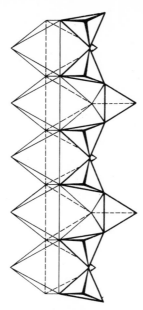

Fig. 25.10. *Development of a triple chain by coupling with a* $[MeO_6]$ *octahedral chain.*

25.3 Band Structures

If two pyroxene chains are so connected that the O atom directed toward the right on one chain is simultaneously the O atom directed to the left on the other chain, bands like those shown in Fig. 25.11 are formed. The general formula is $(Si_4O_{11})_n^{6n-}$. The arrangement of the bands in this group of silicates, called amphiboles, in the crystal is analogous to that in pyroxenes. Because of the greater breadth of the bands, the cleavage angle is smaller, 56°. Tremolite, $Ca_2Mg_5(Si_4O_{11})_2(OH)_2$,[25.21, 25.22] is an example of an amphibole.

This coupling to form one band is also found in single chains as in sillimanite, $Al(AlSiO_5)$, an important component of porcelain[25.23, 25.24, 25.25] (Fig. 25.12). One half of the Al atoms substitutes for one set of Si atoms within the band, the other half is located between the bands.

Xonotlite, $Ca_6(Si_6O_{17})(OH)_2$,[25.26] is an example of a band formed from two triple chains.

25.4 Planar Net Structures

The lateral cross-linking of a pyroxene chain can propagate itself into an infinite, planar net, having the general formula $(Si_2O_5)_n^{2n-}$ (Fig. 25.13).

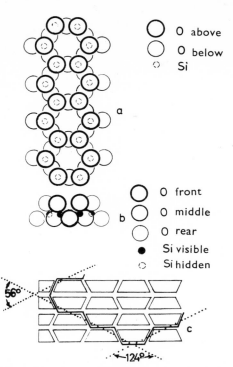

O above   O above
O below   O below
◌ Si

O front   O front
O middle   O middle
O rear
● Si visible
◌ Si hidden

56°

124°

Fig. 25.11. Amphibole structure. (a) Basal view of a $[Si_4O_{11}]^{6-}$-band. (b) Lateral view of a $[Si_4O_{11}]^{6-}$-band. (c) Packing of $[Si_4O_{11}]^{6-}$-bands into a crystal and the position of the cleavage planes.[25.16a]

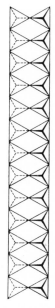

Fig. 25.12. Sillimanite band Al(AlSiO_5).

The apices of the $[SiO_4]$-tetrahedra point only toward one side. These nets are found in a large series of minerals, as for example talc, kaolinite, and mica, which is noted for its extreme cleavability. The neutralization of the net can occur in various ways.

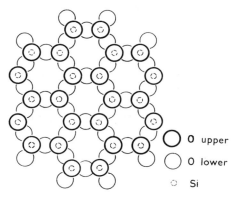

Fig. 25.13. Basal view of a $[Si_2O_5]^{2-}$*-net.*[25.16a]

25.4.1 *Talc-Pyrophyllite Group*[25.27, 25.28]

Between each six O atoms on the apices of the upward-pointing tetrahedra, there is exactly enough room for the addition of an OH^- group. These, together with the above-mentioned O atoms form a densely packed layer. If now, two such $[Si_2O_5]_n^{2n-}$-nets, whose holes are filled by OH, are laid together in such a way that the tetrahedral apices are pointing toward each other, the same ordering for this O, OH layer as that of the O atoms in brucite, $Mg(OH)_2$, is obtained (Figs. 25.14 and 25.15a). The neutralization of these packets comes about from interposed Mg^{2+} or Al^{3+} which are respectively bi- and tervalent ions of similar size. These can take up the metal positions of either the brucite or hydrargillite structure respectively. Talc, $Mg_3(Si_4O_{10})(OH)_2$ and pyrophyllite, $Al_2(Si_4O_{10})(OH)_2$, are examples. All the metal positions of a brucite structure are occupied in talc while in pyrophyllite, all the metal positions of hydrargillite are filled (cf. Fig. 2.1). Every third position of the brucite structure ($\times$ in Fig. 25.14) remains unoccupied in pyrophyllite. The lower part of the figure shows a view of a $[(Si_4O_{10})(OH)_2]^{6-}$-layer. Since only weak van der Waals' forces operate between the layers, these glide easily over one another. Substances with this layer structure thus feel like 'talcum'.

25.4.2 *Chlorite Group*[25.29, 25.30, 25.31]

If other layers, such as brucite layers, are interposed between the talc or pyrophyllite layers, one obtains the chlorite-group (cf. Fig. 25.15b), for example, chlorite itself, $Mg_3(Si_4O_{10})(OH)_2.3Mg(OH)_2 = Mg_6(OH)_8$ (Si_4O_{10}). Part of the Mg atoms can be replaced by bi- and tervalent Fe or Al and other metal atoms of comparable size. Silicon, too, can be replaced by aluminium up to a certain point, so that although the frame as such remains the same, the analytic ratio of the cations can vary.

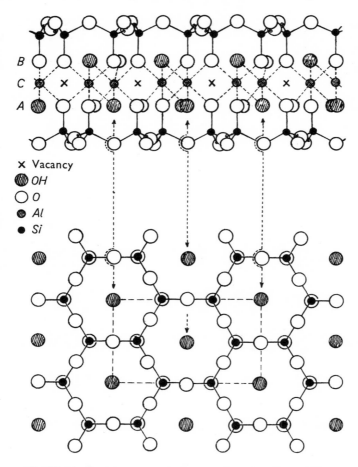

Fig. 25.14. *Structure of a talc layer in basal and lateral views.*

25.4.3 *Kaolin Group*

If a $[(Si_4O_{10})(OH)_2]^{6-}$-layer is removed from pyrophyllite and re-placed by a hydroxyl-layer (as in hydrargillite) we arrive at the layer structure of the kaolins, e.g., kaolinite, $Al_4(OH)_8(Si_4O_{10})$.[25.32, 25.33] Such layers are in this case laid over one another as Fig. 25.15c shows.

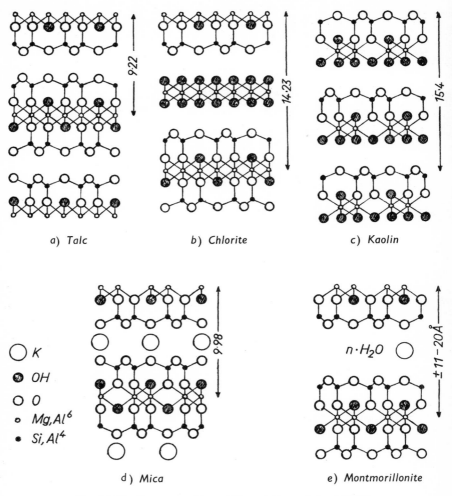

○ K

◉ OH

○ O

∘ Mg, Al⁶

• Si, Al⁴

a) Talc

b) Chlorite

c) Kaolin

d) Mica

e) Montmorillonite

Fig. 25.15. Structure of layer silicates (lateral view).[25.16a]

If Mg atoms are substituted for the Al in kaolin, one obtains chrysotile asbestos, $Mg_6(OH)_8(Si_4O_{10})$, or garnierite, $(Ni,Mg)_6(OH)_8(Si_4O_{10})$ which contains nickel.

Since, when the bivalent elements Mg or Ni are added, the distance between the hydroxyl-groups becomes rather larger than that between the base oxygen atoms of the $[(Si_4O_{10})(OH_2)]^{6-}$-layer, the layers are bent. The layer is rolled up as shown in Fig. 25.16. The inner hole has a diameter of about 100 Å; the outside diameter is about 200 Å. The rolling-up process ends when the curvature is too far from that prescribed by the ideal structure.[25.34, 25.35]

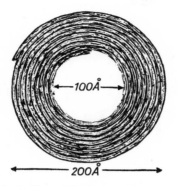

Fig. 25.16. Rolling of the layers of chrysotile asbestos.

25.4.4 *Mica Group*

If every fourth Si atom in pyrophyllite is replaced by an Al atom, alkali must be added in order to make the layers electrically neutral. These alkali atoms are inserted between the pyrophyllite layers as in Muscovite, $KAl_2(AlSi_3O_{10})(OH)_2$.[25.36] (cf. Fig. 25.15d). The space between two superposed hexagonal oxygen-rings of the basis $(Si_4O_{10})(OH_2)^{6-}$-layers, is especially well filled by potassium. Between the layers weak ionic forces are operative. The layers are therefore not so easily slid apart as in talc, but they can still be easily cleaved. If now still more Si is replaced by Al, corresponding amounts of K must be replaced by bivalent ions of appropriate size (Ca, Sr, Ba). The mica then becomes harder and harder until one finally arrives at the so-called brittle micas, as for example margarite, $CaAl_2(Al_2Si_2O_{10})(OH)_2$.

25.4.5 *Montmorillonite Group*[25.37]

If a very small amount of the silicon in pyrophyllite is replaced by aluminium, only few cations are found between the layers. These cations force the layers apart giving rise to holes into which water can come. The amount of interposed water can vary. The identity distance perpendicular to the layer expands then from 10 Å up to generally 20 Å (cf. Fig. 25.15e). The water can also be replaced by other substances with polar groups such as alcohol, sugar, and organic dyes.

25.4.6 *Nets with Disilicate Groups*

Recently, silicates with net structure have been found in which disilicate residues are bound together into four- and eight-membered rings. The combination of eight- and five-membered rings has also been found.

Figure 25.17 shows an idealized structure of apophyllite ($KF \cdot Ca_4Si_8O_{20} \cdot 8H_2O$) which consists of such nets.[25.38] These, however, are not planar but folded so that more stretched eight-member rings result.

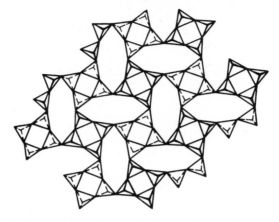

Fig. 25.17. Nets made of four- and eight-membered rings in apophyllite.

25.5 Framework Silicates

The $[SiO_4]$-tetrahedra can also be coupled into a three-dimensional network. Examples are quartz, tridymite, and cristobalite. In Table 17.1, chapter 17, we have already listed the important minerals in which part of the silicon in the framework is replaced by aluminium. An equivalent amount of alkali is then built into the holes.

25.5.1 *Feldspars*

Another kind of space network occurs in the feldspars. Here four $[SiO_4]$-tetrahedra form a ring-like structure having four Si and four O atoms. These rings are then further coupled together forming a crooked chain. These chains are in turn coupled with yet other chains by means of oxygen bridges (shaded in Fig. 25.18), so that a three-dimensional structure made up of disilicate groups, $[Si_2O_7]$, results. If some of the silicon atoms are replaced by aluminium, additional cations are inserted into the holes, as for example: $K(AlSi_3O_8)$-orthoclase (potassium feldspar), $Na(AlSi_3O_8)$-albite (sodium feldspar), $Ca(Al_2Si_2O_8)$-anorthite (calcium feldspar). The frequently very complex structures of the feldspars cannot be treated here. The reader is referred to the specialized literature.[25.39]

25.5.2 *Zeolites*

In addition to these three-dimensional network structures, there are others in which the coupling of the $[SiO_4]$-tetrahedra leads to very large holes so that besides cations, water can be added, too. These minerals,

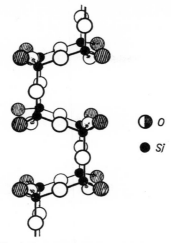

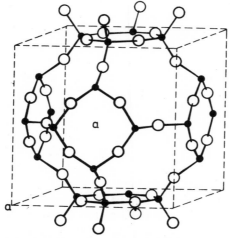

○ O

● Si

Fig. 25.18. Idealized three-dimensional net of the feldspars.

called zeolites, are therefore of unusual interest, especially since the water content can vary greatly as a function of the external vapour pressure. Most importantly, however, the cations can be easily replaced by other cations. They can thus serve in technology as ion exchangers. According to the external form of the crystal one differentiates between:

(a) Fibrous Zeolites, e.g., natrolite, $Na_2(Al_2Si_3O_{10}).2H_2O$

(b) Lamellar Zeolites, e.g., heulandite, $Ca(AlSi_3O_8)_2.5H_2O$

(c) Cubic Zeolites, e.g., chabasite, $(Ca, Na_2)(Al_2Si_4O_{12}).6H_2O$ or faujasite, $(Na, Ca_{0.5})(Al_2Si_5O_{14}).10H_2O$.

a

a

Fig. 25.19. Unit cell of ultramarine (building element of cubic zeolites).

The structural elements of the third group are basket-like forms. In the case of faujasite these consist of rings with four Si(Al) and four O atoms as well as six Si(Al) and six O atoms. (Fig. 25.19.)

If the six corners of an octahedron are truncated by a cube the first kind of rings lie on the surfaces with tetragonal (cube faces) symmetry while the second kind lie on those surfaces with trigonal (octahedron faces) symmetry (Fig. 25.20). The midpoints of the hexagons, when joined together,

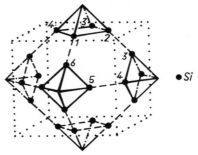

Fig. 25.20. *Formation of four- and six-membered rings by the interpenetration of cube and octahedron.*

form a cube. If these structures are coupled together only via those hexagons whose midpoints form tetrahedra, the centres of the truncated octahedra build up a diamond-like structure (Fig. 25.21). As in that structure the tetrahedral coupling leads here to the especially large vacancies of the faujasite structure.[25.40]

In the ultramarines $Na_{4+x}(Si_{24}Al_xO_{48})(X_2)_2$ with x about 10–12 and $X_2 = S_2^{1-}$, Cl_2^{1-}, SO_4^{2-}, etc., the truncated octahedra are more densely packed. Figure 25.19 illustrates the unit cell in such a way that a ring of four Si and four O atoms is held in common by two neighbouring basket-like networks.[25.41]

The structure is body-centred cubic since the coupling made requires that the net is brought into coincidence with itself by a $\frac{1}{2}\frac{1}{2}\frac{1}{2}$ translation. The atoms Na (or another of similar size) and X are near the centres of the voids a, 000 and $\frac{1}{2}\frac{1}{2}\frac{1}{2}$. They can easily change their position and be exchanged by other ions.

Interestingly, in the mineral helvine $(Mn,Fe)_{16}(Si_{12}Be_{12}O_{48})S_4$, half of the Si atoms are replaced not by Al but by Be.[25.42] In $HPF_6.6H_2O$ the water molecules form the same basket-like skeleton as does $[AlSiO_4]^-$ in ultramarine. This skeleton is held together by hydrogen bonds. The $[PF_6]^-$ octahedra occupy the corners and the centre of the unit cell. These are the centres of vacancies formed by the H_2O-framework.[25.43]

If the rings of four Si and four O atoms are not united but rather lie over one another, the eight Si atoms on two such rings form a cube. The

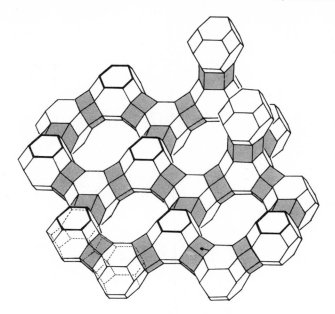

Fig. 25.21. Structure of faujasite.

truncated octahedra are then expanded and in the centre of the cubic cell a large vacancy b (Fig. 25.22) is formed. This describes the structure of the synthetic zeolite 'Linde A' with the idealized composition $Na_{12}(Si_{12}Al_{12}O_{48}).27H_2O$.[25.44, 25.45, 25.46]

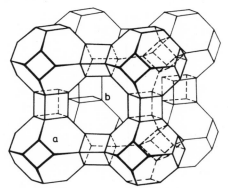

Fig. 25.22. Structure of the zeolite 'Linde A'.

Zeolites exist which have still more complicated structures but they cannot be treated here. The interested reader is referred to the specialized literature.[25.39, 25.47]

21

26

Structures with Polyanions having Several Types of Atoms, Silicates Excepted

26.1 Boron–Oxygen Compounds

Boron, in agreement with the so-called diagonal relationship in the periodic system, is closely related to silicon in its chemical properties. Boric acid like silicic acid has a tendency toward condensation. There are thus a large number of polyborates. Their structures are generally more complex than those of the silicates since boron relative to oxygen can have the co-ordination number 3, ((sp^2)-hybrid and π-bonding), as well as 4, ((sp^3)-hybrid). Only a few characteristic structures will be discussed below.

26.1.1 *Island Structures*

(a) *Orthoboric Acid,* $B(OH)_3$. Although orthoboric acid itself is not a polyacid, we shall discuss its structure first. The $B(OH)_3$-molecules are planar and are arranged in planes into a slightly triclinic distorted hexagonal structure, the construction of which is shown in Fig. 26.1.[26.1,26.2]

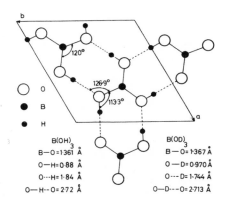

Fig. 26.1. *Structure of a layer in the structure of orthoboric acid.*

A molecule is thrice bonded to neighbouring molecules, each time by two hydrogen bonds. The hydrogen is not located centrally between two oxygen atoms, but stands nearer to one of them, as is general with hydrogen bonds (0·88 Å *vs*. 1·84 Å). The deviations from the full hexagonal symmetry are caused by a weak inclination of the molecular planes with respect to the (001) plane of the lattice.

   (b) *Metaboric Acid III* $(\alpha)H_3B_3O_6$. Metaboric acid crystallizes in three

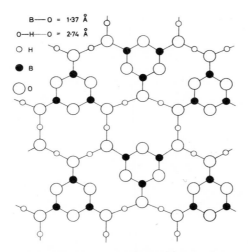

Fig. 26.2. Structure of metaboric acid III.

modifications. At room temperature metaboric acid I is thermodynamically stable. This compound crystallizes in the cubic class with a three-dimensional network. Both the monoclinic metaboric acid II, which has a complex chain-structure, and the orthorhombic metaboric acid III which has the layer structure reproduced in Fig. 26·2,[26.3] are metastable. The condensation of three orthoboric acid molecules leads to the planar trioxyboroxol ring molecules of metaboric acid III. Hydrogen bonds couple these planar rings into a planar layer.

   The sodium and potassium salts, $MeBO_2 = Me_3B_3O_6$[26.4] are also derivatives of trioxyboroxol. KBS_2 is isotypic with KBO_2.[26.5]

   (c) *Potassium Pentaborate* $K[B_5O_6(OH)_4].2H_2O$. In this compound, two boroxol rings are joined via a common boron atom with the co-ordination number 4, to form a spirane-like structure. Figure 26.3 shows the distances within a molecule found by Zachariasen.[26.6] Each of the two rings, which stand perpendicular to one another, is almost planar. The molecules are combined in the crystal in a complex fashion: (i) by electrostatically describable forces between K^+-ions and the polyanions,

(ii) by hydrogen bonds between the hydroxyl groups of neighbouring molecules, and (iii) by hydrogen bonds between water molecules and the anion.

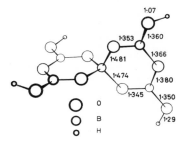

Fig. 26.3. Building block of the structure of potassium tetrahydrogen pentaborate, $K[B_5O_6(OH)_4] . 2H_2O$.

The anhydrous salt $K[B_5O_6O_{4/2}]$ is formed from the same $[B_5O_6]$ ring systems, which now are specially coupled via oxygen bridges.[26.7]

(d) *Borax,* $Na_2[B_4O_5(OH)_4].8H_2O$. In the boroxol ring, too, it is possible for two boron atoms to have the co-ordination number 4. The ring is then no longer planar. Two such rings combined would give the tetraborate ion of borax, which is similar to the camphor molecule. Figure 26.4 shows the structure of the polyion and its coupling to form long chains in the crystal with the help of hydrogen bonds.[26.8, 26.9] Between these chains lie the alkali atoms and water molecules which couple these chains both ionically and via hydrogen bonds.

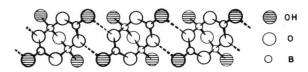

Fig. 26.4. Coupling of the tetraborate ion via hydrogen bridges into long chains in a borax crystal.

The group $[B_4O_5O_{4/2}]$ which structurally resembles camphor is found also in CdB_4O_7.[26.10] In place of the OH-groups there are O atoms which cross-link the tetraborate residues with one another.

26.1.2 *Chain Structures*

(a) *Calcium Metaborate,* $Ca(BO_2)_2$. $[BO_3]$-triangles, like $[SiO_4]$-tetrahedra, can be bound together into a chain. $Ca(BO_2)_2$, in its structure recalls the pyroxenes (Fig. 26.5). Zig-zag chains, not exactly planar, $[BO_2]_\infty^-$ are arranged along the c-axis of an orthorhombic cell.[26.11] These are coupled together via the calcium atoms. That oxygen atom which is bound to only one boron atom has the shortest B–O distance. This is also observed in the P–O distances of the chainlike metaphosphates.[26.12, 26.13] Many factors can be responsible for such an effect in a crystal structure. An increased electron density between these B and O atoms, which in itself brings about the contraction, can also be brought about through the metal atoms whose widely extended valence electron clouds can go into that space.

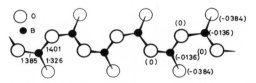

Fig. 26.5. *Metaborate chains in the structure of* $Ca(BO_2)_2$. *On the left are given the inter-atomic distances and on the right side the distances ($\AA$) from the plane containing the O atoms of a chain.*

A similar chain structure is found in $LiBO_2$,[26.14] while $NaBO_2$ and KBO_2 as we have mentioned above are trimetaborates. $LiBO_2.8H_2O$ on the contrary is made up of $[B(OH)_4]^-$ and $[Li(OH_2)_4]^+$ ions.[26.15]

(b) *Metaboric Acid II, $(\beta)HBO_2$.* The metastable, monoclinic form also called the β-modification consists of boroxol rings in which two boron atoms are bound to three oxygen atoms and one boron is bound to four oxygen atoms.[26.16] The coupling in the meta-position leads to approximately planar chains, lying parallel to the crystallographic b-axis (Fig. 26.6). A $[BO_3]$-triangle has one corner in common with a $[BO_4]$-tetrahedron. Those O atoms not built into the chain stand alternately above and below the (201) plane in which, with only slight deviations, the chain lies. The inter-atomic distances are given in Fig. 26.6, as well as the positions of the H-atoms which here can be measured by X-ray techniques to an accuracy of 0·1 Å. Hydrogen bonds join both the chains lying parallel beside one another in a plane and also those which lie over one another. Oxygen atom O_{II} has one neighbouring H atom; together they can be regarded as a hydroxyl group. The O_{VI} atom above or below the plane of the chain has two H atoms in its neighbourhood. It belongs thus to a water molecule. This occupies the fourth co-ordination position in the distorted tetrahedron about the one boron atom. The bond is weak and the associated inter-atomic distance $B_{III}–O_{VI} = 1·553$ Å is relatively large.

26.1.3 *Layer Structures*

Datolite, $CaBSiO_4(OH)$. Only one example will be given here. If half of the silicon atoms in the net structure of apophyllite (see Fig. 25.17, chapter 25) are replaced by boron atoms, so that each $[SiO_4]$-tetrahedron is surrounded by $[BO_4]$-tetrahedra, and vice versa, we have the structure of datolite.[26.17,26.18] Further substitutions lead to minerals of the same structure, herderite $CaBePO_4F$, and gadolinite $YBeSiO_4OFe^{II}_{0.5}$.[26.18]

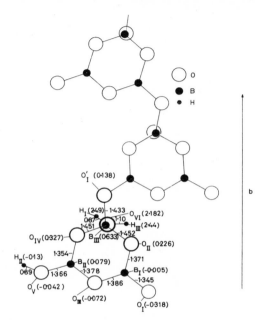

Fig. 26.6. *Coupling of the boroxol rings in a crystal of metaboric acid II. The inter-atomic distances as well as, in parentheses, the distances from the* (201) *plane are given in* Å.

26.1.4 *Three-dimensional Net Structures*

In three-dimensional network structures, the coupling between $[BO_3]$-triangles and $[BO_4]$-tetrahedra is so complicated that only recently has any attempt been made to determine the structure. A pictorial representation of the networks is very difficult and so only the structural principles will be mentioned here.

(a) *CsB_3O_5 and KB_5O_8*. In both these substances boroxol rings are found. In CsB_3O_5[26.19] one boron atom on the ring has the co-ordination number 4. In KB_5O_8[26.20] there are two boroxol rings joined into the spirane structure to which we were introduced in $K[B_5O_6(OH)_4].2H_2O$ (section 26.1.1, Fig. 26.3).

In the caesium salt there are four oxygen atoms available to couple the boroxole rings into a spiral and further into a three-dimensional network. KB_5O_8 has for five boron atoms only four oxygen atoms which can form cross-links. The spirals which are formed here in the crystal are therefore only loosely bound together, producing large cavities. These are so formed that another such network can fit inside. Thus this structure, like that of red P (chapter 12, section 34), Cu_2O (chapter 17, section 5), and $NbF_{2.5}$ (chapter 27, section 2), which will be discussed later, is formed of two, independent, mutually interpenetrating sub-lattices.

In $Ag_2B_8O_{13}$[26.21] the ring systems of Figs. 26.2 and 26.3 are coupled together spatially in the ratio 1:1. Here too the cavities are large enough and are of such a kind that the structure again consists of two interpenetrating sub-lattices between which no chemical bonds exist.

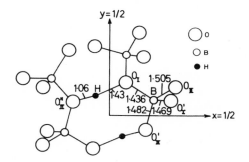

Fig. 26.7. Section of the structure of metaboric acid I.

(b) *Metaboric Acid I*, $(\gamma)HBO_2$. That modification of metaboric acid which is stable at room temperature (I or γ) crystallizes in a cubic cell. All boron atoms are tetrahedrally surrounded by oxygen atoms, so that as in the crystalline modification of SiO_2 each oxygen atom must belong to two other (here boron) atoms. A three-dimensional network results. Every other bridging oxygen atom is now bonded to a hydrogen atom at a distance 1·06 Å (as Fig. 26.7 shows). The other half of the oxygen atoms serve solely as acceptors for hydrogen bonds. Their bond with the boron atom is thus stronger (B–O distance 1·437 Å and 1·469 Å) than the bonds of the first-named boron atoms (B–O distance 1·482 and 1·505 Å).[26.22.26.23]

26.2 Compounds between Oxygen and Transition Metals[26.24]

Compounds whose principal components are oxygen and transition metals have properties which are very similar to those of the previously discussed high polymers, providing that the metal has a high valence, since then the bonding between oxygen and the metal dominates and determines the structure of the crystal. If the metal having a high valence is bound only to oxygen, co-ordination structures are generally formed.

The framework structures appear only rarely as for example in the ReO_3-type where large cavities are characteristic. With the addition of oxides of the mono- and bivalent metals, such as the alkalies and alkaline earths, parallels to the typical inorganic high polymers are apparent. The variety of crystal structures is great. Therefore only a few of the characteristic and easily describable examples will be discussed.

26.2.1 *Derivatives of the Rutile Structure*

The coupling of the $[TiO_6]$-octahedra in rutile is pictorially represented in Fig. 26.8a by a projection parallel to the c-axis. The different heights of the octahedra (centres at $c = 0$ and $c = \frac{1}{2}$) are made apparent by different shadings. In the direction of the c-axis, the octahedra are joined via their common edges like a string of pearls.

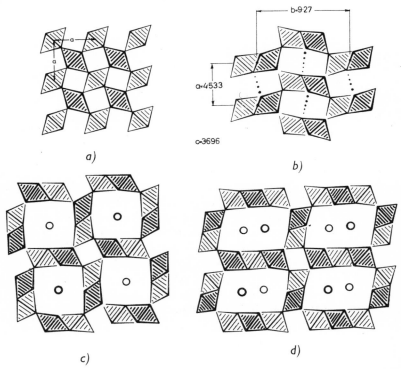

a)

b)

c)

d)

Fig. 26.8. (a) Coupling of $[TiO_6]$-octahedra in rutile. The various relative elevations are given by the darkness of the lines. The octahedrons drawn in heavier lines lie one-half an octahedral edge $(c/2)$ above or below the others. (b) Coupling of $[MnO_6]$-octahedra in ramsdellite . . . . Hydrogen bonds. (c) Coupling of $[MnO_6]$-octahedra in the structure of α-MnO_2. (d) Couplings of $[MnO_6]$-octahedra in the structure of psilomelane.[26.24]

In the rutile structure crystallizes also βMnO_2, as the mineral pyrolusite. There is yet another MnO_2 structure, ramsdellite,[26.25] in which the octahedra are coupled along the c-axis as shown in Fig. 26.8b. The chains of octahedra are half converted into bands in which two chains are joined via common octahedral edges. Depending on the preparation scheme, both pyrolusite and ramsdellite can occur together in MnO_2. Such preparations, in which both structures are found together in the same crystal are called γ-MnO_2.[26.25, 26.26, 26.27] The stoichiometry can vary since the O atoms can be converted into OH-groups. A part of the Mn is then tervalent. Preparations having composition between $MnO_{1.7}$ and MnO_2 are called brown stone.[26.28]

Diaspore (AlOOH) and goethite (FeOOH) also crystallize in the ramsdellite structure type.[26.29, 26.30] The H atoms form hydrogen bonds (see Fig. 26.8b) and shorten the distance O–H$\cdots$O to 2·65 Å,[26.31] while in compounds without hydrogen the distance is approximately 3·35 Å. In the tubes of such a structure smaller atoms can be enclosed, as in $LiMeO_2$ with Me = Sm, Eu, Gd.[26.32, 26.33]

Figure 26.8c shows the structure of α-MnO_2. Here each chain is transformed into a double band and the cavities are so large that they can accept either water or cations, e.g., in the minerals of the hollandite group[26.34] having the general formula, $A_xMnO_2 \cdot yH_2O$, with A = K, Ba, etc. Manganese here, too, becomes partially tervalent. In all cases x remains a small number since the cavities can be either vacant ($x = 0$) or only partially filled, seldom more than half (i.e., $x = \frac{1}{8}$).

Correspondingly built titanates, e.g., K_xTiO_2, are closely related to the tungsten bronzes in their properties, since ter- and tetravalent Ti atoms are on identical lattice points.[26.35] The formation of a hollandite structure is made easy when tetravalent titanium is partially replaced by lower-valent atoms of similar size, as for example in $Ba_x(Ti_{8-x}Mg_x)O_{16}$ with $0.67 < x < 1.14$, which can be obtained as single crystals from the melt.[26.36] Even at $x = 1$ the cavities in the channels are only half filled. Ba ions and vacancies seem to alternate. In this way the barium atoms become somewhat mobile in an electric field, and the crystals show strong dielectric absorption in the direction of the channels. If $x < 1$, the character of the dielectric absorption is not altered, so one can assume that some of the channels are half-filled with barium ions, while the remainder are completely empty.

There is an FeOOH, the water content of which can vary, and which in addition contains chlorine. It has the hollandite structure, the cavities of which contain both water and chlorine.[26.37] The mineral psilomelane, $(Ba_x(H_2O)_{2-x})Mn_5O_{10}$, with $0.5 < x < 0.75$, is formed from double and triple bands like those in Fig. 26.8d.[26.38] The cavities are larger and now give two possible positions for barium and water. Barium in the cavities has the co-ordination number 8; it is co-ordinated three times by two band-oxygen atoms, and twice by water molecules.[26.39]

26.2.2 *Derivatives of the ReO₃ Structure*

Figure 26.9 shows the ReO_3 structure in a projection parallel to the cube edge, $[001]$. WO_3 crystallizes in a distorted ReO_3-type structure, while MoO_3 crystallizes in a layer structure made up of MoO_6-octahedra.

Fig. 26.9. Coupling of the octahedra in ReO_3.

Within these layers, which lie parallel to the (010) planes of an orthorhombic lattice, the octahedra are coupled over a common corner, looking along the $[100]$ lines in the lattice, and over common edges in the $[001]$ direction (Fig. 26.10).[26.40]

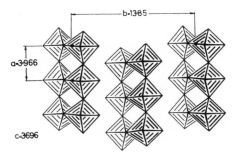

Fig. 26.10. Structure of MoO_3.[26.40]

The easy shift between octahedral coupling via edges or corners combined with the easy variation in the bonding angle on the bridging oxygen atoms on a common edge, leads to an interesting range of structures which are derived from ReO_3. Several examples will be discussed. If two halves of the ReO_3 structures are displaced along the line shown in Fig. 26.11a by the length of one octahedral edge, there results a structure in which the chains which run perpendicular to the plane of the figure are partially coupled, laterally, via the edges. Thus one can observe in Fig. 26.11b four edge-coupled chains of octahedra. In the plane illustrated, there are on four metal atoms six oxygen atoms which form bridges to neighbouring chains, and four oxygen atoms which belong to this group alone. If we include the bridging oxygen atoms in the chain direction, we find a composition $Me_4O_{8/2}O_{6/2}O_4 = Me_4O_{11}$. If those octahedra designated in Fig. 26.11b by $---$ are now combined, the entire crystal can be built

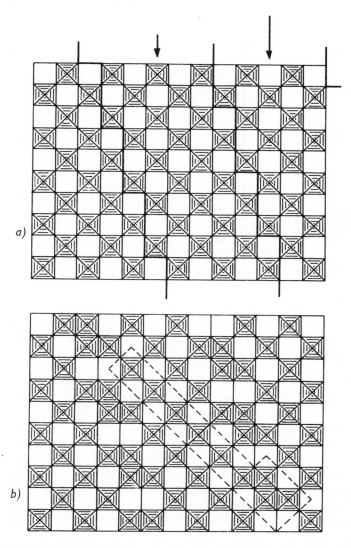

Fig. 26.11. *Transformation of a* ReO_3 *structure (a) into the* Mo_9O_{26} *structure, (b) by translation of structural blocks in the* $[110]$-*direction.*[26.24]

from these structural units, the length of the unit determining the stoichiometry, in our case, $Me_4O_{11} + Me_5O_{15} = Me_9O_{26}$, or more generally, Me_nO_{3n-1}. We come then to a family of oxides having similar structures made up principally of hexavalent but containing also pentavalent metal atoms. These compounds are intensely blue-violet in colour (cf. Table 26.1).[26.41]

Table 26.1. Homologous structures of the series $(Mo, W)_nO_{3n-1}$

Compound	n	Ratio, O:Me	Approximate ratio, Mo:W
WO_3	∞	3·000	0
$(Mo, W)_{14}O_{41}$	14	2·929	1:1
$(Mo, W)_{12}O_{35}$	12	2·917	1:2
$(Mo, W)_{11}O_{32}$	11	2·909	
$(Mo, W)_{10}O_{29}$	10	2·900	1:4
Mo_9O_{26}	9	2·889	∞
Mo_8O_{23}	8	2·875	∞

If six neighbouring chains are combined together in the manner shown for four chains in Fig. 26.11b, one comes to the series Me_nO_{3n-2}, as for example, $W_{20}O_{58} = W_6O_{16} + W_{14}O_{42}$.[26.41, 26.42, 26.43, 26.44] The narrow phase widths of all these compounds is surprising.

A new type of displacement is seen in the compound, PNb_9O_{25} (Fig. 26.12a, b).[26.45] Along the c-axis of a tetragonal system are arranged block-like sectors having the ReO_3 structure, which consist of $3 \times 3 = 9$ chains of $[NbO_6]$-octahedra. Two such sets of chains form the structural unit of the crystal. The common edges are no longer in the (001)-plane, perpendicular to the chain direction, but rather are oblique thereto. Where four such blocks come together, a narrow canal having a tetrahedral arrangement of the O atoms is formed. There are twice as many such tetrahedral holes available as are required by stoichiometry for the P atoms which fill these holes. Within one such channel almost every second hole is occupied. The exact arrangement of the P atoms is, however, unknown. Figure 26.12c shows the position of the Nb and O atoms in two adjacent layers ($c = 0$ and $c = \frac{1}{2}$ for Nb and O) as well as that of P (in $c = \frac{1}{4}$). One recognizes the, in some cases, strong distortions of the octahedra. The inter-atomic distances, Nb–O, vary for Nb_2 and Nb_3 between 1·76 and 2·30 Å, while there is a regular octahedron about Nb_1 with an inter-atomic distance of 1·92 Å.

$Ta_2Nb_4O_{15}$ appears to have this same structure. A corresponding part of the Ta or Nb $(\frac{1}{10})$ goes into tetrahedral holes, which in the structure above were occupied by P atoms. The structure of $GeO_2.9Nb_2O_5$ is very closely related to that of $P_2O_5.9Nb_2O_5$.[26.45]

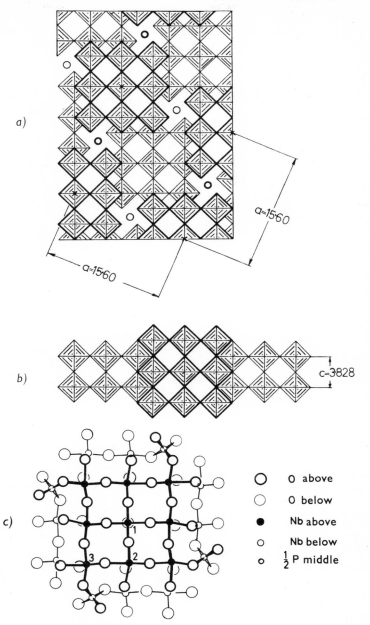

Fig. 26.12. *Coupling of blocks with the* (ReO_3) *structure into the* PNb_9O_{25} *structure.* *(a) Projection in the direction of the c-axis. (b) Section containing the c-axis. (c)* *Real position of the atoms in a projection parallel to the c-axis.*[26.45]

The size of the blocks can be varied. For example, blocks of the size $3 \times 4 \times \infty$ are found in $WNb_{12}O_{33}$, which has W in the tetrahedral holes (Fig. 26.13),[26.46] but otherwise the same packing.

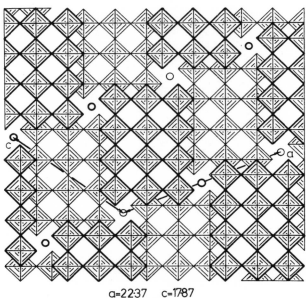

a=22·37   c=17·87

Fig. 26.13. Structure of $WNb_{12}O_3$.[26.46]

In the derivatives of the ReO_3 structure, one finds also coupling via edges of the octahedra in a plane perpendicular to the chain direction. An example is the monoclinic form of $Ti_2Nb_{10}O_{29}$.[26.47] Figure 26.14 shows how blocks $3 \times 4 \times \infty$ are coupled together via edges in the (010)-plane and also via edges which stand oblique to these planes. There are in this structure no longer any tetrahedral holes which can be occupied.

26.2.3 *Structures with Chains of Octahedra*

The tungsten bronzes, A_xWO_3 with the heavy alkali atoms K, Rb, and Cs crystallize in the hexagonal system when the alkali content is in the range $0 < x < 0.33$. The octahedral chains are then so coupled via edges that channels with sixfold symmetry and others with threefold symmetry arise (Fig. 26.15).[26.48] Thereby $x = 0.33$ corresponds to complete filling of the larger channels with alkali atoms. Under high pressure $Rb_{0.27}MoO_3$ also crystallizes in this hexagonal structure.[23.24] If part of the W is substituted by Mo, this structure can be formed without an alkali metal, i.e., with $x = 0$. Surprisingly, the Mo atoms are regularly arranged in the

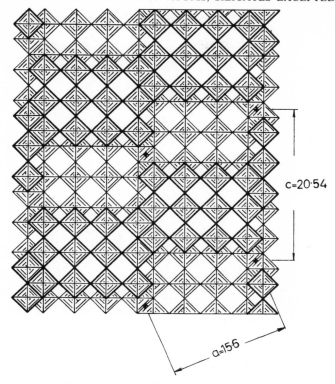

Fig. 26.14. Structure of $Ti_2Nb_{10}O_{29}$.

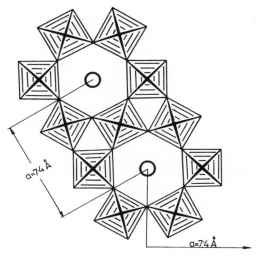

Fig. 26.15. Structure of the hexagonal tungsten bronzes.[26.24]

structure so that the Mo-content is well defined at $MoW_{11}O_{36}$ and $MoW_{14}O_{45}$.[26.49]

Besides the cubic and hexagonal tungsten bronzes there are also bronzes having tetragonal symmetry (Fig. 26.16), as for example.

$$Na_xWO_3 \text{ with } 0{\cdot}28 < x < 0{\cdot}38,[26.50]$$
$$K_xWO_3 \text{ with } 0{\cdot}48 < x < 0{\cdot}54,[26.50]$$
$$Pb_xWO_3 \text{ with } 0{\cdot}17 < x < 0{\cdot}35,[26.51]$$
$$K_xMoO_3 \text{ with } x \approx 0{\cdot}5.[23.24]$$

Here the cross section of the channels is square or pentagonal.

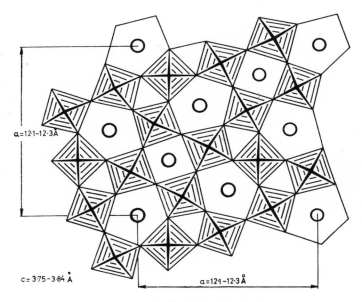

Fig. 26.16. Structure of the tetragonal tungsten bronzes.[26.24]

The high-temperature form of ferroelectric $Pb_{0.5}NbO_3$, crystallizes with tetragonal symmetry and must be closely related to the tetragonal tungsten bronzes. The ferroelectric properties arise from the fact that the Pb in the channels can move. The Nb can be partially replaced by Ta as well as by the tetravalent elements Ti, Zr, Sn. The Pb can be substituted by Ba, Li, Na, K, and Rb, but not Cs. The filling up of the channels can therefore vary without any significant changes in the tetragonal structure.[26.52, 26.53]

27

Structures having Metal–Metal Bonds

In our discussion of the NiAs structure, we mentioned the now long-known theory of W. Klemm that bonds between the metal atoms are characteristic in this structure. The nature of the bonding forces, however, is still no better known today. Several structures will now be described for which metal–metal bonds are characteristic and the structures of which can be more easily understood.

27.1 Structures having Superposed Planar Metal Complexes

Short distances between metal atoms were first found in the planar complexes of Ni, Pd, and Pt whose molecules are laid one over the other like coins in a roll. These compounds are said to have columnar structures. At that time it was considered surprising that the metal atoms along the column axis frequently had short inter-atomic distances. Further, this distance actually became shorter as the metal atom (in the series Ni, Pd, Pt) became larger. Typical examples are dimethylglyoxime-Ni, -Pd, and -Pt;[27.1] N-methylsalicylaldehyde-Ni, -Pd, and also -Cu;[27.2] as well as Magnus' Salt, $[PtCl_4][Pt(NH_3)_4]$.[27.1]

The planar arrangement of the ligands is, as we have seen earlier, due to (dsp^2)-hybrids on the metal atom. In isolated molecules the d_{3z^2-1}-state is doubly occupied while the p_z-orbital is unoccupied.[27.3] In a columnar structure two singly occupied $(d_{3z^2-1} p_z)$-hybrids which effect the bonding can occur.

Nickel forms a columnar structure only when combined with strong complex formers like CN^- in $[Ni(CN)_4]^{2-}$, or the previously mentioned chelates. With the heavier element, Pt, they are more frequent, since the heavy elements tend more to (dsp^2)-hybrid formation. The rearrangement into pairs of the electrons which do not take part in the primary bonding does not require as much energy in the case of the heavier elements (j–j and not Russel–Saunders coupling), and therefore Hund's rule is often broken for these elements. Further, the orbitals of the heavier elements are further extended so that they can better interpenetrate (cf. Figs. 14.13b,

14.15b, chapter 14). In Table 27.1 several of the more recently studied platinum compounds[27.4] are summarized.

Table 27.1. Colour and Me–Me *distance in* Pt-*complexes*

Compound	Pt–Pt distance	Colour
Oxalate Complexes		
$K_2[Pt(C_2O_4)_2].2H_2O$	not columnar	yellow[27.5]
$Ca[Pt(C_2O_4)_2].4H_2O$	3·06 Å	red-violet[27.4]
$K_{1.6}[Pt(C_2O_4)_2].2·5H_2O$	2·77 Å	metallic copper[27.4]
Cyano Complexes		
$KNa[Pt(CN)_4].3H_2O$	3·31 Å	yellow[27.6]
$Mg[Pt(CN)_4].7H_2O$	3·13 Å	red[27.7]
$K_2[Pt(CN)_4].Cl_{0.3}.2·5H_2O$	2·88 Å	metallic copper[27.8]

It is apparent that with decreasing Pt–Pt distance, the colour becomes darker. Especially short distances are observed in the columnar structures of Pt, in which part of the platinum has been transformed by oxidation into the tetravalent state. The $(d_{3z^2-1} p_z)$-hybrid functions are no longer each completely occupied with one electron. Since Pt^{II} and Pt^{IV} occupy identical lattice positions, the defect electron positions are not fixed. We observe metallic lustre and a high electrical conductivity in the columnar direction. The compounds are therefore closely related to the tungsten bronzes. However, their metallic properties exist in only one and not in all three dimensions. One can here speak of a one-dimensional metal.

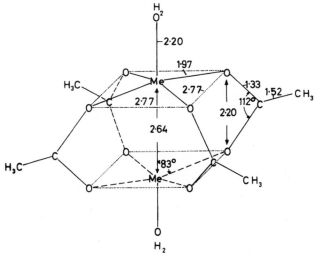

Fig. 27.1. Structure of the $[Cu(ac)_2]_2.2H_2O$ *molecule.*

Another series in which the shortening of the Me–Me distance with increasingly heavy atoms and as a function of the number of electrons is apparent, are the acetates having the general formula $[Me^{II}acet_2]_2.2H_2O$ with metal–metal distances (Fig. 27.1):

Cu: 2·64 Å[27.9]   Cr: 2·46 Å[27.9]
Rh: 2·45 Å[27.10]   Mo: 2·10 Å.[27.11]

In the copper compound the distance is especially large. The rhodium complexes correspond generally to the cobalt complexes. The bonding between the two rhodium atoms is described by (d^2sp^3)-hybrid functions.

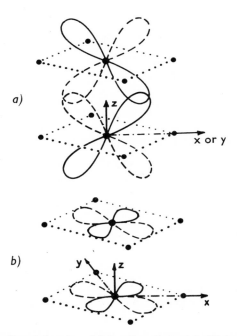

Fig. 27.2. *π-bonding (above) and δ-bonding (below) in* $[Cr(ac)_2]_2 . 2H_2O$.

The three electrons of the t_{2g}-group (d_ε) effect in the chromium and molybdenum compounds two additional π- and one δ-bond, as Fig. 27.2a, b clearly shows. The same bonding system is found in $K_2[Re_2^{III}Cl_8]$ (Fig. 27.3). Two square pyramidal $[ReCl_4]^-$-groups lie perpendicularly over one another; the Re–Re distance is 2·24 Å and the Cl–Cl distance (from layer to layer) 3·32 Å. There must be strong forces operating between the Re atoms which transform a planar $[ReCl_4]^-$-arrangement into a pyramidal configuration. The Cl atoms give the d_{xy}, d_{yz}, and d_{zx}-orbitals a fixed orientation. The π- and δ-bonding systems constrain the Cl atoms to lie perpendicularly over one another and not in the holes. The π-bonding system using d_{zx}- and d_{yz}-functions would have circular symmetry just as do the two π-bonds in acetylene about the z-axis, if this were not disturbed by the Cl atoms.

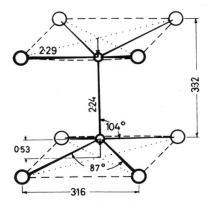

Fig. 27.3. Structure of the $[Re_2Cl_8]^{2-}$-ion.

27.2 Structures with Octahedral [Me₆]-Clusters[27.12]

The elements Nb, Ta, Mo, W, and Re in their lower valence states (2–3) form with the halogens Cl, Br, and I and also occasionally with fluorine, structural units, clusters, in which six metal atoms occupy the corners of an octahedron, the middle of which is vacant. For the halogen atoms there exist three possible arrangements (Fig. 27.4): (a) Eight halogen atoms cubically surround the octahedron. The halogen atoms thus lie over the octahedral surfaces and belong equally to three metal atoms. (b) Twelve halogen atoms lie over the edges of the octahedron. They occupy the corners of a cubo-octahedron, which can be derived from a cube by connecting the centre-points of the edges. Each halogen atom then has two metal atoms as neighbours. (c) Six halogen atoms can lie on the body diagonals of the octahedron at the periphery of the molecule. They can then be easily substituted for by other residues such as OH^- and H_2O. In solution only these halogen atoms dissociate. The complex is otherwise stable.

The Cl atoms of the third type which lie in a plane bind together each two neighbouring $[Mo_6Cl_8]^{4-}$ groups in $MoCl_2$ (Fig. 27.5).[27.13] There thus result planar nets having the composition $[Mo_6Cl_8]Cl_2Cl_{4/2} = 6MoCl_2$. The same structural build-up is shown by $MoBr_2$, WCl_2, and WBr_2.[27.12, 27.13] In $[Nb_6I_8]I_{6/2} = Nb_6I_{11}$ there results with otherwise similar construction, a 3-dimensional linking of the $[Nb_6I_8]^{3-}$-groups.[27.14]

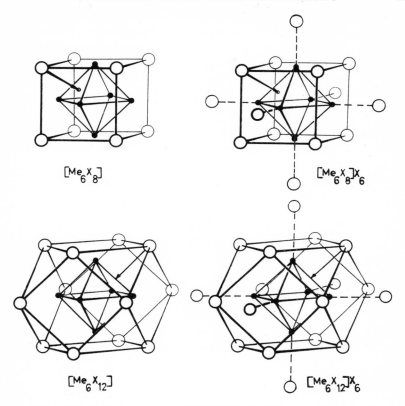

Fig. 27.4. Structure of complexes with octahedral $[Me_6]$-*centres.*[27.12]

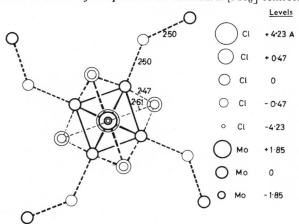

Fig. 27.5. Section from the $MoCl_2$ *structure.*

The type $[Me_6X_{12}]^{n+}X_n^-$ is found with the heavy elements of the fifth sub-group, Nb and Ta. If all the X atoms on the outermost co-ordination sphere (Group 3) are used for three-dimensional coupling, the composition $[Me_6X_{12}]X_{6/12} = 6MeX_{2.5}$ having fractional valence results as, for example, $NbF_{2.5}$,[27.15] $TaCl_{2.5}$, and $TaBr_{2.5}$.[27.12] The structure of $NbF_{2.5}$ is reproduced in Fig. 27.6.[27.15] For the sake of clarity only one of

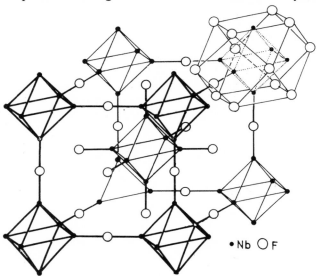

• Nb ◯ F

Fig. 27.6. Structure of $NbF_{2.5}$. Only one cubo-octahedron of twelve atoms is illustrated.

the cubo-octahedra, consisting of 12 fluorine atoms, is shown. One can see that the structure is derived from the ReO_3 structure, when the rhenium atoms are replaced by Nb_6- or more accurately by $[Nb_6F_{12}]$-groups, the oxygen atoms by additional fluorine atoms. Vacancies in this sub-lattice are so large and so arranged that the real crystal consists of two identical sub-lattices which are placed one within the other. Figure 27.7 shows how the $NbF_{2.5}$-structure can be derived from a rock-salt-type structure with vacancies in the Nb- and F-sub-lattices.[27.15]

In the compounds $NbCl_{2.33}$[27.16] and $TaI_{2.33}$[27.17] it is not only the outermost halogen atoms which are used for three-dimensional coupling but also two of the halogen atoms on the inner shell in accordance with the formula, $[Ta_6I_{10}I_{2/2}]I_{2/2}I_{4/2} = 6TaI_{2.33}$. Earlier we considered the NbO structure and saw that it is characterized by Nb_6-octahedra. One can therefore see this structure as a close relative of the last-named group. Here all the O atoms are used for three-dimensional coupling and each O atom belongs equally to two Nb-octahedra, $[Nb_6O_{12/2}] = 6NbO$.

Cotton and Haas have recently developed a molecular orbital treatment of the $[Me_6X_8]^{2+}$ and $[Me_6X_{12}]^{4+}$ structures.[27.18] That for the latter compound will be given here.

Each Me atom is surrounded by an approximate square having four halogen atoms at the corners. Just as with other square-planar complexes (e.g., $PtCl_4^{2-}$) we use (dsp^2)-hybrid functions in order to provide the σ-bond frame. We then assume that each Me atom keeps its own Cartesian co-ordinate system, the axes of which are parallel to the axes of the Me_6-octahedra and the positive z-axes of which point toward the centre of the Me_6-octahedron. The Cartesian co-ordinate system, whose origin is at the

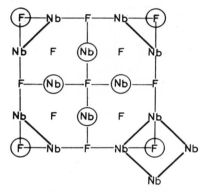

Fig. 27.7. *The development of the* $NbF_{2.5}$ *structure from* NbF *with a rock-salt-type structure by removing those atoms found in the circles.*

centre of the octahedron, has the co-ordinates X, Y, Z. For bonding between the Me atoms of the octahedron there are still available: d_{3z^2-1}, d_{xy}, d_{yz}, d_{zx}, and p_z-functions, while the $d_{x^2-y^2}$-function was used to form the (dsp^2)-hybrid. The first molecular function is obtained when all d_{3z^2-1}-functions $((d_{3z^2-1}p_z)$-hybrids act the same way) have their positive branches directed toward the centre of the octahedron. In all the symmetry operations of the octahedron these molecular functions go into themselves, without changing sign on inversion. The symmetry designation is therefore A_{1g}.

We obtain a further molecular function when the d_{xy}-orbitals are combined as shown in Fig. 27.8a. Over each face of the octahedron occur either only the positive or only the negative branches of the d-functions of the three corner atoms. The signs change on going from one surface to the neighbouring one. By all symmetry operations of the octahedron it is only the sign, at most, that changes. Since the sign is changed under inversion, the function is ungerade and the symmetry designation is A_{2u}.

If we now go back to Fig. 10.4, we recognize immediately how three T_{2g}

molecular functions result. The p_x- and p_y-orbitals of the ligands are to be replaced by appropriate d_{zx}- or d_{yz}-orbitals respectively.

The last group of molecular functions, having symmetry T_{1u}, is depicted in Fig. 27.8b. The d_{yz}- and d_{zx}-orbitals of four Nb atoms in a plane are so combined that the positive branches meet on the positive sides of the X-, Y-, or Z-axes. The molecular function thus transforms like the p_X, p_Y, and p_Z-eigenfunctions which extend out from the centre of the octahedron.

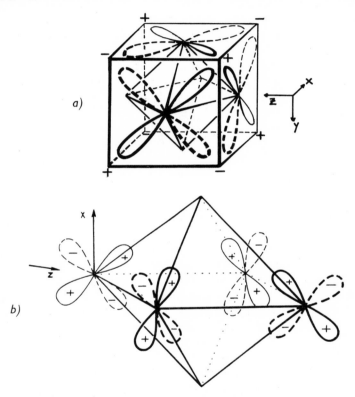

Fig. 27.8. *Molecular functions in* $[Me_6X_{12}]^{4-}$*-complexes with the symmetry:*
(a) A_{2u} *(b)* T_{1u}.

There are thus $1 + 1 + 3 + 3 = 8$ molecular functions, which can be occupied by 16 electrons. $TaI_{2.33} = Ta_6I_{14}$ has exactly the appropriate number of electrons, $6 \times 5 - 14 = 16$, and is diamagnetic. $TaCl_{2.5} = Ta_6Cl_{15}$ has in the system of metal bonds, one electron too few, $6 \times 5 - 15 = 15$ and therefore shows a spin magnetism due to one electron. In the case of $Nb_6I_{11} = [Nb_6I_8]I_{6/2}$ so many electrons are lacking for the full electron occupation of the Me_6X_8-configuration $(24 - 19 = 5)$ that this compound will incorporate H-atoms in a hydrogen atmosphere at a some-what elevated temperature.[27.18d]

$Pt_6Cl_{12} = 6PtCl_2$ forms a crystal from molecules of form b (Fig. 27.4).[27.19] Here the molecules are held together only by Cl-bridges, via (dsp^2)-hybrid functions of the metal atoms, since the complex forming capability of Pd^{II} and Pt^{II} is strongly pronounced. In the elements Nb, Ta, Mo, and W these hybrid functions are further extended and therefore they cannot bind the halogen atoms so tightly. The $[Me_6X_8]$- and $[Me_6X_{12}]$-groupings require for their stabilization the additional weak bonding forces between the metal atoms, corresponding to the above developed theory of Cotton and Haas.

NbO shows metallic lustre and an electrical conductivity which corresponds to that of niobium metal. The above-described bonding systems can be propagated throughout an entire crystal. There result mesomeric bonding systems between atoms of one type (Nb) which according to all experience must lead to metallic conductivity. One must always keep in mind, however, that the orbitals in such a structure can also be combined in other ways. To specify all possible combinations in detail leads to the same difficulties as in a typical metal.

27.3 Metal–Metal Bonds in Structures Made Up of [MeX₆]-Octahedra

The simplest coupling of two $[MeX_6]$-octahedra via one common surface is found in the compounds: Cs_3TlCl_9,[27.20, 27.21] $Cs_3Ti_2Cl_9$, $Cs_3V_2Cl_9$, $Cs_3Cr_2Cl_9$,[27.22] and $K_3W_2Cl_9$ (Fig. 27.9).[27.23, 27.24] Only in

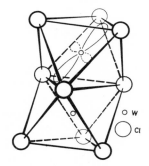

Fig. 27.9. Structure of $[W_2Cl_9]^{3-}$*-ions.*

the W compound is a shorter inter-atomic distance between metal atoms observed, (W–W = 2·409 Å; in tungsten metal it is 2·519 Å). The inter-atomic distances in the other compounds are normal (e.g., Cr–Cr = 3·12 Å). In the tungsten compound, the metal atoms are displaced from the centre of an octahedron to the common face, while in the chromium compound the displacement is in the opposite direction. The tungsten compound is diamagnetic; the chromium is paramagnetic with a spin moment corresponding to 3 unpaired electrons per atom.

The short inter-atomic distances of the $[W_2Cl_9]^{3-}$ ion and its dia-magnetism can be traced back to triple bonding between t_{2g}-electrons on the two W atoms. Each of these d-orbitals points with one branch toward a common edge of the octahedra, so that the two orbitals which geometric-ally correspond to one another, overlap in the region of an edge common to both octahedra.

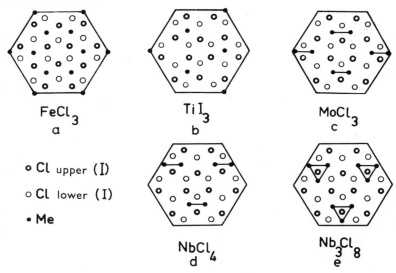

FeCl₃
a

TiI₃
b

MoCl₃
c

o Cl upper (I)

o Cl lower (I)

• Me

NbCl₄
d

Nb₃Cl₈
e

Fig. 27.10. *Structures which can be derived from the* $FeCl_3$-*type.*

This bonding system could be propagated in the direction of the threefold axis of the $[W_2Cl_9]^{3-}$-ion, since d-orbitals are gerade and have the same values on opposite sides of the octahedron. The high negative charge on the complex ion and the large number of cations prevent chain-formation here. In $MoBr_3$ on the other hand, we find a structure in which $MoBr_{6/2}$-octahedra are arranged via common faces into a chain-like molecule (Fig. 27.10b).[27.25] According to X-ray investigations the Mo–Mo distances are all the same, 3·03 Å. The chains are so arranged in the crystal that the Br atoms taken alone have a layer sequence ABAB as in hexagonal close packing, providing that one ignores the fact that every three Br atoms within the layers are displaced toward the chain axis. If one removes every second atom in the metal layer of an $FeCl_3$ structure (Fig. 27.10a), and puts it in the middle between two Fe atoms which lie over one another, one obtains the ordering of Mo atoms in $MoBr_3$. The packing is like that in the WCl_6 structure (chapter 22, section 1) in the c-axis direction; however, we find twice as many metal atoms. In the $MoBr_3$-type crystallize: MoI_3,[27.26] $TiCl_3$, $TiBr_3$, TiI_3,[27.27] $ZrCl_3$, $ZrBr_3$, ZrI_3, HfI_3,[27.28] β-$RuCl_3$,[27.29] and anti-isotypically, Cs_3O.[27.30] NbI_3 can also crystallize in a metastable form having the $MoBr_3$-type structure. This compound shows especially clear superstructure lines in the X-ray pattern. These lines result from a doubling of the lattice parameter a. It follows from this that distortion can occur in the $MoBr_3$ structure type. The nature of these, however, is not yet known.[27.31]

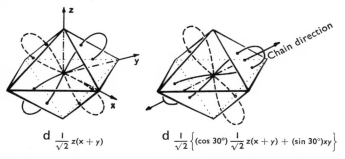

$$d \quad \frac{1}{\sqrt{2}} z(x+y) \qquad d \quad \frac{1}{\sqrt{2}}\left\{(\cos 30°) \frac{1}{\sqrt{2}} z(x+y) + (\sin 30°)xy\right\}$$

Fig. 27.11. Linear combinations of d_ε-orbitals explaining the TiI_3 structure.

The Ti, Zr, and Hf compounds have only one d-electron per metal atom. It then has a free choice as to which of the $d_\varepsilon(t_{2g})$ states, which we discussed for the $W_2Cl_9{}^{3-}$-ion, it occupies. From the three orbitals of the t_{2g}-group, we can form an energetically more favourable linear combination having the angular component:

$$\frac{1}{\sqrt{2}}\left\{(\cos 30°) \frac{1}{\sqrt{2}} z(x+y) + (\sin 30°)xy\right\}.$$

The replacement of x by $x + y$ signifies a rotation of d_{zx} by 45° about the z-axis. The addition of $(\sin 30°)(xy)$ then rotates the two positive branches of the function $(\cos 30°)(1/\sqrt{2})x(x + y)$, so that they stand perpendicular to two opposite octahedral faces. A σ-bond can then be effective in both chain directions (Fig. 27.11). Essentially, all orbitals formed from the above by rotation about the axis of the σ-bond are equivalent. These are formed from the d_ε-function by choosing other coefficients of the linear combination.

If the metal atoms in the $FeCl_3$ structure are displaced as Fig. 27.10c shows, each of two atoms moves somewhat closer to the other and atom pairs are formed. In this way one arrives at the structure of $MoCl_3$.[27.32] The Mo–Mo distances are 2·77 Å and 3·70 Å, $r_2/r_1 = 1·33$. If one reduces the number of atom pairs by 25 per cent one comes to the structure of

$NbCl_4$ (Fig. 27.10d),[27.12] in which type crystallize also the compounds NbI_4, TaI_4,[27.33] and probably $NbBr_4$, $TaCl_4$, and $TaBr_4$.[27.12]

The structure of $NbCl_{2.67} = Nb_3Cl_8$ is derived from that of $NbCl_4 = Nb_2Cl_8$, in that each Nb-pair is supplemented by the addition of a third Nb atom to form a triangular arrangement (Fig. 27.10e).[27.34] The distance between atoms within the triangle is 2·81 Å, that between Nb atoms on neighbouring triangles is 3·93 Å, $r_2/r_1 = 1·40$. Now, each Nb atom is in a position to form a bond to the two neighbours using d_ε-electrons. The $[Nb_3]$-group, however, contains seven d_ε-electrons, so that the superfluous electron is distributed over the three d-states which are still free on the three Nb atoms. Nb_3Cl_8 is therefore paramagnetic, the Curie temperature, $\vartheta = -50°C$. The magnetic moment $(1·86\mu_\beta)$ corresponds to a spin moment of one electron per Nb_3-group. Since the electron, in contrast to that in the tungsten bronzes, is confined to one Nb_3-group, the material is not a metal but rather a semiconductor. The niobium has a fractional valence, $2\frac{2}{3}$, in this compound since all Nb atoms in the crystal are assumed to be equivalent.

In the compounds, $Me_2^{II}Mo_3O_8$, with Me = Mg, Mn, Fe, Co, Ni, Zn, and Cd, the Mo and O atoms form layers just as in the Nb_3Cl_8 structure. Here, however, one finds half of the Me^{II} atoms in tetrahedral and the other half in octahedral holes. Since Mo is tetravalent in this compound, the additional d_ε-electron is missing and the representatives with Me = Mg, Zn, and Cd are therefore only very weakly paramagnetic.[27.35]

Compounds such as Nb_3Cl_8 have a rather wide homogeneity range, e.g., $NbCl_{2.67}–NbCl_{3.13}$, and $NbBr_{2.67}–NbBr_{3.00}$.[22.1] This is related to the easy substitution of Nb_3-groups by Nb_2-groups. One can alternatively consider this a limited mixed crystal region between $NbCl_{2.67}$ and $NbCl_4$.

Metal–metal bonds are found also in structures which are completely different in their construction, as for example the rutile structure. In the c-axis direction, every two metal atoms can move somewhat closer together and form pairs. The following inter-atomic distances have been found:[27.36]

Substance	r_1	r_2	r_2/r_1	No. of d-electrons on the metal
TiO_2	2·959	2·959	1	0
VO_2	2·65	3·10	1·17	1
NbO_2	2·80	3·20	1·14	1
MoO_2	2·50	3·10	1·24	2
WO_2	2·49	3·08	1·24	2
TcO_2	(2·48)	(3·06)	(1·24)	3
ReO_2	(2·49)	(3·08)	(1·24)	3

Figures in parentheses are estimated values.

The bonding between the Nb atoms in NbO_2 is also apparent in a lowered magnetic susceptibility.[27.37] At low temperatures, VO_2 is a semiconductor having a distorted rutile structure.[27.38] Above 60°C, however, it displays metallic conductivity[27.39] and has the ideal rutile structure.[27.40] Increased thermal motion allows the t_{2g}-electron to shift. One can best describe this condition by saying that in a given line of adjacent V atoms, one electron is missing, while then a chain segment follows in which there is one t_{2g}-electron too many.

In IrO_2 (rutile) with the configuration t_{2g}^5 for the non-bonding electrons there is one electron missing from a noble-gas shell. Thereby one can explain the origin of its metallic conductivity.[27.41, 27.42]

28

Alloys

We have already indicated, in section 2 of chapter 12 how difficult it is to derive the structures of metals from theoretical bonding considerations. This is even more of a problem for the crystal structure of alloys, so that one is therefore led to describe phenomenologically the multiplicity of phases found.[28.1, 28.2, 28.3] We shall give only a very compressed survey and shall limit even that discussion to binary systems.

We have already considered many compounds which in their properties are close to alloys. Recall the compounds Al_2Pt (CaF_2 structure), TiC (NaCl), MgTl (CsCl), NaTl, and the NiAs phases. In these the bonding concepts which we have drawn upon to explain the crystal structure of typical chemical compounds were still frequently usable.

28.1 Solid Solution and Superstructure

28.1.1 *The System Cu–Au*

Copper and gold both crystallize in face-centred cubic structures. Their atomic radii differ by about 14 per cent (1·28 Å and 1·44 Å). When the type of chemical bonding is related and the atomic radii do not differ by more than 15 per cent, widespread substitution of one atom for another in a structure can occur. Therefore, at high temperatures one observes a complete solid solution between these two metals. The lattice parameter varies linearly with the composition. According to Vegard (*Vegard's Law*) this is a general property of mixed crystal systems when no unusual circumstances are present.

Only at high temperatures are the Cu and Au atoms statistically distributed over the lattice points of the face-centred cubic structure. If the sample is slowly cooled or annealed at specific temperatures, the Cu and Au atoms will have a definite distribution in the crystal. One speaks then of a *superstructure*. With increasing copper content, as the ratio Cu:Au approaches unity, the tendency toward superstructure formation increases. At the composition CuAu, the ordering is that shown in Fig. 28.1a. The Cu and Au atoms each have the same substructure layers (L1$_0$-type). The crystal loses its cubic symmetry and becomes tetragonally distorted with an axial ratio, $c/a = 0{\cdot}932$. With further addition of copper, the Au atoms are at first statistically replaced by copper. Then, however, there comes a preference for the replacement of the gold atoms in the face centres. When the ratio Cu:Au 3:1 is reached, the structure shown in Fig. 28.1b results, which is again cubic ($L1_2$-type).

The statistical distribution of atoms found at high temperatures can frequently be frozen in at room temperature by quenching. The technological properties of alloys thus often depend on the heat treatment of the sample.

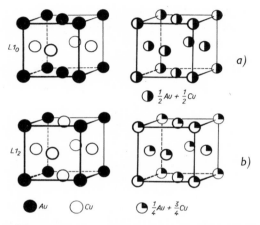

Fig. 28.1. *High- and low-temperature forms of the compounds (a)* AuCu, *(b)* AuCu$_3$.

In the AuCu structure ($L1_0$ type) crystallize LiBi, NaBi, as well as

MeTi with Me = Al, Cu, Ag, Hg
MePd with Me = Zn, Cd, Hg, Fe
MePt with Me = Zn, Cd, Hg, Fe, Ni,

in the Cu$_3$Au structure ($L1_2$ type) crystallize

Ni$_3$Me with Me = Mn, Fe, Pt, Al, Ga, Si, Ge
Pt$_3$Me with Me = Mn, Fe, Co, Ni, Ag
Pb$_3$Me with Me = Na, Ca, Y, RE
Me$_3$Al with Me = Zr, Co, Ni
Me$_3$U   with Me = Ga, Si, Ge, Sn, Pb
Me$_3$Pt with Me = Cr, Mn, Fe, Ni, Cu, Ag
Me$_3$RE with Me = Pd, Pt, In, Tl.[28.3]

28.1.2 *The System Fe–Al*[28.4]

The system Fe–Al is more complicated. Here, at low temperatures, a continuous series of mixed crystals is not possible since iron is body-centred at room temperature and aluminium crystallizes with a face-centred cubic structure.

In the range of 0–25 per cent aluminium, the distribution of aluminium atoms in the body-centred cubic crystal of iron is, in a quenched sample, statistical.

In the range 25–50 atomic per cent aluminium the distribution is no longer statistical. The iron atoms now completely occupy lattice points a and b while additional iron and all the aluminium atoms are statistically distributed among the points c and d in Fig. 28.2. A completely ordered structure is first observed at the composition FeAl with Fe on the a and b places and Al on the c and d places; i.e., a CsCl-type structure is found.

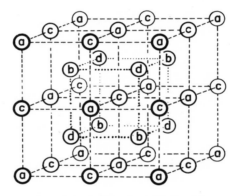

Fig. 28.2. *Occupation of the sites in the cubic* Fe–Al *system (see text).*

With carefully annealed samples, a statistical distribution is found in the range from 0 to 18 atomic per cent aluminium. Then the aluminium begins to concentrate itself in the positions c. At the composition Fe_3Al, about 95 per cent of all aluminium atoms are in the positions c. The structure then resembles that of Li_3Bi. Only after additional aluminium is added are the lattice points d strongly occupied, in part at the expense of the points, c. At 38 per cent aluminium there remain hardly any aluminium atoms in the positions a and b; they are instead statistically distributed over the positions c and d. At the composition FeAl we again observe the —even at high temperature—stable distribution (Fe on a and b, Al on c and d) characteristic of a CsCl structure.

The ordered superstructure of the Fe_3Al (DO_3 type of Li_3Bi) are also shown by the alloy-like phases αFe_3Si, βCu_3Sb, Li_3Hg, Mg_3La, Mg_3Pr, and H_3La.[28.3]

28.2 Hume-Rothery Phases

Figure 28.3 shows the phase diagram of the system Cu–Zn. The system can be divided into five separate phases (α to η) and four two-phase regions. We shall ignore here the δ-phase which occurs at elevated temperatures. The α-phase is face-centred cubic, just as in copper. Up to 37 per cent of all copper atoms can be replaced statistically by zinc. After a two-phase region, comes the β-phase, the phase width of which is narrow at low temperatures, and which contains somewhat less zinc than corresponds to the composition CuZn. At low temperatures, annealed samples

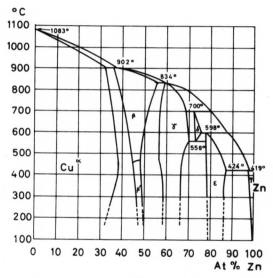

Fig. 28.3. *Phase diagram of the system* Cu–Zn.[28.1]

have the CsCl-type structure. The one atom position, (000), is occupied only by copper atoms while the other $(\frac{1}{2}\frac{1}{2}\frac{1}{2})$, contains the zinc and, depending on the composition, more or less copper. Above 100°C an exchange of the atoms begins, which increases with increasing temperature. Above 470°, the distribution of copper and zinc atoms is statistical. The γ-phase is stable at 58–67 atomic per cent zinc. Its structure can be derived from that of CsCl in which $3 \times 3 \times 3 = 27$ unit cells are combined to form the large cubic unit cell. If we remove the atoms at the corners (000) and centre $(\frac{1}{2}\frac{1}{2}\frac{1}{2})$, of the new cell there remain $54 - 2 = 52$ atoms left over. Because of these holes, small displacements of the atom positions are possible. An ideal composition of the cell would be $Cu_{20}Zn_{32} = Cu_5Zn_8$ with 61·5 atomic per cent zinc. The ε and the η-phase both have hexagonal close-packed structures, although with different lattice parameters and axial ratios. The ε-phase is stable in the range 78–86 atomic per cent zinc. The composition thus is in the neighbourhood of the formula $CuZn^3$ with 75 atomic per cent zinc. The β, ε, and γ phases are characterized by hardness and brittleness.

The crystal structures of these three phases are observed frequently among alloys which are formed from elements of the iron-group and groups I–IV (copper to germanium groups, including aluminium and silicon) of the periodic system. The statistical distribution of the atoms which is almost always observed in the ε-phase and frequently in the β- and γ-phases, at least at higher temperatures, explains the idea that a given atom ratio is not decisive for alloy formation. Hume-Rothery[28.5] showed in 1926 that the occurrence of the above-mentioned phases is coupled with a definite ratio between the number of valence electrons and the number of atoms, providing one assumes that the elements in the iron group have a valence of zero and that other elements have their group valence.

Table 28.1. Hume-Rothery phases

Cubic body centred 21:14		γ-Brass structure 21:13		Hexagonal closest packing 21:12	
CuBe;	Zn	Cu_5Zn_8;	Cd_8, Hg_8	$CuZn_3$;	Cd_3
AgMg;	Zn, Cd	Ag_5Zn_8;	Cd_8, Hg_8	$AgZn_3$;	Cd_3
AuMg;	Zn, Cd	Au_5Zn_8;	Cd_8	$AuZn_3$;	Cd_3
Cu_3Al;	Ga, In	Cu_9Al_4;	Ga_4, In_4	Cu_3Si;	Ge, Sn
Ag_3Al;	In	Ag_9In_4		Ag_3Sn	
		Au_9In_4		Au_3Sn	
Cu_5Si;	Sn				
		$Cu_{31}Si_8$;	Sn_8	Ag_5Al_3	
AlFe;	Co, Ni			Au_5Al_3	
InNi;	Pd	$Zn_{21}Mn_5$;	Fe_5, Co_5, Ni_5, Rh_5, Pd_5, Pt_5		
		$Be_{21}Ni_5$;	Pt_5		

The elements which can substitute for the second element in the formula follow the semicolon in each case.

In Table 28.1 are presented several Hume-Rothery phases. For the β-phase the ratio is 21:14, for γ, 21:13, and for the ε-phase, 21:12. As an example: per formula unit of Cu_3Al there are $3 \times 1 + 3 = 6$ electrons and $3 + 1 = 4$ atoms; or for Co_5Zn_{21} there are $5 \times 0 + 21 \times 2 = 42$ electrons and $5 + 21 = 26$ atoms. The rule is not strictly followed. For example, the above-mentioned phases, CuZn and $CuZn_3$ do not lie within the β- and ε-phase regions but only in the neighbourhood thereof.

It must also be mentioned that at the ratio 21:14, instead of the body-centred cubic β-phase, two complicated structures, called μ and ξ occur.

Today we know that the elements of the iron and copper group also take part in d-electron bonding in metallic systems (cf. section 2 of chapter 11). Pauling[28.6] assumed that in Hume-Rothery phases the elements take part in the bonding with the following electron numbers: Cu 5·53, Zn 4·53, Ga 3·53, and Ge 2·53. One then arrives at new ratios. No matter how the bonding in the Hume-Rothery phases is formulated, the rule says only that between the number of atoms in the unit cell and their position in the periodic system, a simple relation holds, which is analogous to the statement of the Grimm hydride displacement law[28.7] or the Grimm–Sommerfeld rule[28.9] for diamond-like structures.

28.3 Laves Phases

Many intermetallic compounds having the general formula AB_2 crystallize in one of the three closely related structures: (a) $MgCu_2$, cubic (C15-type), (b) $MgZn_2$, hexagonal (C14-type), and (c) $MgNi_2$, hexagonal

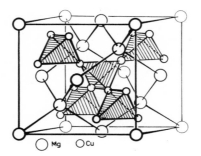

$\bigcirc$ Mg $\bigcirc$ Cu

Fig. 28.4. $MgCu_2$ *structure.*

(C36-type).[28.9] In $MgCu_2$ the Mg atoms alone form a diamond structure or alternately a structure like that of calcium and one half of the fluorine atoms in the CaF_2 structure (Fig. 28.4). The copper atoms form tetrahedra the middles of which are unoccupied. The centres of these tetrahedra lie at those points, which in the CaF_2 structure are occupied by the second half of the F atoms (cf. Fig. 17.1). The tetrahedra themselves are so arranged that the connecting lines from their centres to the corners point into the still empty octants of the CaF_2 structure. There the same tetrahedra are again formed, since the distance from the centre to the corner of a tetrahedron is $[\sqrt{(3)/8}]a$. Each Mg atom is surrounded by four other Mg atoms at a distance $[\sqrt{(3)/4}]a = 0.4325a$ and by $4 \times 3 = 12$ Cu atoms at a distance $0.415a$. Conversely, each Cu atom is surrounded by six Mg atoms at the same distance, and at a distance of $[\sqrt{(2)}/4]a =$ $0·3535a$, by six Cu atoms. The co-ordination numbers are thus very high, $4 + 12 = 16$ for magnesium and $6 + 6 = 12$ for copper. If one considers the magnesium and copper atoms as rigid spheres, which is naturally not justified, then only like atoms touch. The distance Mg–Cu, $0·4145a$, is about 5·5 per cent larger than the average of the Mg–Mg and Cu–Cu distances, $(0·3535 + 0·4325)\,a/2 = 0·393a$. The Mg–Mg distance is 22 per cent greater than the Cu–Cu distance.

In the $MgZn_2$ structure, the Mg atoms considered alone form a wurzite-type structure (Fig. 28.5). Here the Zn atoms form a tetrahedral skeleton, but with the difference, that now the tetrahedra are coupled both over common corners and common faces. In Fig. 28.5 the coupling of the

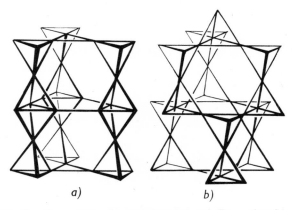

a)   *b)*

Fig. 28.5. (a) Coupling of the Zn-*tetrahedra in* $MgZn_2$. **(b) Coupling of the** Cu-*tetrahedra in* $MgCu_2$.

tetrahedra into the $MgCu_2$ structure is represented such that one body diagonal of the unit cell is parallel to the length of the page while for the $MgZn_2$ structure the crystallographic c-axis is depicted in this direction.

In the $MgNi_2$ structure the two coupling possibilities of the $MgCu_2$ and $MgZn_2$ structures in the direction of the c-axis alternate regularly. On account of the above-derived size relations for the $MgCu_2$ structure, which correspondingly hold also for the $MgZn_2$ and $MgNi_2$ structures, one must assume a size ratio between the atoms on the A and B places of approximately 1·2 in order to form the structure. It can vary from 1·1 to 1·4.[28.9, 28.10] As is apparent from Table 28.2, elements from almost all the groups of the periodic system form Laves phases. Several elements (e.g., Mg, V, and Bi), can assume A as well as B places. At present the structure still cannot be correlated with definite electronic configurations. Typical, however, for these Laves phases are the high co-ordination numbers which also occur in other alloy-like structures and which appear to be co-factors in the formation of these structures.

Table 28.2. Binary Laves phases from references 28.11, 28.5, 28.3, 13.2.

B	MgCu$_2$-type A	MgZn$_2$-type A	MgNi$_2$-type A
V$_2$	Zr, Hf, Ta	Zr	
Cr$_2$	Ti, Zr, Hf, Nb, Ta	Ti, Zr, Hf, Ta	Hf
Mo$_2$	Zr, Hf		Hf
W$_2$	Zr, Hf		
Mn$_2$	Y, RE, U, Pu	Sc, RE, Th, Ti, Zr, Hf, Nb, Ta	Hf
Tc$_2$		Sc, RE, Zr, Hf	
Re$_2$		Sc, Y, RE, Th, U, Pu, Zr, Hf	
Fe$_2$	Y, RE, U, Pu, Zr, Hf	Ti, Zr, Hf, Nb, Ta, Mo, W	
Ru$_2$	RE, Th, Pu	Sc, Y, RE, Zr	
Os$_2$	RE, Th, U	RE, Pu, Zr, Hf	
Co$_2$	Y, RE, U, Pu, Zr, Hf, Nb, Ta	Ta	
Rh$_2$	Ca, Sr, Ba, Y, RE		
Ir$_2$	Ca, Sr, RE, Th, U, Zr	Zr	
Ni$_2$	Sc, Y, RE, Pu	U Zr	Mg
Pd$_2$	Ca, Sr, Ba		
Pt$_2$	Li, Na, Ca, Sr, Ba, Y, RE		U
Li$_2$		Ca	
Na$_2$		K	
Cu$_2$	Mg	Cd	
Ag$_2$	Na		
Au$_2$	Na, Pb, Bi		
Be$_2$	Ti, Nb, Ta, Cu, Ag	V, Cr, Mo, W, Mn, Re, Fe	
Mg$_2$	RE, Th	Ca, Sr, Ba, Er	Th
Zn$_2$	Pu, Zr, Hf	Mg, Ti	Hf, Nb
Cd$_2$		Ca	
Al$_2$	Ca, Sc, Y, RE, U, Nb, Pu	Zr, Hf	
Pb$_2$		K	
Bi$_2$	K, Rb, Cs		

29

Glasses

29.1 Definition of the Vitreous State

It is not easy to divide the vitreous state from the crystalline and the liquid, since there is a continuous transition from one to another. It can perhaps be best defined in the following way: 'A glass is a solid body with dense packing of atoms, which has no long-range ordering into a crystal lattice.' Short-range ordering is, however, present. According to this definition, amorphous $Al(OH)_3$ or $Cr(OH)_3$ are not glasses, since these substances represent loose powders having vacancies down to atomic dimensions.

One distinguishes between glasses in the narrow sense, which are produced by solidification of a melt (e.g., a silicate glass) and those in a broader sense which are obtained by other processes, as by condensation of vapours on cooled surfaces (e.g., glassy arsenic), or by electrolysis (e.g., explosive antimony).

29.2 Causes of Vitrification

29.2.1 *Glasses with Three-dimensional Network Structures*

On the basis of the work of G. Tamman[29.1] and V. H. Goldschmidt,[29.2] W. H. Zachariasen developed the concept that glass formation is connected with the possibility of forming an irregular three-dimensional network.[29.3] Figure 29.1a, b clarifies the difference between an ordered crystalline and a disordered glassy network. In a pure oxide, according to Zachariasen, glass formation requires satisfaction of the following four conditions:

(a) An oxygen atom is bound with at most two central atoms (M).

(b) The co-ordination number x of the $[MO_x]$-polyhedra must be small.

(c) The $[MO_x]$-polyhedra have only corners in common, not edges or faces.

(d) For three-dimensional networks there must be at least three corners of a polyhedron common with neighbouring polyhedra.

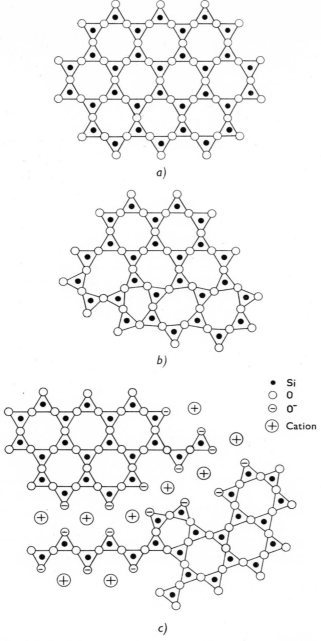

Fig. 29.1. Schematic two-dimensional representation of (a) a crystalline SiO₂-network, (b) a glassy SiO₂-network, (c) a SiO₂-glass with network modifiers (cations).

Glass-forming oxides which satisfy these four conditions are B_2O_3 ($[MO_3]$ = planar triangle), As_2O_3 ($[MO_3]$ = triangular pyramid), and SiO_2, GeO_2, P_2O_5, As_2O_5 ($[MO_4]$ = tetrahedra). If we now look behind these rules to structural chemical principles in order to seek an explanation, we can give the following reasons for the irregular coupling of the co-ordination polyhedra which is essential to glass formation.

There must be free rotation about each M—O bond. This can only result and lead to an irregular coupling of the atoms when oxygen has a co-ordination number of 2. When it has the co-ordination number 3 or 4, the directions for the third and fourth bonds are either partially or completely determined when the position of the first and second co-ordination partners is specified. The possibilities of forming a distorted arrangement of the atoms are then sharply reduced.

We thus can understand not only the first of Zachariasen's conditions but also the second and third. A small co-ordination number on oxygen results automatically in a small co-ordination number on the metal since the ratio of the co-ordination numbers is inversely proportional to the stoichiometric atom ratio. If the co-ordination polyhedra share common edges or faces then two metal and two oxygen atoms form a four-membered ring. In this way the number of possible orientations of the bonding direction is sharply reduced.

The co-ordination number 2 for oxygen is found also in the ReO_3 structure and in perovskites, ($CaTiO_3$ structure) (sections 22.4, 23.1). Both structure types are therefore characterized by atoms which frequently are not at the ideal positions of the cubic lattice. Distortions occur very often as is especially known with those ferroelectric compounds having the perovskite structure. It is thus understandable that for the preparation of optical glasses, the oxides of calcium, strontium, barium, and lanthanum, which readily take the calcium places on a perovskite structure, are used in combination with the oxides of aluminium, zirconium, tantalum, and tungsten. These latter must be able to take up the titanium positions. Of course glass formation with these substances is not so characteristic since the bonding angle does not vary sufficiently from 180°. The crystal structures treated in chapter 26, section 2, show clearly the flexibility of the coupling possibilities of $[MeO_6]$-octahedra where Me = Ti, Nb, Mo, and W, as well as the framework nature of these networks.

In order for the coupling to be irregular, easy variation of the valence angle on oxygen is also important. This angle theoretically can vary from 90° for pure p-bonding to 180° for pure (sp)-hybrids. In the crystalline silicates valence angles of 130°–180° are found.

The technically important silicate glasses contain in addition to SiO_2 large amounts of basic oxides such as Na_2O, K_2O, CaO, BaO, and additional neutral oxides such as Al_2O_3. The basic oxides in the melt contribute their oxygen to the network in accordance with the reaction scheme:

$$Na_2^+O^{2-} + \quad \begin{array}{cc} | & | \\ O & O \\ -O-Si-O-Si-O- \\ O & O \\ | & | \end{array} \quad \longrightarrow$$

$$\begin{array}{ccc} | & & | \\ O & Na^+ & O \\ -O-Si-O^- & & {}^-O-Si-O- \\ O & Na^+ & O \\ | & & | \end{array}$$

The network is then partially broken and thereby becomes more mobile. The softening point drops from $1500°C$ for pure SiO_2-glass to $400–800°C$ for technical silicate glasses. Figure 29.1c gives a two-dimensional representation of one such partially broken-up network. The central Me atoms, such as Si, which form the oxygen polyhedra, are called *network formers*. The basic metal oxides which serve to break up the network are called *network modifiers*. Figure 29.1c shows how some of the oxygen atoms function as bridging atoms both before and after modification. The remainder, however, form only one bond to the network-forming atom while the second valence is ionically saturated.

In so far as the metal atom is strongly basic, the tendency to give up oxygen ions to the network is very great and the two oxides, like Cs_2O and SiO_2 are completely miscible on the silica-rich side (Fig. 29.2).[29.4] With a weakly basic oxide like MgO, CaO, and SrO one observes the formation of two melts, each of which can form a glassy solid. The one melt consists of

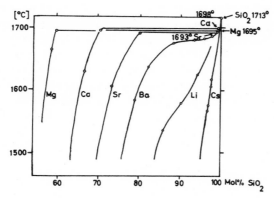

Fig. 29.2. Phase diagram of the system SiO_2—MeO.[29.4]

ca. 40, 30, or 20 mole-per cent metal oxide and 60, 70, or 80 mole-per cent SiO_2. Cristobalite is in equilibrium with the melt at 1695°C, 1698°C, or 1693°C.

The basis for the formation of two melts is that less strongly basic metal ions, such as Mg^{2+}, have a greater tendency to develop oxygen polyhedra in accordance with their own requirements.[29.5] One can thus assume that magnesium atoms both in the melt and in the glassy state are surrounded by octahedra of six oxygen atoms just as they are in magnesium–oxygen compounds. Apparently the network of a SiO_2-melt can form only few octahedral holes (ca. 1 per cent) of the proper size to accept the Mg atoms. A complete alteration in the coupling of the $[SiO_2]$-tetrahedra must occur so that $[MgO_6]$-octahedra can be formed.

The rules set forth by Zachariasen have only limited validity. Thus TeO_2 with at least 9 mole-per cent Li_2O forms a glass in which most of the Te atoms are surrounded mainly by six O atoms.[29.6, 29.7] In oxide glasses containing GeO_2 and Ga_2O_3 one observes, in the presence of 10 mole-per cent alkali oxide a maximum in density and in refractive index.[29.8] By adding O^{2-} ions in the form of alkali oxides one makes it possible for part of the Ge and Ga atoms to take on the co-ordination number 6, without requiring the bridging oxygen atoms simultaneously to increase their co-ordination number to three,

$$[GeO_{4/2}] + Na_2O \longrightarrow Na_2^+[GeO_{6/2}]^{2-}.$$

In addition there are very many glasses in which the atoms are not coupled in three dimensions. By the addition of sufficient amounts of a network-modifying oxide, it is possible to break so many Si—O—Si bridges that a space net is no longer possible.

29.2.2 Glasses with Chain Structures

In a glass having the composition $Na_2O.2SiO_2$, each silicon atom is bound to three bridging oxygen atoms. To what extent planar networks are formed as in the clay minerals is still unknown. At the composition of a metasilicate, $Na_2O.SiO_2$, a glass can form which probably has a chain structure, like that in a pyroxene, and in which rings occur like those in benitoite. The basis for glass formation is that the chains in the melt are no longer linear but more or less tangled. Ordering into the long, straight chains of a crystal is only possible with great difficulty.

Many organic high polymeric compounds, e.g., the polystyrenes, form chain-like glasses. The role of bridging members with co-ordination number 2 (O or CH_2) is evident here and has been frequently mentioned in the literature.[29.9]

29.2.3 *Glasses from a Mixture of Differently Shaped Molecules*

A melt with the composition $58Na_2O.42SiO_2$ still solidifies into a glass. The glass must now consist of a mixture of shorter chains and individual rings. Crystallization is greatly hindered by the different shapes and sizes of the anionic components. Phosphate glasses with a comparable structure, e.g., the composition $Na_8P_6O_{20}$, are soluble in water and in this case, it was possible to show the existence of a mixture of chains and rings by paper chromatography.[29.10, 29.11, 29.12]

29.2.4 *Glasses from Uniform Molecules in which Packing into a Crystal Structure is Hindered*

The melting point of toluene, at $-95°C$, is very low compared to that of benzene, at $+6°C$. Obviously, the packing of the plane benzene ring into a crystal structure is greatly hindered by the attachment of an aliphatic group. Toluene, therefore, solidifies as a glass if quenched with liquid air. In the same way, glasses are easily formed by branched-chain hydro-carbons when they are quickly cooled. Likewise, molten mixtures of nitrates, carbonates, or sulphates can easily form glasses for the same reason.[29.13] In the system KNO_3–$Ca(NO_3)_2$, for example, the glass-forming region extends from 53 to 70 mole per cent KNO_3.[29.14]

29.3 Microstructure of Glasses

When a glass melts, depending on the composition and the addition of certain impurities (e.g., $SO_4{}^{2-}$) one observes an opalescence whose origin is in a drop-shaped emulsion. As can be shown by X-ray diffraction and electron microscopy, many glasses which appear clear to the naked eye have such inhomogeneities, the size of which can be on the border of detectability (*ca.* 20 Å). In the system Li_2O–SiO_2 these droplets do not occur in pure silica or at the composition of the disilicate $Li_2Si_2O_5$ and the metasilicate Li_2SiO_3. In the intermediate region and with still higher Li_2O content, the size of the droplets becomes greater as one departs more and more from these limits. As could be shown also through chemical analysis, the droplets and the material in which they are embedded have a composition which is similar to that of the limits SiO_2, $Li_2Si_2O_5$, and Li_2SiO_3.[29.15]

We are thus led to the surmise that in a glass down to the smallest regions generally only definite compositions are possible just as in crystalline compounds. A homogeneous glass (without droplets), often has only a narrow phase width. The condition for the retention of definite short-range ordering, which can somehow be propagated through space, is apparently connected with a definite atomic ratio with small deviations from the stoichiometry. The great variability in the composition of a silicate glass appears therefore to rest not so much on irregularity in the ordering of atoms but rather on the mixing ratios of two finely divided phases.[29.16, 29.17, 29.18]

The two-phase character of a glass can also lead to the possibility that one component is crystalline while the other is glassy. For example, in the study of a glass of the composition $58MgO.42P_2O_5$ an evidently crystalline phase which probably consists of $Mg(PO_3)_2$ has been observed.[29.19] Or, in a SiO_2-glass having large amounts of PbO, a phase can first melt which is strongly enriched in PbO, while a finely divided SiO_2-rich glass phase is distributed throughout it. The relationship to the formation of ceramic materials is here seen.

29.4 Special Glasses

29.4.1 *Boron Oxide Glasses*

B_2O_3 itself, as also its melts with other oxides, easily form glasses. An essential question is how is the boron surrounded by oxygen. Are $[BO_3]$-triangles or $[BO_4]$-tetrahedra bound together? Only recently has it been possible to approach solutions to this problem, in some cases by the use of infrared absorption and especially by nuclear magnetic resonance.[29.20]

In B_2O_3-glass, each boron atom is surrounded by three oxygen atoms in the form of an equilateral triangle; each oxygen atom couples two boron atoms together. By the addition of alkali oxide up to 30 mole-per cent, each additional O^{2-}-ion is used to increase the co-ordination number of boron to 4.

$$Me_2O + B_2O_3 \longrightarrow 2Me[BO_2].$$

The proportion of tetrahedra remains approximately constant with increasing alkali oxide content from 30 up to 50 mole-per cent, and then rapidly decreases. At 70 mole-per cent Me_2O, which is somewhat more than would correspond to the formula, $Me_4[B_2O_5]$, all the boron atoms have again the co-ordination number 3.

29.4.2 *Lead Glasses*

We have previously explained that polyvalent cations such as Mg^{2+} have the tendency in a glass to form the co-ordination polyhedra which are appropriate to them. To these cations must be added especially Be^{2+}, Zn^{2+}, Pb^{2+}, Bi^{3+}, Al^{3+}, Ti^{4+}, and Zr^{4+}. As the tendency of the cation to fill its own co-ordination sphere with oxygen increases, its role as a net work modifier becomes increasingly diluted and it goes over into a network former. The above-named cations are frequently called *intermediates* in the literature.

Especially interesting are those glasses with Pb^{2+}. First it is noteworthy that the PbO content in binary glasses can be very high: e.g., up to 67 mole-per cent in SiO_2, 77 mole-per cent in B_2O_3, 62 mole-per cent in P_2O_5. While pure PbO under normal conditions is not obtained as a glass, from the high PbO contents of the above-mentioned glasses one can see that the Pb atom must be in a position to build networks with oxygen. The ionization energy of lead, $Pb \rightarrow Pb^{2+} + 2e^- + 517$ kcal/mole, is relatively high. This means that the oxygen atoms are strongly bound to lead.

To ascertain the type of atomic coupling is very difficult, since bivalent lead can develop various co-ordination polyhedra relative to oxygen. Thus Pb^{2+} has a co-ordination number of 12 in perovskites, 6 in magneto-plumbites, 4 in red tetragonal PbO, three in Pb_3O_4, and two in yellow orthorhombic PbO. It is therefore not surprising that in glasses lead can take on various roles.

By nuclear magnetic resonance measurements[29.20] it could be shown that in the system PbO/B_2O_3, PbO acts first as a network modifier just like an alkali oxide. The Pb^{2+}-ion then has a high co-ordination number and the oxygen is used in order to transform $[BO_3]$-triangles into $[BO_4]$-tetrahedra, which are cross-linked with the $[BO_3]$-triangles. However, from 15 mole-per cent PbO, the content of $[BO_4]$-tetrahedra is found to be lower. At 50 mole-per cent PbO, i.e., a composition $Pb[BO_2]_2$, the content of $[BO_4]$-tetrahedra is not 100 per cent but 50 per cent. This is the maximum concentration of $[BO_4]$-tetrahedra in this system. With still further PbO addition, the concentration of tetrahedral boron is again reduced.

From NMR signals one can observe that lead with low co-ordination numbers relative to oxygen is coupled only with $[BO_3]$-triangles and not with $[BO_4]$-tetrahedra. This can be explained very simply if one refers back to the concept of the electrostatic bond strength according to Pauling.[29.21] This is defined as the ratio of oxidation number of a central atom (here B and Pb) and its co-ordination number. In stable ionic lattices, the sum of the bond strengths between anions (here O) and the central atom is equal, or nearly so, to the value of the charge of the anion. For the grouping the charge of the oxygen is seen to be 2 (B—O = 3/3; Pb—O = 2/2). If an oxygen atom belongs to a $[BO_4]$-tetrahedron and an angular $[PbO_2]$-group, a value of 1·75 is calculated (B—O = 3/4; Pb—O = 2/2). The charge 2 could be attained if part of the oxygen atoms assume a higher co-ordination number than 2. This is, however, as discussed earlier, unfavourable for glass formation.

29.4.3 Glasses with Hydrogen Bonds

Molecules with hydrogen bonds easily form glasses. Thus when ethyl alcohol is cooled by 'dry ice', a glass is formed which consists of molecular chains associated through hydrogen bonding.[29.22]

The free rotation about each hydrogen bridge combined with the bent-chain structure leads here to the defective structures which are necessary for glass formation. If we now go to water, each molecule has the tendency to surround itself with four other water molecules as in the tridymite structure. Alternatively the water can be surrounded by three other molecules since in the crystalline state water often shows this reduced co-ordination number. Since the hydrogen bond is linear, the bent bridging atoms, which are required for irregular coupling of the atoms, are missing. Glassy water can therefore be obtained only with great difficulty, through a very definite quenching procedure with liquid air. If other materials which enter into hydrogen bonds are added to water, the disorder is increased and glass formation is made easier.

The easy vitrification of concentrated sulphuric acid, concentrated phosphoric acid, and concentrated sugar solutions is well known. Of several other organic compounds which solidify in the glassy state glycol, glycerine, and water containing phenol may be mentioned.

29.4.4 Metals and Salts in the Vitreous State

When alkali halide or metal vapours are condensed on surfaces at a temperature of 20°K, with the exception of a few metals, crystalline layers are formed. If, however, impurities are also vaporized, glassy condensation products can be obtained under the same conditions. Examples include: KI with 10 per cent KF, and Sn with some Cu. Bismuth can be obtained in the glassy form by the intermediate vaporization of Ga. This form of bismuth is stable at room temperature.[29.23] CuCl, AgCl, AgBr behave like the alkali halides on sublimation. TlCl, TlBr, and TlI, however, form amorphous sublimates. TlBr and TlI do not crystallize until 110°K and 140°K, respectively. This difference between the halides of Tl and those of Ag and Cu, is undoubtedly a function of the tendency of thallium compounds to crystallize in more complex structures, as for example the pronounced layer structure of TlI (see chapter 15, section 4).[29.24]

29.5 Chalcogenide Glasses

By a chalcogenide glass, is meant a glass in which S, Se, or Te, take the place of oxygen as the divalent element. However, this name is not strictly correct since oxygen, too, is a chalcogen.

29.5.1 *Elements in the Glassy State*

Among the glasses made from differently shaped molecules can be listed the elements plastic sulphur and glassy selenium, and the compounds phosphonitrilfluoride and phosphonitrilchloride $(PNF_2)_n$ and $(PNCl_2)_n$. [12.39, 12.40, 29.25] Tellurium forms a glass only in a broader sense, since the glass can be obtained only by condensation from the vapour.

The elements As, Sb, Si, and Ge, which frequently occur in chalcogenide glasses where they aid in glass formation, themselves form only glasses in the broader sense. The extreme cross-linking of these elements in the glassy and crystalline states makes mobility of the atoms impossible, so that melting can occur only with a structure transformation, as we previously mentioned in chapter 15 with reference to Ge and Sb. Since the melts have a fundamentally different structure, they cannot be supercooled to a three-dimensionally cross-linked state. Indeed, the elements mentioned form a glass in the broader sense only when condensation occurs in such a way that polymerization can take place. The condensation temperature for As_4-vapour is for example between 100° and 200°C. At lower temperatures one obtains yellow arsenic since it, like the vapour, consists of As_4-molecules.

29.5.2 *Binary Chalcogenide Glasses*

Table 29.1 shows which compounds of the type Me_2X_3 can solidify in the glassy state when quenched at a rate of *ca.* 200°/sec (which corresponds to quenching in water).[29.26]

Table 29.1. Glass formation in Me_2X_3 *compounds*

	S_3	Se_3	Te_3	
P_2	−	+	?	
As_2	+	+	−	+ = Glass Forming
Sb_2	−	−	−	− = No Glass Formation
Bi_2	−	−	−	? = No Data Available

One can see that glass formation is more difficult as the atoms become heavier. There are three reasons for this:

(a) The bonds which involve heavier atoms are generally weaker, so that easy dissociation and rearrangement of the atoms into a crystal lattice can occur.

(b) The heavy atoms, as we have previously said (chapters 12 and 15) can loosely add atoms in addition to those atoms corresponding to the valence and which are tightly bound. At higher temperatures and especially in the melt, the role of tightly and loosely bound atoms can be easily interchanged, in that the reference atom moves away from a near neighbour and another then comes closer. This is approximately equivalent to the breaking of a strong bond and the formation of a new one. In this way the rearrangement of atoms, and therefore crystallization, is possible.

(c) The melt is metallic (see section 29.5.3).

P_2S_3 is an exception to this rule. The reason for this is the ease of forming such molecules as P_4S_3, P_4S_5, P_4S_7, and P_4S_{10}.

The composition of these glasses can be varied within wide limits.[29.27, 29.28] However, in the systems As–Se, and As–S, the As content cannot go over 60 atomic per cent, while the glassy region on the chalcogenide side goes to 100 atomic per cent Se, and about 90 atomic per cent S. Here again, as in oxide glasses, the influence of elements with the co-ordination number 2 and a bonding angle which is less than 180° is seen. Free rotation, combined with a certain variability in bonding angle on the bivalent bridging atom, makes possible irregular coupling of the atoms in the glass as well as in the melt.

29.5.3 *Ternary Chalcogenide Glasses*

Ternary chalcogenide glasses are generally obtained by simply melting the components together.[29.29, 29.30]

The glass-forming region in the system As–S–Br is shown in Fig. 29.3.[29.31] Point 3 has the approximate composition $As_1S_{1.8}Br_{2.5}$. The glass has a softening point of $-60°C$ and at room temperature is as fluid as water. Here certainly vitrification is due to a mixture of small molecules the compositions of which are not yet known. If the halogen content is lowered and that of sulphur raised, the molecules are forced to become larger, since sulphur always bonds two atoms together. The softening point then increases. At the approximate composition $As_1S_{1.5}Br_{0.5}$ (point 2) it is 90°C, and for $As_1S_{1.5}$ (point 1), 200°C.

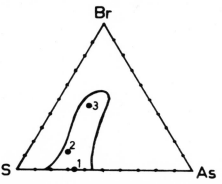

Fig. 29.3. Vitreous region in the system As–S–Br.[29.31]

In the last few years ternary chalcogenide glasses have been prepared which have relatively high softening points and some of which are transparent to infrared light.[29.32, 29.33] Figure 29.4 shows a direct comparison of the glass-forming regions in the systems Ge–P–S, Ge–P–Se, and Ge–P–Te; the corresponding regions for the systems Si–As–Te, Ge–As–Te,

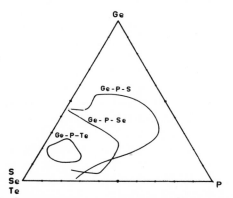

Fig. 29.4. Glass-forming region in the systems Ge–P–S, Ge–P–Se, *and* Ge–P–Te.
[29.33, 29.34]

Si–P–Te, and Ge–P–Te are shown in Fig. 29.5. The following regularities can be observed.

(a) A large percentage of bivalent elements is necessary for glass formation. The often stated role of the bridging atom as a necessary constituent of three-dimensionally cross-linked glasses in the narrow sense is here again confirmed.

(b) As the atoms in the series Si, Ge, Sn, and S, Se, Te become heavier, the extent of the glassy regions becomes narrower. Systems with Sn and Bi have only very narrow glassy regions.[29.34] The same regularity has been found for binary chalcogenide glasses and has been thoroughly established.

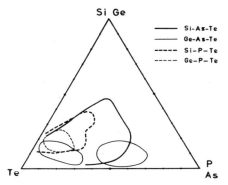

Fig. 29.5. Glass-forming region in the systems Si–As–Te, Ge–As–Te, Si–P–Te, *and* Ge–P–Te.[29.32, 29.33, 29.34]

From the relatively high softening points, which sometimes can rise to 500°, one can conclude that the glasses are three-dimensionally cross-linked.

The formation of glasses in regions having high tellurium concentrations is surprising, since these are not observed in binary chalcogenide glasses. From the densities of the glasses one can determine that the Te atoms, like the Sb atoms in explosive antimony, have in addition to two near, tightly bound neighbours, further weakly bound ones, so that the surroundings can have the form of a distorted octahedron. The tendency of tellurium to break up the network is apparently compensated for by the tetravalent elements Si or Ge so that the glasses are stable.[29.35]

Figure 29.5 shows that the regions of glass formation are smaller with phosphorus than with the heavier arsenic. This contradicts the observation that the ease of crystallization increases with increasing atomic weight, and is probably due to the fact that Si and Ge form definite compounds with As, but not with P and Sb. It can be assumed, therefore, that Si and Ge do not form bonds with P in glasses either, and that they prefer instead chalcogenides as neighbours. This renders the formation of a three-dimensional network more difficult.

These ternary chalcogenide glasses undoubtedly have the same short range order as their melts, since they easily form from them. The bridging

atoms make possible a mobility in the melt even in the case of larger
molecules. An especially high mobility of the melt can be obtained by the
addition of halogens. On the other hand, if there are insufficient amounts
of uni- or bivalent elements available the network has to break apart in
order to achieve a high mobility of atoms in the melt. The atoms are then
forced to higher co-ordination numbers, as in the melting of germanium.

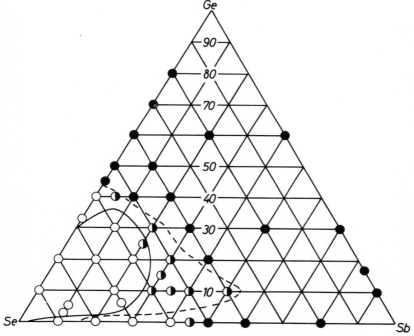

Fig. 29.6. Glass-forming region in the Ge–Sb–Se *system*
——— *Glass-forming region by air quenching.*[29.37]
– – – – *Glass-forming region by water quenching.*
○   *Semiconducting melts,* $\Delta E \approx$ 2 eV.
◑   *Highly conducting melts.*
●   *Melts with metallic conductivity.*

A mobile bonding system as discussed in section 15.2 is formed. The melts
then show a metallic-like electrical conductivity. The valence electrons
can move freely and are thus highly reactive, so that the atoms can order
themselves into a crystal lattice on cooling. On the other hand, melts
which show a wide forbidden energy gap solidify as glasses, as has
been shown in the systems Ge–Sb–Se, illustrated in Fig. 29.6, and
Ge–As–Se.[29.36] The width of the forbidden gap of melts in the glass-
forming region is about 2 eV, representing the energy necessary to remove

an electron from a localized bond. Melts which solidify as glasses (or, in some cases, partly as glasses) only upon very rapid quenching are more or less characterized by a high, but not metallic, electrical conductivity. These melts presumably contain in microregions a second phase in which the atoms have a high co-ordination number, similar to the co-ordination in metallic melts.

29.6 Electrical Conductivity in Ordered and Disordered Structures

In conclusion, a word is in order concerning the relationship between the width of the forbidden zone and the structure.

As the atomic distribution curve of liquid germanium at 1270°C shows, (see Fig. 15.3), metallic conductivity can also be observed when the short-range order of the atom in the melt is so strongly disturbed that only one first co-ordination sphere with a large half-width (ca. 1 Å) appears. Similarly, the atomic distribution curve of molten tin at high temperatures (ca. 1000°C) is also blurred.[29.36] The extensive destruction of order is not, however, reflected in the electrical conductivity. One must, therefore, conclude that electrical conductivity has its origin principally in a marked mesomeric bonding system and not in the periodicity of a lattice. This is also made apparent by the fact that when typical metals are melted the electrical conductivity is only slightly (up to about 40 per cent) diminished. In contrast to the situation with melts, a marked mesomeric bonding system in solids is generally possible only when a crystal lattice exists, since a system of electrons bonding to several sides of an atom brings with it extensive ordering of the atoms throughout the crystal lattice.

If we now consider glasses, the coupling of the atoms results primarily from hybrid functions which bond only to one side and which must permit free rotation around the inter-atomic line between two atoms. For glasses, localized bonding electron pairs are characteristic and marked mesomeric bonding systems do not occur. Therefore, the width of the forbidden zone in glasses is comparable with that in crystalline phases only when the latter are characterized by similar bonding systems. As an example, in As_2Se_3 the width of the forbidden zone in the vitreous and in the crystalline state is about 45 kcal/mol.[29.30] In contrast thereto stands the poor electrical conductivity of glassy arsenic and of explosive antimony, while the rhombohedral, crystalline phases (As and Sb) are metallic conductors with extensive mesomeric bonding systems. (See sections 12.34 and 12.4.)

Further Reading

Theory of the Chemical Bond
(The books are listed approximately in order of increasing mathematical complexity.)

L. Pauling, *The Nature of the Chemical Bond*, Cornell Univ. Press, Ithaca/New York, 3rd ed. 1960.

L. E. Sutton and E. Fluck, *Chemische Bindung und Molekülstruktur*, Springer, Berlin-Göttingen-Heidelberg, 1961.

C. A. Coulson, *Valence*, Oxford University Press, Oxford 1961.

H. Hartmann, *Die chemische Bindung*, Springer, Berlin 1964.

H. Preuss, *Quantenchemie für Chemiker*, Verlag Chemie, Weinheim/Bergstraße 1966.

H. Preuss, *Grundriß der Quantenchemie*, Bibliographisches Institut, Mannheim 1962.

H. Preuss, *Quantentheoretische Chemie*, Bibliographisches Institut, Mannheim, Vol. I 1963, Vol. II 1965, Vol. III in preparation.

F. A. Cotton, *Chemical Applications of Group Theory*, Interscience Publ., New York 1964.

B. N. Figgis, *Introduction to Ligand Fields,* Interscience Publ., New York 1966.

H. L. Schäfer and G. Gliemann, *Einführung in die Ligandenfeldtheorie*, Akad. Verlagsgesellschaft, Frankfurt a. M. 1967.

C. J. Ballhausen, *Introduction to Ligand Field Theory*, McGraw-Hill, New York 1962.

H. Hartmann, *Theorie der chemischen Bindung*, Springer, Berlin 1954.

Crystal Chemistry

(a) *Text Books*

R. C. Evans, *An Introduction to Crystal Chemistry*, Cambridge (Engl.), Univ. Press, 1964.

J. E. Hiller, *Grundriß der Kristallchemie,* W. de Gruyter & Co., Berlin 1952.

W. Kleber, *Einführung in die Kristallographie*, VEB Technik, Berlin 1961.

A. F. Wells, *Structural Inorganic Chemistry*, Clarendon Press, Oxford 1962.

J. Zemann, *Kristallchemie*, W. de Gruyter & Co., Berlin 1966.

(b) *Monographs*

N. V. Belov, *Crystal Chemistry of Large-Cation Silicates*, Consultants Bureau, New York 1963. (Original Russian.)

L. Bragg and G. F. Claringbull, *Crystal Structures of Minerals*, Bell, London 1965.

W. Eitel, *Silicate Science*, Academic Press, New York 1964.

N. A. Goryunova, *The Chemistry of Diamond-like Semiconductors*, Chapman and Hall, London 1965. (Original Russian.)

W. Hume-Rothery, *The Structure of Metals and Alloys*, The Institute of Metals, London, 1962.

E. Parthé, *Crystal Chemistry of Tetrahedral Structures*, Gordon and Breach, Science Publ., New York 1964.

J. P. Suchet, *Chimie Physiques des Semiconducteurs*, Dunod, Paris 1962, Engl. translation, *Chemical Physics of Semiconductors*, Van Nostrand, London 1964.

(c) *Reference Works*

W. B. Pearson, *A Handbook of Lattice Spacings of Metals and Alloys*, Pergamon Press, London 1958.

K. Schubert, *Kristallstrukturen zweikomponentiger Phasen*, Springer, Berlin 1964.

Landolt-Börnstein, *Zahlenwerte und Funktionen*, Vol. I, Part IV, *Kristalle*, Springer, Berlin 1955.

R. W. G. Wyckoff, *Crystal Structures*, Interscience Publ., New York, 2nd ed. Vol. I, 1963, Elements and Compounds, RX and RX_2; Vol. II, 1964, Comp. RX_n, R_nMX_2, R_nMX_3; Vol. III, 1965, Comp. $(R_x(MX_4)_y, R_x(M_nX_p)_y$, Hydrates and Ammoniacates; Vol. IV and Vol. V in preparation.

Strukturbericht, supplement of the *Z. Kristallographie*, edit. by P. P. Ewald, C. Hermann, K. Herrmann and C. Gottfried, Akademische Verlagsgesellschaft Leipzig; Vol. I (1931) to Vol. VII (1943), covering the literature 1913–1939.

Structure Reports, Publ. for the International Union of Crystallography, Edit. by A. J. C. Wilson and W. B. Pearson, N. V. A. Oosthoek, Utrecht; starting with Vol. VIII, covering the literature 1940–1941.

References

1.1 G. Schoknecht. *Z. Naturf.* **12a**, 983 (1957)
2.1 E. Schrödinger. *Ann. d. Phys.* **79**, 361, 489 and 734 (1926); **80**, 437 (1926); **81**, 109 (1926)
3.1 W. Pauli. *Z. Physik* **31**, 765 (1925)
3.2 F. Hund. *Z. Physik* **33**, 345 (1925)
4.1 W. Heitler and F. London. *Z. Physik* **44**, 455 (1927)
4.2 L. Pauling. *J. Am. Chem. Soc.* **53**, 1367 (1931)
4.3 J. C. Slater. *Phys. Rev.* **37**, 481 (1931); **38**, 1109 (1931)
4.4 F. Hund. *Z. Physik* **51**, 759 (1928); **63**, 719 (1929)
4.5 R. S. Mulliken. *Phys. Rev.* **32**, 186, 761 (1928); **33**, 730 (1929)
4.6 L. Pauling. *J. Am. Chem. Soc.* **53**, 1367 (1931); *Proc. Nat. Acad. Sci. Wash.* **14**, 359 (1928)
4.7 S. Mensger. Diss. Stuttgart (1966)
4.8 A. Jucys. *Proc. Roy. Soc.* (London) A, 173, 59 (1939)
5.1 E. Hückel. *Z. Physik* **60**, 423 (1930); **70**, 204 (1931); **72**, 310 (1931); **76**, 628 (1938)
5.2 L. Pauling. *J. Chem. Soc.* (1948) 1461
5.3 L. Pauling. *The Nature of the Chemical Bond*, Cornell Univ. Press, Ithaca New York (1960)
5.4 L. Pauling. *Proc. Nat. Acad. Sci. Wash.* **18**, 293 (1932); *J. Chem. Phys.* **1**, 362 (1933)
5.5 J. Thiele. *Ann. Chem.* **306**, 87 (1899)
5.6 C. K. Ingold and E. H. Ingold. *J. Chem. Soc.* 1310 (1926)
5.7 F. Arndt, E. Scholz, and F. Nachtwey. *Ber.* **57**, 1903 (1924) F. Arndt, *Ber.* **63**, 2963 (1930)
5.8 F. Arndt and B. Eistert. *Ber.* **71**, 237 (1938)
5.9 B. Eistert. *Tautomerie und Mesomerie*, Enke, Stuttgart (1938)
5.10 R. E. Watson, A. J. Freeman. *Phys. Rev.* **123**, 521 (1961)
6.1 Don T. Cromer. *J. Phys. Chem.* **61**, 1388 (1957)
6.2 F. E. Ilse and H. Hartmann. *Z. Phys. Chem.* Leipzig **197**, 239 (1951); *Z. Naturf.* **6a**, 751 (1951); H. Hartmann and H. L. Schläfer. *Z. Phys. Chem.* Leipzig **197**, 116 (1951); *Z. Naturf.* **6a**, 754, 760 (1951)
7.1 See: J. Goubeau. *Angew. Chem.* **69**, 77 (1957)
8.1 J. C. Slater. *Phys. Rev.* **34**, 1293 (1929)
9.1 H. Bethe. *Ann. Phys.* [5] **3**, 135 (1929) and in book form: *Splitting of Terms in Crystals*, Consultants Bureau, New York (1958)
9.2 H. van Vleck. *J. Chem. Phys.* **3**, 803 and 807 (1935) See also: *Theory of Magnetic and Electric Susceptibilities*, Oxford Univ. Press, Oxford and New York (1932)
9.3 F. A. Cotton. *Chemical Applications of Group Theory*, Intersc. Publ., New York–London (1963)
9.4 Y. Tanabe and Y. Sugano. *J. Phys. Soc. Japan* **9**, 753 and 766 (1954)

360   FUNDAMENTALS OF INORGANIC CRYSTAL CHEMISTRY

9.5   H. HARTMANN and H. FISCHER-WASELS. *Z. Phys. Chem.* N.F. **4**, 297 (1955)
9.6   H. A. JAHN and E. TELLER. *Proc. Roy. Soc.* (London) **A 161**, 220 (1937)
      H. A. JAHN. *Proc. Roy. Soc.* (London) **A 164**, 117 (1938)
12.1 H. T. HALL, L. MERRIL, and J. D. BARNETT. *Science* **146**, 1297 (1964)
12.2 A. JAYARAMAN, N. W. KLEMENT JR., and G. C. KENNEDY. *Phys. Rev.* **131**, 644 (1963)
12.3 L. PAULING. *Phys. Rev.* **54**, 899 (1938); cf. also 5.3
12.4 K. GANZHORN. *Z. Naturf.* **7a**, 291 (1953); **8a**, 330 (1953)
12.5 U. DEHLINGER. *Theoretische Metallkunde,* Springer, Berlin–Göttingen–Heidelberg (1955)
12.6 J. DONOHUE and ST. H. GOODMAN. *Acta Cryst.* **18**, 568 (1965)
12.7 R. L. COLLIN. *Acta Cryst.* **5**, 431 (1952); **9**, 539 (1956)
12.8 B. VONNEGUT and B. E. WARREN. *J. Am. Chem. Soc.* **58**, 2459 (1936)
12.9 J. J. KITAIGORODSKII, V. KHOTSYANOVA, and M. STRUCKKOV. *Zh. fiz. Khim.* **27**, 780 (1953)
12.10 M. SCHMIDT and E. WILHELM. *Angew. Chem.* **78**, 1020 (1966); *Angew. Chem. intern. Edit.* **5**, 964 (1966)
12.11 J. DONOHUE, A. CARON, and E. GOLDISCH. *J. Am. Chem. Soc.* **83**, 3748 (1961)
12.12 A. CARON and J. DONOHUE. *Acta Cryst.* **18**, 562 (1965)
12.13 S. C. ABRAHAMS. *Acta Cryst.* **18**, 566 (1965); **14**, 311 (1961); **8**, 661 (1955)
12.14 D. E. SANDS. *J. Am. Chem. Soc.* **87**, 1395 (1965)
12.15 A. KUTOGLU and E. HELLNER. *Angew. Chem.* **78**, 1021 (1966); *Angew. Chem. intern. Edit.* **5**, 965 (1966)
12.16 R. E. MARSH, L. PAULING, and J. D. MCCOLLOUGH. *Acta Cryst.* **6**, 71 (1953)
12.17 R. D. BURBANK. *Acta Cryst.* **4**, 140 (1951)
12.17a H. KREBS. *Angew. Chem.* **70**, 615 (1958)
12.18 H. KREBS, P. DRODTEN, K. H. MÜLLER, and H. THURN. Unpublished
12.19 A. R. v. HIPPEL. *J. Chem. Phys.* **16**, 372 (1948)
12.20 R. J. DE SANDO and R. C. LANGE. *J. inorg. nucl. Chem.* **28**, 1837 (1966)
12.21 H. KREBS and H. U. GRUBER. *Z. Naturf.* **22a**, 96 (1967)
12.22 H. THURN and H. KREBS. *Angew. Chem.* **78**, 1101 (1966); *Angew. Chem. intern. Edit.* **5**, 1047 (1966); Acta Cryst. in print
12.23 R. HULTGREN, N. S. GINGRICH, and B. E. WARREN. *Phys. Rev.* **47**, 808 (1935); *J. Chem. Phys.* **3**, 351 (1935)
12.24 A. BROWN and S. RUNDQVIST. *Acta Cryst.* **19**, 684 (1965)
12.25 H. KREBS, W. HOLZ, and K. H. WORMS. *Ber.* **90**, 1031 (1957)
12.26 Z. JOHAN. *Chem. Erde* **20**, 71 (1959)
12.27 J. C. JAMIESON. *Science* **139**, 1291 (1963)
12.28 C. S. BARETT, P. CUCKA, and K. HAEFFNER. *Acta Cryst.* **16**, 451 (1963)
12.29 S. S. KABALKINA. *Soviet Physics Doklady* **8**, (9) 917 (1964)
12.30 P. CUCKA and C. S. BARETT. *Acta Cryst.* **15**, 865 (1962)
12.31 H. STÖHR. *Z. anorg. allg. Chem.* **242**, 138 (1939)
12.32 H. KREBS and R. STEFFEN. *Z. anorg. allg. Chem.* **327**, 224 (1964)
12.33 H. KREBS. *Angew. Chem.* **65**, 293 (1953)
12.34 R. HILSCH in *Non-Crystalline Solids,* edited by V. D. Fréchette, p. 351, John Wiley & Sons Inc. (1960)
12.34a F. HERMAN and S. SKILLMAN. *Atomic Structure Calculations,* Prentice-Hall, Englewood Cliffs, N.J. (1963)
12.35 H. KREBS. *Acta Cryst.* **9**, 95 (1956)
12.36 AJIT KUMAR DUTTA. *Phys. Rev.* **90**, 187 (1953)

12.37 O. Foss. *Acta Chem. Scand.* **7**, 1221 (1953)

12.38 H. Krebs and H. Beine. *Z. anorg. allg. Chem.* **355**, 113 (1968)

12.39 H. Krebs. *Z. Naturf.* **12b**, 795 (1957); *Z. anorg. allg. Chem.* **272**, 288 (1953)

12.40 H. Krebs. *Z. anorg. allg. Chem.* **265**, 156 (1951)

12.41 S. O. Ross, E. R. Coburn, W. A. Leach, and W. B. Robinson. *J. Pol. Sci.* **13**, 406 (1954); H. Zahn et. al. *Angew. Chem.* **68**, 229 (1956); 69, 270 (1957)

12.42 H. P. Boehm and U. Hofmann. *Z. anorg. allg. Chem.* **278**, 58 (1955); F. Laves and Y. Baskin. *Z. Krist.* **107**, 337 (1956)

12.43 G. E. Bacon. *Acta Cryst.* **4**, 558 (1951); R. E. Franklin. *Acta Cryst.* **4**, 253 (1951)

12.44 K. Lark-Horovitz et al. *Phys. Rev.* **69**, 258 (1946)

12.45 W. Ringer and H. Welker. *Z. Naturf.* **3a**, 20 (1948)

12.46 R. H. Wentorf and J. S. Kasper. *Science* **139**, 338 (1961)

12.47 J. C. Jamieson. *Science* **139**, 762 and 845 (1961)

12.48 J. D. Barnett, R. B. Bennion, and H. T. Hall. *Science* **141**, 1041 (1963); *Rev. Sci. Instr.* **35**, 175 (1964)

13.1 E. Zintl. *Angew. Chem.* **52**, 1 (1939); F. Laves. *Naturw.* **29**, 241 (1941); discussion of bonding, see 12.35

13.2 See summary by: O. D. McMasters and K. A. Gschneider jr. in J. T. Waber, P. Chiotti, and W. N. Miner. *Compounds of Interest in Nuclear Reactor Technology*, J.M.D. Special Report No. 13, p. 93, Am. Inst. of Mining, Metallurgical and Petroleum Engineers, Inc., Edwards Brothers, Inc., Ann Arbor, Mich. (1964) and K. A. Gschneider jr., *Rare Earth Alloys*, Van Nostrand, Princeton N.J. (1961)

13.3 G. J. Piermarini and G. E. Weir. *J. Research Natl. Bur. Std.* **A 66**, 325 (1962); **68**, 105 (1964)

13.4 C. W. F. T. Pistorius. *Nature, Lond.*, **201**, 1321 (1964); **204**, 467 (1964); *J. Phys. Chem. Sol.* **25**, 1477 (1964)

13.5 V. Evdokimova and L. F. Vereshchagin. *Soviet Physics J.E.T.P.* **16**, 855 (1963); *Soviet Physics Solid State* **4**, 1438 (1963)

13.6 W. E. Spicer, A. H. Sommer, and J. G. White. *Phys. Rev.* **115**, 57 (1959)

13.7 S. Minomura and H. G. Drickamer. *J. Phys. Chem. Sol.* **23**, 451 (1962)

13.8 C. H. Bates, W. B. White, and R. Roy. *Science* **137**, 993 (1962)

13.9 A. M. Mariano. *Science* **142**, 672 (1963)

13.10 M. D. Banus, R. E. Hanneman, M. Strongin, and K. Gooen. *Science* **142**, 662 (1963)

13.11 A. Jayaraman, R. C. Newton, and G. C. Kennedy. *Proc. I. Intern. Congr. on Diamonds in Industry*, Paris (1962)

13.12 R. Hoppe. *Bull. Soc. Chim. France* 1115 (1965)

13.13 C. Keller, L. Koch, and K. H. Walter. *J. Inorg. Nucl. Chem.* **27**, 1205 (1965)

13.14 G. Gattow and J. Zemann. *Z. anorg. allg. Chem.* **279**, 324 (1955)

13.15 J. W. Boon. *Rec. Trav. Chim. Pays-Bas* **63**, 32 (1944)

13.16 S. Geller and J. H. Wernick. *Acta Cryst.* **12**, 46 (1959)

13.17 A. Stegherr, F. Wald, and P. Eckerlin. *Z. Naturf.* **16a**, 130 (1961)

13.18 L. D. Dyer. *J. Am. Chem. Soc.* **76**, 1499 (1954)

13.19 E. F. Hockings and J. G. White. *Acta Cryst.* **14**, 328 (1961)

13.20 G. Blasse. *Z. anorg. allg. Chemie* **326**, 44 (1963)

13.21 J. S. Kasper and J. S. Prenner. *Acta Cryst.* **7**, 24 (1954)

13.22 E. Parthé. *Crystal Chemistry of Tetrahedral Structures*, Gordon and Breach Science Publ. New York, London (1964)

13.23 N. A. GORYUNOVA. *The Chemistry of Diamond-like Semiconductors,* Chapman & Hall Ltd., London (1965); Original Russian (1963)

13.24 O. G. FOLBERTH and H. PFISTER. *Acta Cryst.* **14**, 325 (1961)

13.25 L. S. PALATNIK, YU. F. KOMNIK, V. M. KOSCHKIN, and E. K. BELOVA, *Soviet Physics Doklady* **6**, 241 (1961); *Dokl. Akad. Nauk. S.S.R.* **137**, 68 (1961)

13.26 H. HAHN, G. FRANK, W. KLINGLER, A. D. MEYER, and G. STÖRGER. *Z. anorg. allg. Chem.* **271**, 153 (1953)

13.27 H. HAHN and W. KLINGLER. *Z. anorg. allg. Chem.* **259**, 135 (1949)

13.28 J. GOODYEAR and G. A. STEIGMANN. *Acta Cryst.* **16**, 946 (1963)

13.29 H. HAHN, G. FRANK, W. KLINGLER, A. D. STÖRGER, and G. STÖRGER. *Z. anorg. allg. Chem.* **279**, 241 (1955)

13.30 H. HAHN, G. FRANK, and W. KLINGLER. *Z. anorg. allg. Chem.* **279**, 271 (1955)

13.31 J. FLAHAUT et al. *Cull. Soc. Chim. Fr.* **102**, (1961); *Compt. Rend.* **256**, 427 (1963); **257**, 1530 (1963)

14.1   V. M. GOLDSCHMIDT. *Ber. dtsch. chem. Ges.* **60**, 1263 (1927); *Geochem. Verteilungsgesetze der Elemente* VII Sk. Norske Vid.-Akad. Oslo, Math. Nat. Kl. No. 2 (1926)

14.2   For further tables of ionic radii, see:
   (a) L. H. AHRENS. *Geochim. Cosmochim. Acta* **2**, 155 (1952)
   (b) D. H. TEMPLETON and C. H. DAUBEN. *J. Am. Chem. Soc.* **76**, 5237 (1954) (radii of the rare earths)
   (c) N. EFREMOV. *Bull. Am. Phys. Soc.* [2] **1**, 203 (1956) (radii of the actinides)
   (d) J. H. VAN SANTEN and J. S. VAN WIERINGEN. *Rec. Trav. Chim. Pays-Bas* **71**, 420 (1952)
   (e) N. S. HUSH and M. H. L. PRYCE. *J. Chem. Phys.* **28**, 244 (1958) (radii of the transition metals)
   (f) E. KORDES. *Z. Krist.* **115**, 169 (1961)
   (g) E. G. FUMI and M. R. TOSI. *Phys. Chem. Solids* **25**, 31 and 45 (1964) (radii in alkali halogenides)
   (h) W. H. ZACHARIASEN. *Z. Krist.* **80**, 137 (1931)

14.3   S. GELLER. *Acta Cryst.* **10**, 248 (1957)

14.4   E. MADELUNG. *Phys. Z.* **19**, 524 (1918)

14.5   P. NAOR. *Bull. Res. Council Israel* **3**, 439 (1954); *Z. Krist.* **110**, 112 (1958)
   See also: F. BERTAUT. *C. R. Acad. Science Paris* **239**, 234 (1954); F. G. FUMI and M. R. TOSI. *Phil. Mag.* [8] **2**, 284 (1957); R. HOPPE. *Z. anorg. allg. Chem.* **283**, 196 (1956); **291**, 4 (1957)
   See summarizing literature: M. F. C. LADD and W. LEE. 'Lattice Energies and Related Topics' *Progress in Solid State Chemistry* **1**, 37 (1964)

14.6   M. BORN and A. LANDÉ. *Verh. Dtsch. Phys. Ges.* **20**, 210 (1918); **21**, 533 (1919)

14.7   E. WOLFEL et al. *Z. Phys. Chem.* New series **4**, 36 (1955); *Z. Elektrochem,* **63**, 891 (1959)

14.8   V. FOCK and M. J. PETRASHEN. *Phys. Z. USSR* **8**, 547 (1935); F. W. BROWN. *Phys. Rev.* **44**, 214 (1933)

14.9   H. KREBS and H. WEYAND. Unpublished

14.10 W. W. SCANLON. *Solid State Phys.* **9**, 83 (1959)

14.11 R. F. BREBRICK. *J. Phys. Chem. Sol.* **24**, 27 (1963)

14.12 J. ROSENBERG, R. GRIERSON, J. C. WOOLEY, and P. NIKOLIC. *Transactions of the Metallurgical Soc. of AIME* **230**, 342 (1964)

14.13 S. GELLER and G. W. HULL. *Phys. Rev. Letters* **13**, 127 (1964); S. GELLER, A. JAYARAMAN, and G. W. HULL, JR. *J. Phys. Chem. Sol.* **26**, 353 (1965)

14.14 J. J. LANDER, in 14.24, p. 52

14.15 S. GELLER, *Preprint Symposium on the Chemical Bond in Semiconductors.* **28**, v.–3. vi–1967, Minsk, USSR

14.16 C. J. M. ROOYMANS. *Ber. Bunsen Ges. Phys. Chem.* **70**, 1036 (1966)

14.17 S. METHFESSEL. *Z. angew. Phys.* **18**, 414 (1965)

14.18 A. JANDELLI. *Rare Earth Research,* edited by E. V. KLEBER, p. 135, Macmillan Company, New York (1961)

14.19 P. EHRLICH. *Z. anorg. allg. Chem.* **259**, 1 (1949); *Z. Elektrochem.* **45**, 362 (1939)

14.20 U. KUYLENSTIERNA and A. MAGNÉLI. *Acta Chem. Scand.* **10**, 1195 (1965)

14.21 A. RABENAU, cited in 27.12

14.22 D. REINEN. *Ber. Bunsen ges. phys. Chem.* **69**, 82 (1965); O. SCHMITZ-DUMONT, A. LULÉ and D. REINEN. *ibid.* **69**, 76 (1965)

14.23 C. WAGNER et al. *Z. Phys. Chem.* **B 22**, 181 (1933); **23**, 199 (1933); **24**, 59 (1934); **32**, 439 (1936)

14.24 F. J. MORIN in *Semiconductors,* edited by N. B. HANNAY, p. 1047, Rheinhold, New York (1959)

14.25 G. H. JONKER and S. VAN HOUTEN in *Halbleiterprobleme VI*, p. 118, Friedrich Vieweg, Braunschweig (1961)

14.26 H. A. KRAMERS. *Physica* **1**, 182 (1934)

14.27 P. W. ANDERSON. *Phys. Rev.* **79**, 350 (1950)

15.1 K. SCHUBERT and H. FRICKE. *Z. Metallk.* **44**, 457 (1953)

15.2 H. KREBS and H. U. GRUBER, will appear in *Z. Naturf. a*

15.3 H. KREBS, H. WEYAND, and M. HAUCKE. *Angew. Chem.* **70**, 466 (1958)

15.4 H. KREBS, V. B. LAZAREV, and L. WINKLER. *Z. anorg. allg. Chem.* **352**, 277 (1967)

15.5 J. A. KAFALAS. *Science* **143**, 952 (1964)

15.6 E. PARTHÉ and O. SCHOB et al. *Acta Cryst.* **19**, 214 (1965); *Naturw.* **52**, 155 (1965)

15.7 J. A. KAFALAS, H. C. GATOS, M. C. LAVINE, and M. D. BANUS. *J. Phys. Chem. Solids* **23**, 159 (1962)

15.8 P. W. BRIDGMAN. *Proc. Am. Acad. Arts. Sci.* **74**, 21 (1940)

15.9 J. S. KASPER, unpublished

15.10 K. AURIVILLIUS. *Acta Chem. Scand.* **10**, 852 (1956)

16.1 R. H. WENTORF. *J. Chem. Phys.* **26**, 956 (1957)

16.2 M. ATOJI and W. N. LIPSCOMB. *Acta Cryst.* **7**, 597 (1954)

16.3 M. J. KAY. *Acta. Cryst.* **14**, 80 (1961)

16.4 See survey paper by: A. KJEKSHUS and W. P. PEARSON. *Progr. Solid State Chem.* **1**, 83 (1964)

16.5 W. KLEMM. *Naturw.* **37**, 150 (1950)

16.6 See S. RUNDQVIST. 'Binary Transition Metal Phosphides'. *Arkiv för Kemi,* **20**, 67–113 (1962)

16.7 For survey literature on the structure of sulphides, see H. HAHN. The Chemical Society London, Special Publication Nr. 12, p. 263 (1958); F. JELLINEK. *Arkiv för Kemi,* **20**, 447 (1963)

17.1 W. H. ZACHARIASEN. *Acta Cryst.* **2**, 388 (1949)

17.2 R. HOPPE and C. HEBECKER. *Z. anorg. allg. Chem.* **335**, 85 (1965)

17.3 Compare also: C. KELLER. *Angew. Chem.* **78**, 85 (1966)

17.4 W. H. ZACHARIASEN. *Acta Cryst.* **4**, 231 (1951)

17.5   M. v. STACKELBERG and F. QUATRAM. *Z. Phys. Chem.* **B 27**, 50 (1934)
17.6   H. J. BECHER. *Z. anorg. allg. Chem.* **317**, 346 (1962)
17.7   E. ZINTL, A. HARDER, and W. HAUKE. *Z. Phys. Chem.* **B 35**, 354 (1937)
17.8   C. D. WEST and A. W. PETERSON. *Z. Krist.* **88**, 93 (1934); U. DEHLINGER. *Z. Elektrochem.* **41**, 344 (1935)
17.9   F. WEIBKE and G. HESSE. *Z. anorg. allg. Chem.* **240**, 289 (1939)
17.10 O. KUBASCHEWSKI and F. WEIBKE. *Z. Elektrochem.* **44**, 870 (1938)
17.11 R. JUZA and F. HUND. *Z. anorg. allg. Chem.* **257**, 1 (1948)
17.12 H. NOWOTNY and W. SIEBERT. *Z. Metallk.* **33**, 391 (1941)
17.13 H. NOWOTNY. *Z. Metallk.* **34**, 237 (1942)
17.14 R. JUZA and F. HUND. *Z. anorg. allg. Chem.* **257**, 13 (1948)
17.15 R. JUZA, H. H. WEBER, and E. MEYER-SIMON. *Z. anorg. allg. Chem.* **273**, 48 (1953)
17.16 R. JUZA and W. SCHULZ. *Z. anorg. allg. Chem.* **275**, 65 (1954)
17.17 A. PEBLER and W. A. WALLACE. *J. Phys. Chem.* **66**, 148 (1962)
17.18 C. E. HOLLEY Jr., R. N. R. MULFORD, F. H. ELLINGER, W. C. KOEHLER, and W. H. ZACHARIASEN. *J. Phys. Chem.* **59**, 1226 (1955)
17.19 H. L. YAKEL et al. *Acta Cryst.* **11**, 46 (1958)
17.20 G. G. LIBOWITZ. *J. Nucl. Mats.* **2**, 1 (1960)
17.21 R. E. RUNDLE et al. *Acta Cryst.* **5**, 22 (1952)
17.22 H. WELKER. *Erg. exakt. Naturw.* **29**, 275 (1956)
17.23 E. ZINTL and A. UNGARD. *Z. anorg. allg. Chem.* **240**, 150 (1939)
17.24 W. RÜDORFF and G. VALET. *Z. anorg. allg. Chem.* **271**, 257 (1953)
17.25 Mixed phases with fluorspar structure, see F. HUND. *Ber. Dtsch. Ker. Ges.* **42**, 251 (1965)
17.26 W. H. ZACHARIASEN. *Am. Rev. Phys. Chem.* **3**, 369 (1952)
17.27 F. HUND and R. FRICKE. *Z. anorg. allg. Chem.* **258**, 198 (1948)
17.28 W. R. COOK and H. JAFFE. *Phys. Rev.* **90**, 375 (1953)
17.29 E. ZINTL and G. BRAUER. *Z. Elektrochem.* **41**, 297 (1935)
17.30 E. MOOSER and W. B. PEARSON. *Phys. Rev.* **10**, 492 (1956)
17.31 E. MOOSER and W. B. PEARSON. *J. Phys. Chem. Sol.* **7**, 65 (1958); *Canad. J. Phys.* **34**, 1369 (1956); F. HULLIGER and E. MOOSER. *J. Phys. Chem. Sol.* **24**, 283 (1963)
17.32 H. U. SCHUSTER. *Naturw.* **52**, 639 (1965) and **53**, 360, 361 (1966)
17.33 D. CHAPIN and T. HONIG. *J. Phys. Chem.* **69**, 1402 (1965)
17.34 T. J. SWOBODA, P. ARTHUR et al. *J. appl. Phys.* **32**, 3745 (1961)
17.35 A. D. LICH and C. J. BALLHAUSEN. *Ann. Phys. N.Y.* **3**, 304 (1958)
17.36 W. H. ZACHARIASEN, C. E. HOLLEY jr. and J. F. STAMPER jr. *Acta Cryst.* **16**, 352 (1963)
17.37 S. M. STISHOW and S. V. POPOVA. *Geokhimiy* **10**, 837 (1961)
17.38 A. PREISINGER. *Naturw.* **49**, 345 (1962)
17.39 K. H. JACK and R. MAITLAND. *Proc. Chem. Soc.* London, 232 (1957)
17.40 C. BILLY and H. HAENDLER. *J. Am. Chem. Soc.* **79**, 1049 (1957)
17.41 W. H. BAUR. *Acta Cryst.* **11**, 488 (1958)
       See also: J. D. DUNITZ and L. E. ORGEL 'Stereochemistry of Ionic Solids' in *Advanced Inorganic Chemistry and Radiochemistry*, **2**, 1–60 (1960)
17.42 D. REINEN. *Habilitationsschrift,* Universität Bonn, 1965.
17.43 GORO HONJO and KOHJI SHIMAOKO. *Acta Cryst.* **10**, 710 (1957)
17.44 S. W. PETERSON and H. A. LEVY. *Acta Cryst.* **10**, 70 (1957)
17.45 P. P. KEAT. *Science* **120**, 328 (1954)
17.46 J. SHOPSHIRE, P. P. KEAT, and P. A. VAUGHAN. *Z. Krist.* **112**, 409 (1959)

17.47 L. Coes jr. *Science* **118**, 131 (1953)

17.48 T. Zoltai and M. J. Buerger. *Z. Krist.* **111**, 129 (1959)

17.49 F. Dachille and R. Roy. *Z. Krist.* **111**, 451 (1959)

17.50 G. E. R. Schulze. *Z. Phys. Chem.* **24 B**, 215 (1934)

17.51 F. Dachille and R. Roy. *Z. Krist.* **111**, 459 (1959)

17.52 E. C. and M. W. Shafer and R. Roy. *Z. Krist.* **108**, 263 (1956)

17.53 H. G. F. Winkler. *Acta Cryst.* **1**, 27 (1948)

17.54 T. F. W. Barth, *J. Chem. Phys.* **3**, 323 (1935)

17.55 H. G. v. Schnering, R. Hoppe, and J. Zemann. *Z. anorg. allg. Chem.* **305**, 24 (1960)

17.56 P. Eckerlin, C. Langereis, T. Maak, and A. Rabenau. *Angew. Chem.* **72**, 268 (1960)

17.57 W. Rüdorff and K. Brodersen. *Z. anorg. allg. Chem.* **274**, 323 (1953)

17.58 S. D. Arora, W. N. Lipscomb, and M. C. Sneed. *J. Am. Chem. Soc.* **73**, 1015 (1951)

17.59 K. Brodersen and W. Rüdorff. *Z. anorg. allg. Chem.* **287**, 24 (1956)

17.60 For mixed crystal systems with these structures, see F. Hund. *Z. anorg. allg. Chem.* **321**, 1 (1963)

17.61 F. Hulliger. *Nature, Lond.,* **200**, 1064 (1963)

17.62 F. Hulliger. *Helv. Phys. Acta* **35**, 535 (1962)

17.63 E. F. Hockings and J. G. White. *J. Phys. Chem.* **64**, 1042 (1960)

17.64 G. W. W. Hoffman et al. *J. Am. Chem. Soc.* **81**, 3830 (1959)

18.1 E. Dönnges. *Z. anorg. allg. Chem.* **265**, 56 (1951)

18.2 R. Hilsch, G. v. Minnigerode, and H. v. Wartenberg. *Naturw.* **44**, 463 (1957)

18.3 L. H. Brixner. *J. Inorg. Nucl. Chem.* **24**, 257 (1962)

18.4 W. Rüdorff. *Chimica* **19**, 489 (1965)

18.5 H. Krebs. *Z. anorg. allg. Chem.* **278**, 82 (1955)

18.6 F. Hulliger and J. Müller. *Phys. Letters,* **5**, 226 (1963)

18.7 R. M. Douglas. *Acta. Cryst.* **10**, 423 (1957)

18.8 W. Feitknecht. *Helv. Chim. Acta* **21**, 766 (1938); *Fortschr. Chem. Forsch.* **2**, 670 (1953)

18.9 Compare also: Glemser. *Fortschr. Chem. Forsch.* **2**, 273 (1951)

18.9a H. Krebs, *Z. Naturf. a*, 1968 in press

18.9b B. T. Matthias, T. H. Geballe and V. B. Compton, *Rev. Mod. Phys.* **35**, 1 (1963)

18.9c B. W. Roberts in *Intermetallic Compounds*, ed. by J. H. Westbrook, John Wiley 1967, p. 581

18.9d B. W. Roberts in *Progress in Cryogenics*—4, Heywood Books, London 1964, p. 159

18.9e John Piper, *Int. Symp. on Compounds of Interest in Nuclear Reactor Technology*, 3–5, VIII, 1964, Boulder, Cal., ed. by J. T. Waber, P. Chiotti and W. Miner, I.M.D. Special Report Nr. 13, Edward Brothers Inc., 1964

18.9f M. Robbins, R. H. Willens and R. C. Miller, *Solid State Commun.* **5**, 933 (1967)

18.9g J. Goubeau, personal communication

18.9h R. Hilsch, *Proc. Int. Conf. on Low Temp. Physics*, ed. by R. Bowers, Oxford 1951, p. 119

W. Buckel and R. Hilsch, *Z. Phys.* **138**, 109 (1954)

18.9i B. T. Matthias, *Progr. in Low Temp. Physics*, Vol. II, p. 138, Interscience, New York, 1955; *Phys. Rev.* **97**, 74 (1955).

18.10 B. E. Brown. *Acta Cryst.* **20**, 264 and 268 (1966)
18.11 W. Rüdorff. *Angew. Chem.* **71**, 127 and 487 (1959)
18.12 B. Brehler. *Z. Krist.* **115**, 373 (1961); *Fortschr. Mineral.* **39**, 338 (1961)
18.13 F. A. Bannister and M. H. Hey. *Mineral. Mag.* **24**, 49 (1935)
18.14 L. G. Sillén. *Svensk. Kem. Tidskr.* **53**, 39 (1941)
18.15 L. G. Sillén and A. L. Nylander. *Svensk. Kem. Tidskr.* **53**, 369 (1941)
18.16 D. H. Templeton and C. H. Dauben. *J. Am. Chem. Soc.* **75**, 6069 (1953)
18.17 H. Bärnighausen, G. Brauer, and N. Schultz. *Z. anorg. allg. Chem.* **338**, 250 (1965)
18.18 W. H. Zachariasen. *Acta Cryst.* **2**, 291 (1949)
18.19 R. Juza et al. *Naturw.* **52**, 538 (1965) and **53**, 552 (1966)
18.20 P. Ehrlich et al. *Z. anorg. allg. Chem.* **283**, 58 (1956); **288**, 148, 156 (1956)
18.21 H. Hahn and R. Schmid, *Naturw.*, **59**, 475 (1965)
18.22 L. G. Sillén. *Naturw.* **30**, 318 (1942)
19.1   Alarich and Arnim Weiss. *Z. anorg. allg. Chem.* **276**, 95 (1954)
19.2   A. I. Snow and R. E. Rundle. *Acta Cryst.* **4**, 348 (1951)
19.3   A. F. Wells. *Z. Krist.* **100**, 189 (1938); *J. Chem. Soc. London* 1670 (1947)
20.1   H. Krebs. *Z. Elektrochem.* **61**, 925 (1957)
21.1   J. O. Sawyer, B. G. Hyde, and L. Eyring. *Bull. Soc. Chim. France* 1190 (1965)
21.2   Compare also: G. Brauer. *Science and Technology of the Rare Earths,* Vol. 2, p. 312, Pergamon Press, Oxford–New York (1966)
21.3   H. K. Müller-Buschbaum and H. G. v. Schnering. *Z. anorg. allg. Chem.* **340**, 232 (1965)
21.4   For exact atomic positions, see: R. E. Newnham and Y. M. de Haan. *Z. Krist.* **117**, 235 (1962)
21.5   U. Ventriglia. *Periodico Mineral.* (Rome) **26**, 345 (1957)
21.6   W. H. Cloud. *Phys. Rev.* **111**, 1046 (1958)
21.7   T. J. Swoboda, R. C. Toole, and J. D. Vaughan. *Phys. Chem. Solids* **5**, 293 (1958)
21.8   A. E. Ringwood and M. Seabrook. *J. Geophys. Res.* **67**, 1690 (1962)
21.9   S. Geller. *J. Chem. Phys.* **33**, 676 (1960)
21.10 D. Harker. *Z. Krist.* **89**, 175 (1934)
21.11 P. W. Lange. *Naturw.* **27**, 133 (1939)
21.12 A. J. Rosenberg and A. J. Strauss. *J. Phys. Chem. Solids* **19**, 105 (1961)
21.13 R. W. M. D'Eye, P. G. Sellman, and J. R. Murray. *J. Chem. Soc. London* 2555 (1952)
21.14 N. Morimoto. *Mineral. J.* (Japan) **1**, 160 (1954)
21.15 K. A. Becker, K. Plieth, and J. N. Stranski. *Z. anorg. allg. Chem.* **275**, 297 (1954)
21.16 K. E. Almin and A. Westgren. *Arkiv Kemi, Mineral. Geol.* **15B**, 22 (1942)
22.1   H. G. v. Schnering, personal communication
22.2   B. Morogin and A. Narath. *J. Chem. Phys.* **40**, 1958 (1964)
22.3   J. A. A. Ketelaar, C. H. MacGillavry, and P. A. Renes. *Rec. Trav. Chim.* **66**, 501 (1947)
22.4   K. Brodersen and F. Moers, personal communication cf. *Angew. Chem.* **76**, 690 (1964)
22.5   H. Bärnighausen and B. K. Handa. *J. Less Common Metals* **6**, 226 (1964)
22.6   J. A. A. Ketelaar and G. W. van Oosterhout. *Rec. Trav. Chim.* **62**, 197 (1943)

22.7 H. D. MEGAW. *Z. Krist.* **87**, 185 (1934)

22.8 E. ZINTL and G. BRAUER. *Z. Elektrochem.* **41**, 102 (1935)

22.9 J. OFTEDAL. *Z. Phys. Chem.* **5B**, 272 (1929)

22.10 K. SCHLYTER. *Arkiv Kemi* **5**, 73 (1952)

22.11 G. GNUTZMANN, F. W. DORN, and W. KLEMM. *Z. anorg. allg. Chem.* **309**, 210 (1961)

22.12 K. DEHNICKE. *Naturw.*, **52**, 660 (1965)

22.13 K. S. VORRES and J. DONOHUE. *Acta Cryst.* **8**, 25 (1955)

22.14 H. SCHÄFER et al. *Naturw.* **51**, 241 (1964)

22.15 R. HOPPE and K. BLINNE. *Z. anorg. allg. Chem.* **293**, 251 (1958)

22.16 K. SCHUBERT and A. SEITZ. *Z. anorg. allg. Chem.* **256**, 226 (1948)

22.17 M. A. HEPWORTH, K. H. JACK, R. D. PEACOCK, and G. J. WESTLAND. *Acta Cryst.* **10**, 63 (1957)

22.18 J. F. KEGGIN and F. D. MILES. *Nature Lond.* **137**, 577 (1936)

22.19 H. B. WEISER, W. D. MILLIGAN, and H. B. BATES. *J. Phys. Chem.* **46**, 99 (1942)

22.20 E. FLUCK, W. KERLER, and W. NEUWIRTH. *Z. anorg. allg. Chem.* **333**, 235 (1964)

23.1 C. KELLER, B. KANELLAKOPULOS and W. WASSILOPULOS. *Radiochim. Acta.*, **5**, 87 (1966)

23.2 W. RÜDORFF and B. REUTER. *Z. anorg. allg. Chem.* **253**, 177 (1947)

23.3 F. GALASSO, L. KATZ, and R. WARD. *J. Am. Chem. Soc.* **80**, 820 and 5898 (1959)

23.4 F. GALASSO and W. DARBY. *Inorg. Chem.* **4**, 71 (1965)

23.5 Compare: C. KELLER. *J. inorg. nucl. Chem.* **27**, 321 (1965)

23.6 K. KNOX. *Acta Cryst.* **14**, 583 (1961)

23.7 W. RÜDORFF and D. KRUG. *Z. anorg. allg. Chem.* **329**, 211 (1964)

23.8 A. FERRARI and A. BARONI. *Atti R. Accad. Lincei* **6**, 418 (1927)

23.9 G. NATTA and L. PASSERINI. *Gazz. Chim. Ital.* **58**, 472 (1928)

23.10 N. ELLIOT and L. PAULING. *J. Am. Chem. Soc.* **60**. 1846 (1938)

23.10a H. J. SEIFERT, personal communication

23.10b H. J. SEIFERT and F. W. KOGNAT, *Z. anorg. allg. Chem.* **341**, 269 (1965)

23.11 H. HAHN and U. MUTSCHKE. *Z. anorg. allg. Chem.* **288**, 269 (1956)

23.12 A. CLEARFIELD. *Acta Cryst.* **16**, 135 (1963)

23.13 B. REUTER and K. HARDEL. *Z. anorg. allg. Chem.* **340**, 158 and 168 (1965)

23.14 Compare: F. JONA and G. SHIRANE. *Ferroelectric Crystals*. Pergamon Press, Oxford–London–New York–Paris (1962)

23.15 A. J. EDWARDS and R. D. PEACOCK. *J. Chem. Soc.* 4126 (1959)

23.16 A. OKASAKI and Y. SUEMUNE. *J. Phys. Soc. Japan* **16**, 176 and 671 (1961)

23.17 D. REINEN, *Theor. Chim. Acta*, **5**, 312 (1966)

23.18 R. G. SHULMAN and K. KNOX. *Phys. Rev. Letters* **4**, 603 (1960)

23.19 H. D. MEGAW. *Proc. Roy. Soc.* London, **A 189**, 261 (1947)

23.20 B. C. FRAZER, H. R. DANNER, and R. PEPINSKY. *Phys. Rev.* **100**, 745 (1955)

23.21 G. SHIRANE, R. PEPINSKY, and B. C. FRAZER. *Acta Cryst.* **9**, 131 (1956)

23.22 H. T. EVANS jr. *Acta Cryst.* **14**, 1019 (1961)

23.22a W. RÜDORFF and F. PFITZNER, *Z. Naturf.* **10b**, 178 (1955)

23.22b C. KELLER, *Nukleonik*, **4**, 271 (1962); **5**, 89 (1963)

23.23 G. HÄGG. *Z. Phys. Chem.* **B 29**, 192 (1935)

23.24 T. A. BITHER, J. L. GILLSON, and H. S. YOUNG. *Inorg. Chem.* **5**, 1559 (1966)

23.25 R. HOPPE and W. DÄHNE. *Naturw.* **49**, 254 (1962)

23.26 F. P. GORTSEMA and R. DIDSCHENKO. *Inorg. Chem.* **4**, 182 (1965)

23.27 H. Schäfter and H. G. v. Schnering. *Angew. Chem.* **76**, 833 (1964)
23.28 C. Brosset. *Z. anorg. allg. Chem.* **235**, 139 and 301 (1937)
23.29 D. Balz and K. Plieth. *Z. Elektrochem.* **59**, 545 (1955)
23.30 W. Rüdorff, J. Kändler, and D. Babel. *Z. anorg. allg. Chem.* **317**, 261 (1962)
23.31 W. Rüdorff, G. Lincke, and D. Babel. *Z. anorg. allg. Chem.* **320**, 150 (1963)
23.32 H. Remy and F. Hansen. *Z. anorg. allg. Chem.* **283**, 277 (1956)
23.33 S. N. Ruddlesden and P. Popper. *Acta Cryst.* **10**, 538 (1957)
23.34 G. Wagner and H. Binder. *Z. anorg. allg. Chem.* **298**, 12 (1959)
23.35 W. Rüdorff, personal communication
23.36 M. Foëx. *Bull. Soc. Chim. France* 109 (1961)
23.37 A. Rabenau and P. Eckerlin. *Acta Cryst.* **11**, 304 (1958)
23.38 H. J. Seifert and K. Ktutyk. *Naturw.* **49**, 539 (1962)
23.39 S. N. Ruddlesden and P. Popper. *Acta Cryst.* **11**, 54 (1958)
23.39a M. Perez y Jorba, G. Tilloga and R. Collongues, *Compt. Rend.* **260**, 170 (1965)
23.39b C. Brisi, M. Succo-Borlera, *J. Inorg. Nucl. Chem.* **27**, 2129 (1965)
23.40 B. Aurivillius. *Arkiv Kemi* **1**, 463 and 499 (1949); **2**, 519 (1950) and **5**, 39 (1952)
23.41 H. G. v. Schnering. *Angew. Chem.* **76**, 607 (1964) and *Habilitationsschrift*, Münster (1963)
23.42 See survey in: E. W. Gorter. *Philips Res. Rept.* **9**, 245 (1954)
23.43 See survey in: G. Blasse. *Crystal Chemistry and some magnetic properties of mixed metal oxides with spinel structure,* Dissertation, Universität Leiden (1964)
23.44 T. W. F. Barth and E. Posnjak. *Z. Krist.* **82**, 325 (1932)
23.45 E. J. W. Verwey, P. B. Braun, E. W. Gorter, F. C. Romeijn, and J. H. van Santen. *Z. Phys. Chem.* **198**, 6 (1951)
23.46 E. J. W. Verwey and P. W. Haaijman. *Physica* **8**, 979 (1941)
23.47 P. B. Braun. *Nature, Lond.* **170**, 1123 (1952)
23.48 E. W. Gorter. *Philips Res. Rept.* **9**, 403 (1954)
23.49 C. J. M. Rooymans. *J. Inorg. Nucl. Chem.* **11**, 78 (1959)
23.50 G. A. Steigmann, H. H. Sutherland, and J. Goodyear. *Acta Cryst.* **19**, 967 (1965)
23.51 H. P. Rooksby and C. J. M. Rooymans. *Clay Minerals Bull.* **4**, 234 (1961)
23.52 W. L. Roth. *Acta Cryst.* **13**, 140 (1960)
23.53 W. Rüdorff, J. Kändler, and D. Babel. *Z. anorg. allg. Chem.* **317**, 261 (1962)
23.54 R. G. Dickinson. *J. Am. Chem. Soc.* **44**, 774 (1922)
23.55 J. Adams, T. R. AuCoin, and G. A. Wolff. *J. Electrochem. Soc.* **109**, 1050 (1962)
23.56 J. Flahaut et al. *Bull. Soc. Chim. France* 2382 (1961)
23.57 H. Hahn et al. *Z. anorg. allg. Chem.* **264**, 184 (1951); **283**, 138 (1956)
23.58 J. Dulac and A. Durif. *Compt. Rend.* **251**, 747 (1960)
23.59 A. M. Gaines, A. J. Perrotta, and D. A. Stephenson. *Am. Cryst. Assoc. Meeting*, Gatlinburg, Tenn. USA, 27.6–2.7.1965
23.60 A. E. Ringwood. *Nature, Lond.* **198**, 79 (1963); **187**, 1019 (1960)
23.60a D. Reinen, *Z. anorg. allg. Chem.* **356**, 172 (1968)
23.61 P. Cosse. *J. inorg. nucl. Chem.* **8**, 483 (1958)
23.62 J. D. Dunitz and L. E. Orgel. *J. Phys. Chem. Solids* **3**, 318 (1957)
23.63 D. S. McClure. *Phys. Chem. Sol.* **3**, 31 (1957)

23.64 L. Neél. *Ann. Physique* **3**, 137 (1948)

24.1 M. Atoji and R. C. Medrud. *J. Chem. Phys.* **31**, 332 (1959)

24.2 M. Atoji et al. *J. Am. Chem. Soc.* **80**, 1804 (1958)

24.3 A. E. Austin. *Acta Cryst.* **12**, 159 (1959)

24.4 S. C. Abrahams and J. Kalnajs. *Acta Cryst.* **8**, 503 (1955)

24.5 E. B. Hunt and R. E. Rundle. *J. Am. Chem. Soc.* **73**, 4777 (1951)

24.6 W. H. Zachariasen. *Acta Cryst.* **5**, 17 (1952)

24.7 W. Klemm and E. Busmann. *Z. anorg. allg. Chem.* **319**, 297 (1963)

24.8 R. E. Marsh and D. P. Shoemaker. *Acta Cryst.* **6**, 197 (1953)

24.9 E. Busmann. *Z. anorg. allg. Chem.* **313**, 90 (1961)

24.10 J. Witte and H. G. v. Schnering. *Z. anorg. allg. Chem.* **327**, 260 (1964)

24.11 H. Schäfer, K. H. Janzon, and A. Weiss. *Angew. Chem.* **75**, 451 (1963); **77**, 258 (1965)

24.12 J. Oftedal. *Z. Krist.* **66**, 517 (1928)

24.13 N. N. Zhuravley and G. S. Zhdanov. *Kristallografiya* **1**, 509 (1956)

24.14 S. Rundqvist. *Nature, Lond.* **185**, 31 (1960)

24.15 For survey, see: E. H. Wiebenga, E. E. Havinga, and K. H. Boswijk. *Adv. Inorg. Chem. Radiochem.* **3**, 133 (1961)

24.16 R. C. L. Mooney. *Z. Krist.* **90**, 143 (1935)

24.17 R. C. L. Mooney Slater. *Acta Cryst.* **12**, 187 (1959)

24.18 R. J. Hack and R. E. Rundle. *J. Am. Chem. Soc.* **73**, 4321 (1951); see also J. Broekema, E. E. Havinga, and E. H. Wiebenga. *Acta Cryst.* **10**, 596 (1957)

24.19 For survey, see: O. Foss. *Adv. Inorg. Chem. Radiochem.* **2**, 237 (1960)

24.20 S. C. Abrahams and E. Grison. *Acta Cryst.* **6**, 206 (1953)

24.21 Don T. Cromer. *Acta Cryst.* **12**, 36 and 41 (1959)

24.22 E. Busmann and S. Lohmeyer. *Z. anorg. allg. Chem.* **312**, 53 (1961)

24.23 H. Krebs and Th. Ludwig. *Z. anorg. allg. Chem.* **294**, 257 (1958)

24.24 H. Krebs. *Z. Phys.* **126**, 769 (1949); *Z. anorg. allg. Chem.* **256**, 156 (1951)

24.25 J. Böhm and O. Hassel. *Z. anorg. allg. Chem.* **160**, 152 (1927)

24.26 R. Kiessling et al. *Acta Chem. Scand.* **3**, 90, 595 and 603 (1949)

24.27 V. Russel et al. *Acta Cryst.* **6**, 870 (1953)

24.28 B. Post, F. W. Glaser, and D. Moskovitz. *Acta Met.* **2**, 20 (1954)

24.29 W. Obrowski. *Naturw.* **48**, 428 (1961)

24.30 F. Laves. *Naturw.* **31**, 145 (1943)

24.31 A. Zalkin, D. E. Sands, R. G. Bedford, and O. H. Krikorian. *Acta Cryst.* **14**, 63 (1961)

24.32 For summarizing literature, see: W. Rüdorff. *Adv. Inorg. Chem. Radiochem.* **1**, 224 (1959); G. R. Hennig. *Progr. Inorg. Chem.* **1**, 125 (1959); R. C. Croft. *Quart. Rev.* (London) **14**, 1 (1960)

24.33 W. Rüdorff and G. Rüdorff. *Z. anorg. allg. Chem.* **253**, 281 (1947)

24.34 W. Rüdorff and E. Schulze. *Z. anorg. allg. Chem.* **277**, 156 (1954)

24.35 A. R. Ubbelohde, L. C. F. Blachman, and J. F. Mathews. *Nature, Lond.* **183**, 454 (1959)

24.36 W. Rüdorff. *Chimia* (Aarau) **19**, 489 (1965)

24.37 R. Juza and V. Wehle. *Naturw.* **52**, 560 (1965)

24.38 W. Rüdorff. *Z. anorg. allg. Chem.* **245**, 383 (1941)

24.39 W. T. Eeles and J. A. Turnbull. *Proc. Roy. Soc.* London, A **283**, 179 (1965)

24.40 R. Juza and A. Schmeckenbecher. *Z. anorg. allg. Chem.* **292**, 34 and 46 (1957)

25

24.41 W. RÜDORFF. *Angew. Chem.* **75**, 130 (1963)
24.42 J. M. COWLEY and J. A. IBERG. *Acta Cryst.* **9**, 421 (1956)
24.43 G. R. HENNING. *J. Chem. Phys.* **20**, 1443 (1952)
24.44 E. ZINTL and W. DULLENKOPF. *Z. Phys. Chem.* **B 16**, 183 and 195 (1932)
24.45 G. GRUBE et al. *Z. Elektrochem.* **42**, 201 (1936) and *Z. anorg. allg. Chem.* **38**, 869 (1932)
24.46 W. KLEMM. *Proc. Chem. Soc.* London 329 (1958)
24.47 G. BRAUER and A. MITIUS. *Z. anorg. allg. Chem.* **249**, 325 (1942)
24.48 W. H. ZACHARIASEN. *Acta Cryst.* **2**, 94 (1949)
24.48a A. F. WELLS. *Structural Inorganic Chemistry*, Clarendon Press, Oxford (1962), p. 774
24.49 M. V. STACKELBERG and F. NEUMANN. *Z. Phys. Chem.* **B 19**, 314 (1932)
24.49a *Strukturbericht II, Akad. Verlagsges*, Leipzig (1937)
24.50 W. H. ZACHARIASEN. *Acta Cryst.* **7**, 81 (1954)
24.51 F. BERTAUT and P. BLUM. *Compt. Rend.* **229**, 666 (1949)
24.52 Survey paper on borides and silicides: B. ARONSSON. *Arkiv Kemi* **16**, 379 (1960); B. ARONSSON, T. LUNDSTRÖM, and S. RUNDQVIST. *Borides, Silicides and Phosphides*, Methuen, London (1965)
25.1   Compare: F. LIBAU. 'Die Systematik der Silikate', *Naturw.* **49**, 481 (1962) and 388; A. WITTMANN, 'Beiträge zur Strukturchemie der Germanate', *Fortschr. Miner.* **43**, 230 (1966); and 25.39
25.2   F. RINNE et al. *Z. Krist.* **59**, 230 and 548 (1924)
25.3   K. HAUKE and J. ZEMANN. *Naturw.* **50**, 91 (1963)
25.4   G. V. GIBBS et al. *Acta Cryst.* **16**, A 13 (1963)
25.5   D. K. SMITH, A. MAJUMDAR, and F. ORDWAY. *Acta Cryst.* **18**, 787 (1965)
25.6   W. H. TAYLOR and J. WEST. *Proc. Roy. Soc.* **A 117**, 517 (1928) and *Z. Krist.* **70**, 461 (1929)
25.7   W. H. ZACHARIASEN. *Z. Krist.* **73**, 1 (1930)
25.8   D. W. J. CRUICKSHANK, H. LYNTON, and G. A. BARCLAY. *Acta Cryst.* **15**, 491 (1962)
25.9   Kh. S. MAMEDOV, R. F. KLEVTSOVA, and N. V. BELOV. *Dokl. Akad. Nauk SSSR* **126**, 574 (1959); English translation see 25.18, p. 79
25.10 W. H. ZACHARIASEN. *Z. Krist.* **74**, 139 (1930)
25.11 D. E. HENSHAW. *Mineral. Mag.* **30**, 585 (1955)
25.12 W. L. BRAGG and J. WEST. *Proc. Roy. Soc.* London, **A 111**, 59 (1926)
25.13 H. G. HEIDE and K. BOLL-DORNBERGER. *Acta Cryst.* **8**, 425 (1955)
25.14 M. J. BUERGER, C. W. BURNHAM, and D. R. PEACOR. *Acta Cryst.* **15**, 583 (1962)
25.15 A. BYSTRÖM. *Arkiv Kemi Min. Geol.* **15 B**, 7 (1941)
25.16 B. E. WARREN and W. L. BRAGG. *Z. Krist.* **69**, 168 (1928)
25.16a J. M. BIJVOET, N. H. KOLKMEYER, and C. H. MACGILLAVRY, *X-Ray Analysis of Crystals*, Butterworths, London (1951)
25.17 F. LIBAU. *Acta Cryst.* **12**, 180 (1959)
25.18 N. V. BELOV. *Crystal Chemistry of Large Cation Silicates*, Consultants Bureau New York, pp. 14 and 16 (1963)
25.19 E. THILO. *Angew. Chem.* **77**, 1056 (1965)
25.20 H. G. V. SCHNERING and R. HOPPE. *Z. anorg. allg. Chem.* **312**, 99 (1961)
25.21 B. E. WARREN. *Z. Krist.* **72**, 42 (1929)
25.22 J. ZUSSMAN. *Acta Cryst.* **12**, 309 (1959)
25.23 W. H. TAYLÓR et al. *Z. Krist.* **68**, 503 (1920); **71**, 205 (1929); **80**, 428 (1931)
25.24 C. W. BURNHAM. *Z. Krist.* **118**, 127 (1963)
25.25 S. ĎUROVIČ and S. DÁVIDOVÁ. *Acta Cryst.* **15**, 1051 (1962)

25.26 KH. S. MAMEDOV and N. V. BELOV. *Doklady Akad. Nauk. SSSR* **104**, 615 (1955); see also 25.18, p. 17

25.27 L. PAULING. *Proc. Nat. Acad. Sci.* **16**, 123 (1930)

25.28 J. W. GRUNER. *Z. Krist.* **88**, 412 (1934)

25.29 L. PAULING. *Proc. Nat. Acad. Sci.* **16**, 578 (1930)

25.30 G. W. BRINDLEY, B. M. OUGHTON, and K. ROBINSON. *Acta Cryst.* **3**, 408 (1950)

25.31 H. S. STEINFINK. *Acta Cryst.* **11**, 191 and 195 (1958)

25.32 G. W. BRINDLEY and K. ROBINSON. *Mineral. Mag.* **27**, 242 (1946)

25.33 R. E. NEWNHAM and G. W. BRINDLEY. *Acta· Cryst.* **9**, 759 (1956) and *Mineral. Mag.* **32**, 683 (1961)

25.34 W. NOLL and H. KIRCHER. *Naturw.* **37**, 540 (1950); **39**, 158 (1952); *Neues Jahrb. Mineral. Monatsh.* 219 (1951)

25.35 H. JAGODZINSKI. *Neues Jahrb. Mineral. Monatsh.* 97 (1953)

25.36 W. W. JACKSON and J. WEST. *Z. Krist.* **76**, 211 (1931); **85**, 160 (1933)

25.37 U. HOFMANN et al. *Z. Krist.* **86**, 340 (1933); **98**, 299 (1937); *Angew. Chem.* **68**, 53 (1956)

25.38 W. H. TAYLOR and ST. NÁRAY-SZABÓ. *Z. Krist.* **77**, 146 (1931)

25.39 L. BRAGG and G. F. CLARINGBULL. *Crystal Structures of Minerals,* G. Bell and Sons Ltd., London (1965); W. EITEL. *Silicate Science,* Vol. I, Academic Press, New York (1964)

25.40 G. BERGERHOFF, W. NOWACKI et al. *Experientia* **12**, 418 (1956); *Neues Jahrb. Mineral.* **9**, 193 (1958)

25.41 H. SAALFELD. *Z. Krist.* **115**, 132 (1961)

25.42 T. F. W. BARTH. *Norsk Geol. Tidsskr.* **9**, 40 (1926); L. PAULING. *Z. Krist.* **74**, 213 (1930)

25.43 H. BODE and G. TEUFER. *Acta Cryst.* **8**, 611 (1955)

25.44 T. B. REED and D. W. BRECK. *J. Am. Chem. Soc.* **78**, 5972 (1956)

25.45 P. A. HOWELL. *Acta Cryst.* **13**, 737 (1960)

25.46 L. BROUSSARD and D. P. SHOEMAKER. *J. Am. Chem. Soc.* **82**, 1041 (1960)

25.47 K. F. FISCHER and W. M. MEIER. *Fortschr. Mineral.* **42**, 50 (1965)

26.1 W. H. ZACHARIASEN. *Acta Cryst.* **7**, 305 (1954)

26.2 B. M. CRAVEN and T. M. SABINE. *Acta Cryst.* **20**, 214 (1966)

26.3 H. TAZAKI. *J. Sci. Hiroshima Univ.* **10** *A*, 55 (1940); *Chemical Abstracts* **34**, 4318 (1940)

26.4 M. MAREZIO, H. A. PLETTINGER, and W. H. ZACHARIASEN. *Acta Cryst.* **16**, 594 (1963)

26.5 F. CHOPIN and A. HARDY. *Compt. Rend.* Paris, 261 (1965)

26.6 W. H. ZACHARIASEN and H. A. PLETTINGER. *Acta Cryst.* **16**, 376 (1963)

26.7 J. KROGH-MOE. *Acta Cryst.* **18**, 1088 (1965)

26.8 N. MORIMOTO. *Mineral. J.* (*Japan*) **2**, 1 (1956)

26.9 Structure of $K_2[B_4O_5(OH)_4].2H_2O$: M. MAREZIO, H. A. PLETTINGER, and W. H. ZACHARIASEN. *Acta Cryst.* **16**, 975 (1963)

26.10 M. IHARA and J. KROGH-MOE. *Acta Cryst.* **20**, 132 (1966)

26.11 M. MAREZIO, H. A. PLETTINGER, and W. H. ZACHARIASEN. *Acta Cryst.* **16**, 390 (1963)

26.12 D. E. CORBRIDGE. *Acta Cryst.* **13**, 263 (1960)

26.13 K. H. JOST. *Acta Cryst.* **17**, 1539 (1964); comp. also W. S. MCDONALD and D. W. J. CRUICKSHANK. *Acta Cryst.* **22**, 37, 43, and 48 (1967)

26.14 W. H. ZACHARIASEN. *Acta Cryst.* **17**, 749 (1964)

26.15 W. H. ZACHARIASEN, in press

26.16 W. H. ZACHARIASEN. *Acta Cryst.* **16**, 385 (1963)

26.17 T. Ito and H. Mori. *Acta Cryst.* **6**, 24 (1953)
26.18 P. V. Pavlov and N. B. Belov. *Kristallografiya* **4**, 324 (1960), reprinted in 25.18, p. 82
26.19 J. Krogh-Moe. *Acta Cryst.* **13**, 889 (1960)
26.20 J. Krogh-Moe. *Arkiv Kemi* **14**, 439 (1959)
26.21 J. Krogh-Moe. *Acta Cryst.* **18**, 77 (1965)
26.22 W. H. Zachariasen. *Acta Cryst.* **16**, 380 (1963)
26.23 Summarizing literature on borates: Ch. Tennyson. *Fortschr. Mineral.* **41**, 64 (1963)
26.24 See survey article, A. D. Wadsley in L. Mandelcorn. *Non Stoichiometric Compounds,* p. 98, Academic Press, New York–London (1964)
26.25 A. M. Byström. *Acta Chem. Scand.* **3**, 162 (1949)
26.26 O. Glemser. *Ber. dtsch. chem. Ges.* **72**, 1879 (1939)
26.27 W. C. Vosburgh. *J. Electrochem. Soc.* **106**, 839 (1959)
26.28 O. Glemser, G. Gattow, and H. Meisick. *Z. anorg. allg. Chem.* **309**, 1 and 20 (1961)
26.29 F. J. Ewing. *J. Chem. Phys.* **3**, 203 (1935)
26.30 W. Hoppe. *Z. Krist.* **103**, 73 (1941); **104**, 11 (1942)
26.31 W. R. Büsing and H. A. Levy. *Acta Cryst.* **11**, 798 (1958)
26.32 H. Bärnighausen. *Acta Cryst.* **16**, 1073 (1963)
26.33 M. Gondrand and F. Bertaut. *Bull. Soc. France, Mineral Crist.* **86**, 301 (1963)
26.34 A. Byström and A. M. Byström. *Acta Chem. Scand.* **3**, 146 (1950)
26.35 A. D. Wadsley and S. Andersson. *Nature, Lond.* **192**, 551 (1961)
26.36 J. S. Dryden and A. D. Wadsley. *Trans. Faraday Soc.* **54**, 1574 (1958)
26.37 A. L. Mackay. *Mineral. Mag.* **32**, 545 (1960)
26.38 M. Fleischer. *Am. Mineralogist* **45**, 176 (1960)
26.39 A. D. Wadsley. *Acta Cryst.* **6**, 443 (1953)
26.40 G. Andersson and A. Magnéli. *Acta Chem. Scand.* **4**, 793 (1950)
26.41 A. Magnéli et al. *Akiv Kemi* **6**, 133 (1953); *Acta Chem. Scand.* **2**, 50 (1948); **9**, 1382 (1955)
26.42 O. Glemser and H. Sauer. *Z. anorg. allg. Chem.* **252**, 144 (1943)
26.43 A. Magnéli. *Arkiv Kemi* **1**, 513 (1950)
26.44 See survey article: L. Kihlborg. *Arkiv Kemi* **21**, 471 (1963)
26.45 R. S. Roth and A. D. Wadsley. *Acta Cryst.* **18**, 643 (1965)
26.46 R. S. Roth and A. D. Wadsley. *Acta Cryst.* **18**, 724 (1965); **19**, 32 (1965)
26.47 A. D. Wadsley. *Acta Cryst.* **14**, 664 (1961)
26.48 A. Magnéli, B. Blomberg et al. *Acta Chem. Scand.* **5**, 372 (1951); **9**, 1382 (1955)
26.49 J. Graham and A. D. Wadsley. *Acta Cryst.* **14**, 379 (1961)
26.50 A. Magnéli. *Arkiv Kemi* **1**, 213 and 269 (1949)
26.51 R. A. Bernoff and L. E. Conrey. *J. Am. Chem. Soc.* **82**, 6261 (1960)
26.52 G. Goodman. *J. Am. Ceram. Soc.* **43**, 105 (1960)
26.53 F. Galasso, L. Katz, and R. Ward. *J. Am. Chem. Soc.* **81**, 5898 (1959)
27.1   R. E. Rundle et al. *Acta Cryst.* **6**, 487 (1933); *J. Phys. Chem.* **61**, 45 (1957); *J. Am. Chem. Soc.* **79**, 3017 (1957); **81**, 755 (1959)
27.2   B. Meuthen and M. v. Stackelberg. *Z. anorg. allg. Chem.* **305**, 279 (1960)
27.3   H. B. Gray and C. J. Ballhausen. *J. Am. Chem. Soc.* **85**, 260 (1963)
27.4   K. Krogmann. *Habilitationsschrift*, Stuttgart (1964); *Z. anorg. allg. Chem.* in press
27.5   K. Krogmann and R. Mattes. *Z. anorg. allg. Chem.* **332**, 247 (1964)

27.6   F. Mondorf. *Bull. Soc. Roy. Sci.* Liège **11**, 567 (1942)
27.7   R. M. Bozorth and L. Pauling. *Phys. Rev.* **39**, 537 (1932)
27.8   K. Krogmann and H. D. Hausen. *Z. anorg. allg. Chem.* **358**, 67 (1968)
27.9   J. N. van Niekerk et al. *Acta Cryst.* **6**, 227 and 501 (1953)
27.10 M. A. Porai-Koshits and A. S. Antsyshkina. *Dokl. Akad. Nauk SSSR*, **146**, 1102 (1962)
27.11 D. Lawton and R. Mason. *J. Am. Chem. Soc.* **87**, 921 (1965)
27.12 See survey article: H. Schäfer and H. G. v. Schnering. *Angew. Chem.* **76**, 833 (1964)
27.13 H. Schäfer, H. G. v. Schnering, J. Tillack, F. Kuhnen, H. Wöhrle and H. Baumann. *Z. anorg. allg. Chem.* **353**, 281 (1967)
27.14 A. Simon, H. G. v. Schnering, and H. Schäfer. *Z. anorg. allg. Chem.* **355**, 295 (1967)
27.15 H. Schäfer, H. G. v. Schnering, K. J. Niehues, and H. G. Nieder-Vahrenholz. *J. Less-Common Metals* **9**, 95 (1965)
27.16 A. Simon, H. G. v. Schnering, H. Wöhrle, and H. Schäfer. *Z. anorg. allg. Chem.* **339**, 155 (1965)
27.17 D. Bauer, H. G. v. Schnering, and H. Schäfer. *J. Less-Common Metals* **8**, 388 (1965)
27.18 F. A. Cotton and T. E. Haas. *Inorg. Chem.* **3**, 10 (1964)
27.18a A. Simon. *Z. anorg. allg. Chem.* **355**, 311 (1967)
27.19 K. Brodersen, G. Thiele, and H. G. v. Schnering. *Z. anorg. allg. Chem.* **337**, 120 (1965)
27.19a H. Schäfer, U. Wiese, K. Rinke, and K. Brendel. *Z. Angew. Chem.* **79**, 244 (1957)
27.20 H. M. Powell and A. F. Wells. *J. Chem. Soc.* 1008 (1935)
27.21 J. L. Hoard and L. Goldstein. *J. Chem. Phys.* **3**, 199 (1935)
27.22 G. J. Wessel and D. J. W. IJdo. *Acta Cryst.* **10**, 466 (1957)
27.23 C. Brosset. *Arkiv Kemi Min. Geol.* **12 A** 4 (1935)
27.24 W. H. Watson jr. and J. Waser. *Acta Cryst.* **11**, 689 (1958)
27.25 D. Babel and W. Rüdorff. *Naturw.* **51**, 84 (1964)
27.26 J. Lewis, D. L. Machin, R. S. Nyholm, L. Pauling, and P. W. Smith. *Chem. Ind.* (London) 259 (1960)
27.27 H. G. v. Schnering. *Habilitationsschrift*, Münster, 1963
27.28 L. F. Dahl, Tao-J Chiang, P. W. Seabaugh, and M. M. Larsen, *Inorg. Chem.* **3**, 1236 (1946)
27.29 For β $RuCl_3$, $RuBr_3$, RuI_3, $IrBr_3$, and IrI_3 see: K. Brodersen. *Angew. Chem.* **80**, 155 (1968)
27.30 K. R. Tsai, P. M. Harris, and E. N. Lassettre. *J. Phys. Chem.* **60**, 345 (1956)
27.31 H. G. v. Schnering. *Naturw.* **53**, 359 (1966)
27.32 H. G. v. Schnering and H. Wöhrle. *Naturw.* **50**, 91 (1963)
27.33 L. F. Dahl and D. L. Wampler. *Acta Cryst.* **15**, 903 (1962); *J. Am. Chem. Soc.* **81**, 315 (1959)
27.34 H. G. v. Schnering, H. Wöhrle, and H. Schäfer. *Naturw.* **48**, 159 (1961)
27.35 W. H. McCarrol, L. Katz, and R. Ward. *J. Am. Chem. Soc.* **79**, 5410 (1957); G. B. Angell and L. Katz. *Acta Cryst.* **21**, 482 (1966)
27.36 A. Magnéli and G. Andersson. *Acta Chem. Scand.* **9**, 1378 (1955)
27.37 G. Brauer. *Z. anorg. allg. Chem.* **248**, 1 (1941); **256**, 10 (1948)
27.38 G. Andersson. *Acta Chem. Scand.* **8**, 1599 (1954)
27.39 F. J. Morin. *Phys. Rev. Letters* **3**, 34 (1959)

27.40 S. WESTMAN. *Acta Chem. Scand.* **13**, 217 (1961)
27.41 M. LEBLANC and H. SACHSE. *Phys. Z.* **32**, 887 (1931)
27.42 W. RÜDORFF and F. RODI, personal communication
28.1   Compare also: M. HANSEN. *Constitution of Binary Alloys*, McGraw-Hill, New York–Toronto–London (1958)
28.2   Compare also: C. S. BARRETT. *Structure of Metals*, McGraw-Hill, New York–Toronto–London (1952)
28.3   Compare: W. B. PEARSON. *Lattice Spacings and Structures of Metals and Alloys*, Pergamon Press, London–New York–Paris–Los Angeles (1958)
28.4   A. J. BRADLEY and A. H. JAY. *Proc. Roy. Soc.* London, A **136**, 210 (1932); *J. Iron Steel Inst.* **125**, 339 (1932)
28.5   W. HUME-ROTHERY. *J. Inst. Metals* **35**, 309 (1926)
28.6   See reference 5.3, p. 430
28.7   H. G. GRIMM. *Z. Elektrochem.* **31**, 474 (1925)
28.8   H. G. GRIMM and A. SOMMERFELD. *Z. Physik* **36**, 36 (1926)
28.9   F. LAVES et al. *Metallwirtschaft* **14**, 645 (1935); *Z. Krist.* A **101**, 78 (1939)
28.10 U. DEHLINGER and G. E. R. SCHULZE. *Z. Krist.* **102**, 377 (1940)
28.11 K. SCHUBERT. *Kristallstrukturen zweikomponentiger Phasen*, Springer, Berlin–Göttingen–Heidelberg (1964)
29.1   G. TAMMAN. *Aggregatszustände*, Voss, Leipzig 1923, translated by R. F. MEHL. *The States of Aggregation*, D. van Nostrand Company, New York (1925); *Der Glaszustand*, Voss, Leipzig (1933)
29.2   V. M. GOLDSCHMIDT. *Geochemische Verteilungsgesetzte der Elemente*, VIII. Vid. Akad. Ser. Oslo Nr. 8, 137 (1926)
29.3   W. H. ZACHARIASEN. *J. Am. Chem. Soc.* **54**, 3841 (1932)
29.4   F. C. KRACEK. *J. Am. Chem. Soc.* **52**, 1436 (1930)
29.5   A. DIETZEL. *Z. Elektrochem.* **48**, 9 (1942)
29.6   G. W. BRADY. *J. Chem. Phys.* **27**, 300 (1957)
29.7   R. W. DOUGLAS in '*Non-Crystalline Solids*', edited by V. P. FRÉCHETTE, p. 382, John Wiley & Sons (1960)
29.8   M. K. MURTHY et al. *J. Am. Cer. Soc.* **47**, 328, and 444 (1964); *Nature Lond.* **201**, 285 (1964)
29.9   E.g., A. SMEKAL in *Zur Struktur und Materie der Festkörper*, p. 223, Springer (1952)
29.10 E. THILO. *J. Polymer Science* **48**, 69 (1960)
29.11 H. GRUNZE. *Silikattechnik* **7**, 134 (1956)
29.12 K. H. JOST and F. WODKE. *Makromol. Chemie* **53**, 1 (1962)
29.13 A. DIETZEL and H. J. POEGEL. *Atti III Congr. Int. Vetro*, p. 219, Venice (1953)
29.14 E. THILO, CH. WIEKER, and W. WIEKER. *Silikattechnik* **15**, 109 (1964)
29.15 W. VOGEL. *Angew. Chem.* **77**, 109 (1965) and *Struktur und Kristallisation der Gläser*, VEB Deutscher Verlag für Grundstoffindustrie, Leipzig (1965)
29.16 W. BILTZ and F. WEIBKE. *Z. anorg. allg. Chem.* **203**, 845 (1932); *Glastechn. Ber.* **10**, 577 (1932)
29.17 A. DIETZEL. *Glastechn. Ber.* **22**, 212 (1949)
29.18 M. A. PORAI-KOSHITS in *The Structure of Glass I*, Proc. of a Conference on the Structure of Glass, Leningrad (1953); Consultants Bureau New York (1958)
29.19 W. VOGEL. *Silikattechnik* **10**, 241 (1959)
29.20 P. J. BRAY et al. *Phys. Chem. Glasses* **4**, 37 and 47 (1963); **6**, 113 (1965)
29.21 See: 5.3, p. 548

29.22 A. Prietzschk. *J. Physik* **117**, 483 (1941)

29.23 R. Hilsch in 29.7, p. 351

29.24 For further methods of preparing glassy films, see: J. D. Mackenzie. *Modern Aspects of the Vitreous State*, Vol. III, p. 149, Butterworth, London (1964) and *J. Am. Ceram. Soc.* **48**, 487 (1965)

29.25 O. Schmitz-DuMont. *Z. anorg. allg. Chem.* **243**, 113 (1939); *Angew. Chem.* **50**, 415 (1937)

29.26 N. S. Goryunova and B. T. Kolomiets. *The Structure of Glass II*, pp. 58 and 410, Proc. of the third All-Union Conference on the Glassy State, Leningrad 1959, Consultants Bureau New York (1960)

29.27 S. S. Flaschen, A. D. Pearson, and W. R. Northover. *J. Am. Ceram. Soc.* **42**, 450 (1959) and **43**, 274 (1960)

29.28 N. A. Goryunova, B. T. Kolomiets, and V. P. Shilo. *Soviet Phys., Tech. Phys.* **3** [5] 912 (1958)

29.29 Compare: A. D. Pearson. 'Sulphide, Selenide and Telluride Glasses' in J. D. Mackenzie. *Modern Aspects of the Vitreous State*, Vol. III, p. 29, Butterworth, London (1964)

29.30 Compare: B. T. Kolomiets. *Physica status solidi* **7**, 359 and 713 (1964)

29.31 A. D. Pearson, W. R. Northover, J. F. Dewald, and W. F. Peck jr. *Advances in Glass Techn.*, VI. Congress on Glass, p. 357, Washington DC (1962), Plenum Press New York (1962)

29.32 A. R. Hilton and M. Brau. *Infrared Phys.* **3**, 69 (1963)

29.33 A. R. Hilton, C. E. Jones, and M. Brau. *Infrared Phys.* **4**, 213 (1964), *Phys. and Chem. of Glasses* **7**, 105 (1966)

29.34 A. R. Hilton and M. Brau, personal communication

29.35 H. Krebs. *Angew. Chem.* **78**, 577 (1966); *Angew. Chem.* intern. Edit. **5**, 544 (1966)

29.36 R. W. Haisty and H. Krebs, unpublished

29.37 W. Patterson and M. Brau, presented at the Electrochemical Society Meeting, May 1966, Cleveland, Ohio

29.38 H. Krebs, H. Hermsdorf, H. Thurn, H. Welte, and L. Winkler. *Z. Naturf. a,* **23a**, 491 (1968)

Name Index

Subject Index

Substance Index

Formula Index

THIS BOOK HAS BEEN SET IN MONOPHOTO TIMES NEW ROMAN 10 ON 12 POINT
AND PRINTED AND BOUND IN GREAT BRITAIN BY
WILLIAM CLOWES AND SONS, LIMITED, LONDON AND BECCLES